A Note From The Publisher

The Educational Book Division of Prentice-Hall, Inc., is committed to the publication of outstanding textbooks. One important measure of a book's excellence is how well it communicates with its readers. To assure a highly readable book, the content for this text was selected, organized, and written at a level appropriate for the intended audience. The Fry readability formula was used to control readability level. An attractive design was created to enhance the book's visual appeal as well as to facilitate the reading process. The authors, editors, and designers are confident that the student for whom this book is intended will comprehend it and learn from it.

Physical Science: The Key Ideas offers a number of special features that will make the study of physical science an effective and meaningful experience for students. A list of these features follows. Page references are given to provide an example of each feature.

- Every chapter teaches one key idea. The Table of Contents includes the key idea, or goal, of each chapter. (pages 3-8)
- Each of the five units in the book begins with at least one science competency, or skill, which the student will master in that unit. (page 10)
- Important science terms are introduced in capital letters and defined within the text. (page 11)
- Key facts and ideas are printed in bold type within the text. (page 26)
- Important concepts often appear within boxes, which are set apart from the chapter text. (page 38)
- Chapters are divided into sections. Each section ends with review questions. (page 39)
- Forty-eight Activities that use easy-to-obtain materials reinforce the text content. No special equipment kits are necessary to undertake the Activities. Questions at the end of each Activity help students evaluate their data. (page 64)
- Many photographs and drawings throughout the book illustrate key facts and concepts. (page 75)
- Each chapter closes with a Summary section that includes vocabulary words, a list of key facts and concepts, a concluding paragraph, and a final question that reinforces the key idea of the chapter. (page 82)
- A Glossary and an Index help students use and find significant terms and information. In the Glossary, many of the terms are phonetically pronounced. (pages 318–334)

PHYSICAL SCIENCE THE KEY IDEAS

HARRY K. WONG
Las Lomitas School District
Menlo Park, California

MALVIN S. DOLMATZ
Woodside High School
Woodside, California

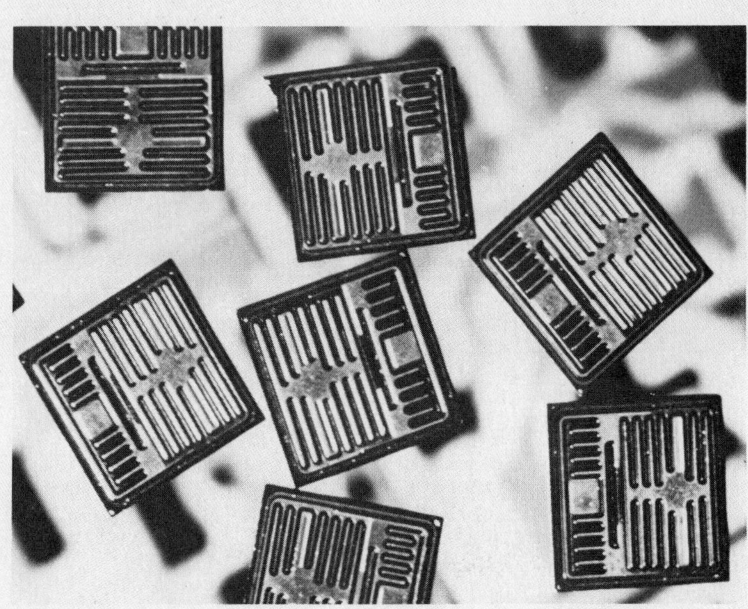

Prentice-Hall, Inc., Englewood Cliffs, New Jersey

PHYSICAL SCIENCE: THE KEY IDEAS **Harry K. Wong** **Malvin S. Dolmatz**

Supplementary Materials:

Teacher's Manual

Laboratory Data Book

Contributing Authors:

Fred L. Beyer
Cumberland County Board of Education
Fayetteville, North Carolina

Douglas W. Green
Binghamton City Schools
Binghamton, New York

The photograph on the cover shows several highly magnified silicon chips. These particular chips are used in the production of computers for automobiles. Photo by T. E. Adams/Bruce Coleman Inc.

Printed in the United States of America.

ISBN 0-13-671545-1

10 9 8 7 6 5 4 3

Prentice-Hall International, Inc., London
Prentice-Hall of Australia, Pty. Ltd., Sydney
Prentice-Hall Canada, Inc., Toronto
Prentice-Hall of India Private Ltd., New Delhi
Prentice-Hall of Japan, Inc., Tokyo
Prentice-Hall of Southeast Asia Pte. Ltd., Singapore
Whitehall Books Limited, Wellington, New Zealand
Editora Prentice-Hall do Brasil Ltda., Rio de Janeiro

Contents and Key Ideas

UNIT ONE Method of Science

UNIT TWO **Matter**

CHAPTER **19: Families of Elements** Different elements have atoms of different masses.

CHAPTER **20: Analyzing the Atom** There are charged particles in atoms.

CHAPTER **21: Analyzing Atomic Structure** The atom is made up of subatomic particles.

CHAPTER **22: Electrons and Chemical Properties** The chemical properties of atoms are determined by the electrons in the outer level.

UNIT THREE **Work and Energy**

CHAPTER **23: Forms of Energy** Energy is the ability to do work.

CHAPTER **24: Motion** Work is done when force acts over a distance.

CHAPTER **25: Simple Machines** Simple machines are mechanical devices that change force.

CHAPTER **26: Heat Engines** Engines transform energy into motion.

UNIT FOUR **Energy and Change**

UNIT FIVE **Technology**

Activities

Chapter numbers, Activity titles, and page numbers are listed below. A dot next to an Activity step means that data must be recorded in a chart, graph, or diagram. Students can either draw their own chart, graph, or diagram or use the art provided in the *Laboratory Data Book*.

UNIT ONE

Method of Science

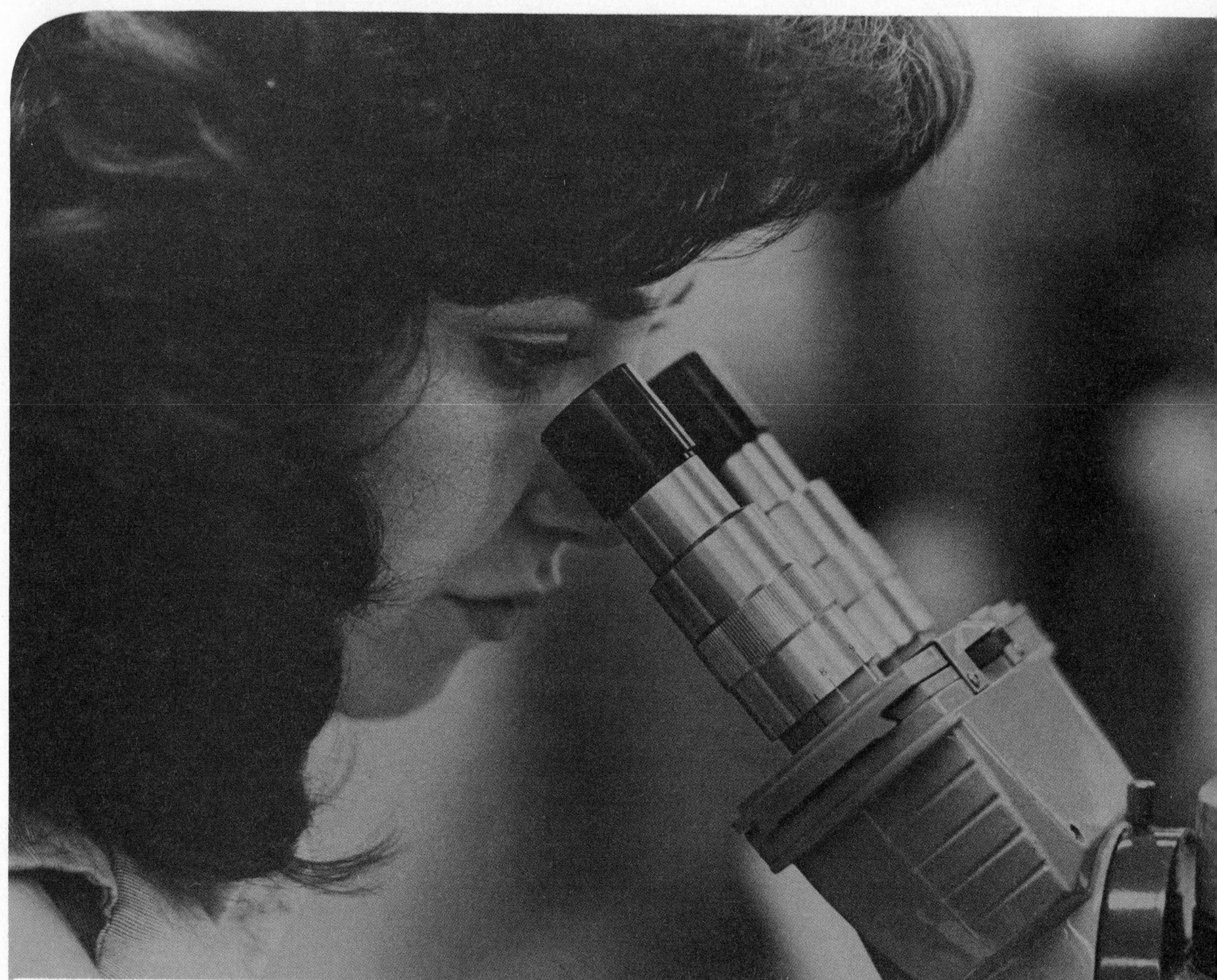

SCIENCE COMPETENCIES

Competencies are LIFE SKILLS you need for living. You will be asked to master five competencies in this book. Unit 1 will help you to master the first one.

SOLVING PROBLEMS—How to Use the Scientific Method

USING MATERIALS AND ENERGY—How to Use Matter and Energy Wisely

RESPECTING THE EARTH—How to Cope with Environmental Changes

UNDERSTANDING NATURAL PROCESSES—How to Conserve the Earth's Resources

APPLYING TECHNOLOGY—How to Be a Functionally Literate Citizen

CHAPTER

1 Observation

The First Step in Making Discoveries

1A INTRODUCTION

Much of what you know about the world around you was discovered by SCIENTISTS. **Scientists are people whose job it is to find out how nature works.** They start by OBSERVING. The scientist looks for CLUES about what is happening and how it happens. If a scientist stops observing carefully, then too much will be missed that is important.

Scientists do many other things, too. They ask questions. Scientists also think of possible answers. They test ideas with experiments. And above all else, scientists measure. They measure the tiniest bits of matter and the distance from the earth to the edge of the universe. At the same time scientists are doing these things, they continue to look, see, and observe. **They are finding out how the world works.**

The observing, questioning, experimenting, and measuring that scientists do lead to knowledge. It is the search for knowledge as well as the knowledge itself that is called SCIENCE.

Observing is not just for scientists. It is an important activity for everyone. A golfer has to see the hole to sink a putt. The golfer also has to know which way the wind is blowing, which way the green slopes, and which way the grass is bent. A basketball player has to see the basket. The player also has to see the positions of teammates, the other team, and the officials.

Observing is for you, too. Your clues as to how the world works are traffic signals, price tags, umpires' signals, uniforms, and direction signs, to name just a few. They are too important to miss. You must keep looking all the time.

1. What is every scientist's job?
2. What are some ways scientists find out about how nature works?

1B OBSERVATION

Observing is not just an important activity in science. Observing is important in all the activities of life. Use the following pictures to test how well you see.

Look at Picture A.

Picture A

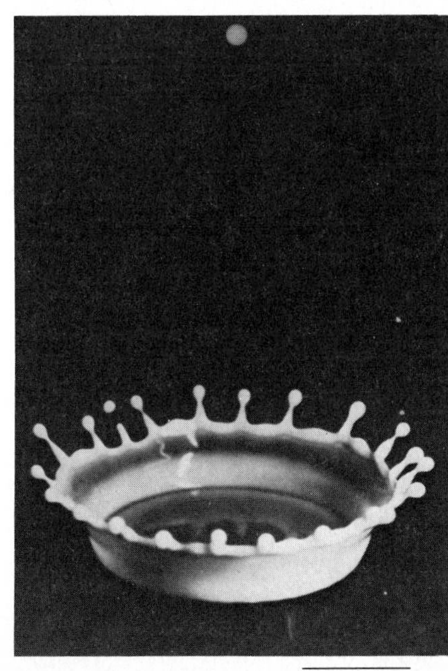

3. What is this a photograph of?
4. How do you know? The picture is not what you probably thought it was at first glance.
5. What tells you what is happening?

If you saw the clues that tell you what is happening, you were observant. You have taken the first step a scientist would take.

Look at Picture B.

Picture B

6. Was this a party celebrating New Year's, a birthday, Halloween, Valentine's Day, or Thanksgiving?

7. How did you know?

Picture C

Look at Picture C at the left.

8. What kind of team used this room last?

9. How did you know?

Now look at Picture D.

Picture D

10. What kind of work does this woman do?

11. How do you know?

12. What did you have to do with all of these pictures to answer the questions?

1C CAREFUL OBSERVERS

Scientists do not get up in the morning and decide, "Today, let's discover gravity." Scientists do not work that way.

What scientists do is carefully observe the world around them. They look for something they don't already understand as a place to start working. When scientists explain something beyond what was already known, they have expanded the boundaries of knowledge.

> Observing carefully enough to discover the unexplained is the key to working in science.

To see something different takes careful looking. But to use your observations you must tell someone else what you saw. If you can't communicate, then all your observations and discoveries are useless.

ACTIVITY: Observation, Description, and Identification

MATERIALS: Paper bags, assorted objects

a. Each pair of students will be given a paper bag full of objects. Do not show the contents of the bag to anyone.

b. If you are chosen to go first, take out one object. Be careful not to let the rest of the class see it. Describe what the object looks like to the class. Do this without actually naming the object.

c. The rest of the class can now look in their bags. When students have heard enough description to be able to identify the object, they should pull it out of their bags and hold it up.

d. Take turns describing other objects from the bag. See how fast the rest of the class can guess which object is being described.

e. Scientists keep records of what they see. Practice carefully recording what you have seen.

• f. Write down what each of the things in the bag looks like. Be sure you describe, not name, each item in your sack.

g. To test how well you can describe things, take turns reading your descriptions aloud. See if other students can pick out the right object by listening to your description.

13. Did all students guess correctly the first time?
14. If they did, what helped them? If they didn't, what was missing?
15. When the descriptions were written down, did everyone guess the answer quickly?
16. When the descriptions were written down, what did everyone need for a correct answer?

Seeing, or observing carefully, is not just for scientists. There are many people who must be good observers, such as airline pilots, nurses, teachers, and cashiers. These people must observe and act upon what they observe.

17. What must a scientist do to study nature?
18. List some other jobs in which observing is important.
19. What must you do to know what is going on around you?

SUMMARY

VOCABULARY

scientist   observing   clue   science

KEY FACTS AND CONCEPTS

The first step in understanding nature is careful observation.
The scientist's job is learning how nature works.
Scientists observe, question, experiment, and measure.
The search for knowledge about how the world works, as well as the knowledge itself, is called science.

CONCLUSION

The scientist starts studying nature by observing. When something in nature doesn't fit what is already known, there is a chance for new discoveries. Careful observing is the way to find the pieces of the puzzle that do not fit.

Each chapter in this book has one central concept, or idea. At the end of each chapter you will be asked what that idea is.

20. What is the KEY IDEA of this chapter?

CHAPTER

2 Dependability

Nature Is Reliable and Consistent

2A INTRODUCTION

You have already learned something about scientists. They look at things carefully. They watch distant stars with telescopes and study tiny cells with microscopes. Scientists also use such devices as stethoscopes, lasers, and seismographs. A laser produces a thin beam of light that can burn a hole through steel or repair the delicate tissue in a human eye. A seismograph is used to record the size of an earthquake.

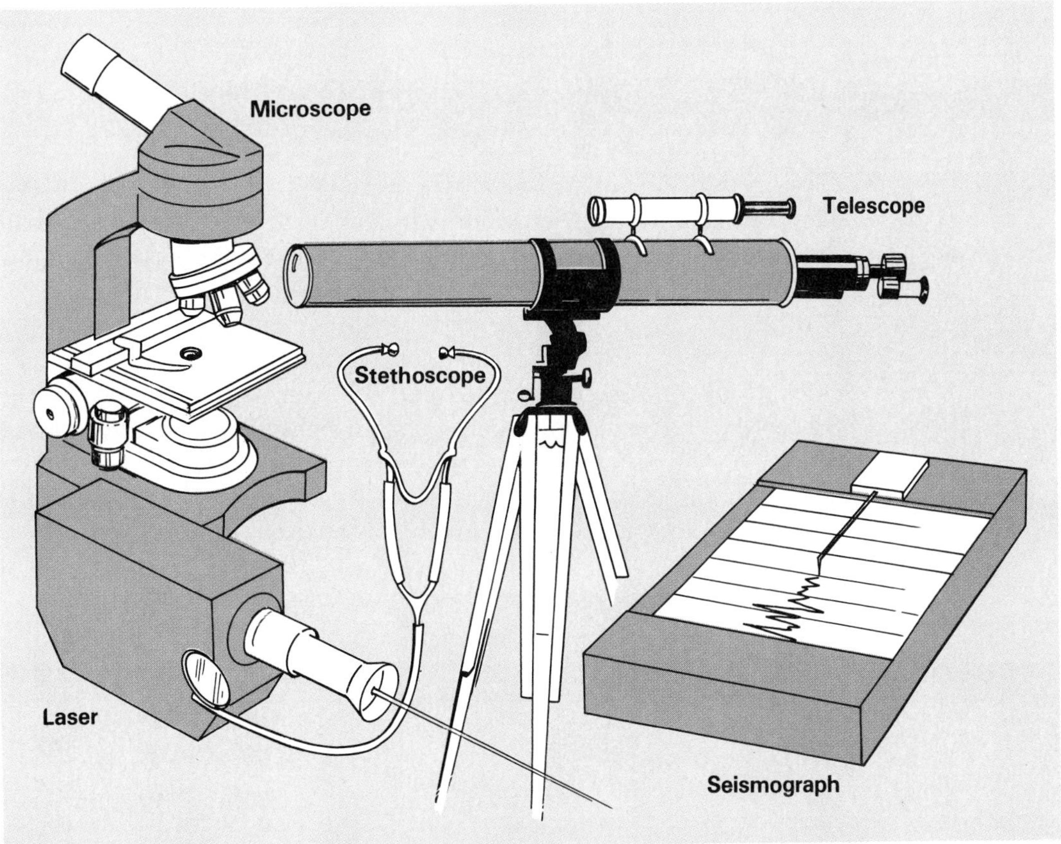

Scientists do many different things, yet they have one important belief in common. All scientists believe that nature is DEPENDABLE. That is, things in nature can be counted on to behave always in the same way. No matter who asks the questions about nature, the answers should be the same.

For example, suppose a scientist finds a new atomic particle in an experiment in Berkeley, California. Another scientist should be able to duplicate these findings in an experiment in Novosibirsk, Russia.

You expect nature to be dependable, too. Every time you shoot a basket in the school gym, it takes the same amount of push to get the ball up there. If you boil an egg at home for breakfast each morning, cooking time is always the same. You are depending on nature to work the same way each time. You can't get along without a dependable world and neither can scientists.

1. What can scientists rely on in their work?

2B THE CONSISTENCY OF NATURE

One way to describe nature's most important property is to say that nature is CONSISTENT. In the 17th century, Isaac Newton discovered how gravity controls the motions of objects in space. GRAVITY is the force of attraction, or pull, between all objects in the universe. In the 20th century, 300 years later, Newton's findings about gravity are still valid. The astronauts who went to the moon depended upon Newton's discoveries about gravity to make the trip. You will learn more about gravity later in this book.

> Scientists depend upon nature to be consistent. They expect the same set of conditions to always produce the same results.

Scientists often do things to see what will happen. **They do this believing that the same set of conditions will produce the same result every time.** When the same conditions do not seem to produce the same result, scientists ask why. This is how they question nature.

In the 16th century, Galileo measured how long it took balls to roll down a grooved board. He found a mathematical relationship between the length of time the balls rolled and the speeds they reached. In the 17th century, Newton shined light through a glass prism. He discovered that white light was composed of different colors. The same activities are done today in science classes all over the world. Students get the same results that Galileo and Newton got hundreds of years ago.

White light passing through a prism is separated into light of different colors.

Scientists study the past as well as the present. Scientists who study the earth try to determine its age. One method of doing this is by measuring how much radioactivity remains in certain minerals. Radioactivity refers to the way some substances give off particles and turn into other substances. You will learn more about radioactive substances in Unit 2.

By measuring the remains of radioactive minerals, scientists can determine how long the minerals have been in existence. The scientists are depending on the consistency of nature. They assume the rate of radioactive change has been the same for millions of years.

Scientists study stars that are tremendous distances from the earth. Light from these stars has taken many years to reach the earth. The events on these stars that are just being seen now took place thousands of years ago. The events on distant stars seem to follow the same patterns as the events on stars much closer to the earth. The rules of nature that are working now were working thousands of years ago. **Nature is consistent in time.**

Light from the Andromeda galaxy has traveled for millions of years to reach the earth.

2. Why will scientists list exactly what they have done to get a result?

3. Why would you expect the same result from bouncing a ball in your yard as you would from bouncing a ball in your neighbor's yard?

4. Why would you expect to get the same result from bouncing a ball on Friday as you did when you bounced it on Monday?

ACTIVITY: Testing the Reliability of Nature

MATERIALS: Plastic tube, medicine dropper, rubber stopper, water

a. Fill the plastic tube with water. It should be almost full. Put enough water in the medicine dropper so that it barely floats.
b. Put the dropper in the tube. Put the stopper in the top of the tube.
c. Place your thumb over the hole in the stopper and gently squeeze the tube. Release it.

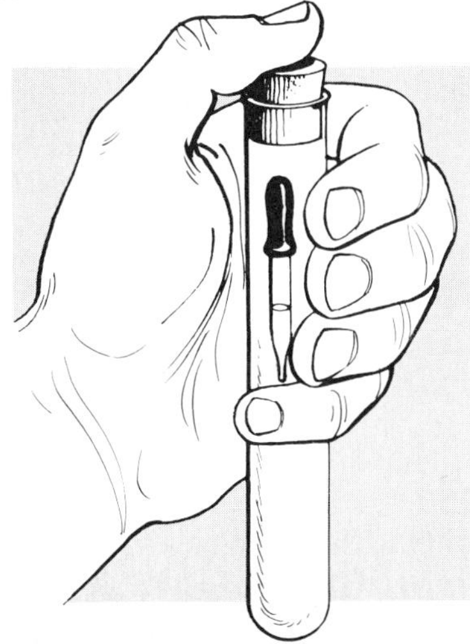

d. Squeeze the tube a second time, then release it. Be sure you covered the hole.
e. Test to see if it matters who squeezes the tube. Have your lab partner squeeze the tube while covering the hole.

5. What happened to the dropper when you squeezed the tube?
6. What happened when you stopped squeezing the tube?
7. What happened the second time you squeezed and released the tube?
8. What happens if you squeeze and release the tube a few more times?
9. What happened when your lab partner squeezed the tube?
10. Does it make any difference if the tube is squeezed by someone who is tall or short, male or female, blond or brunette?
11. How different are conditions in the tube if different people squeeze the tube just as hard?
12. How consistent was nature in this activity?

ACTIVITY: The Pendulum

MATERIALS: String, paper clip, washer, tape

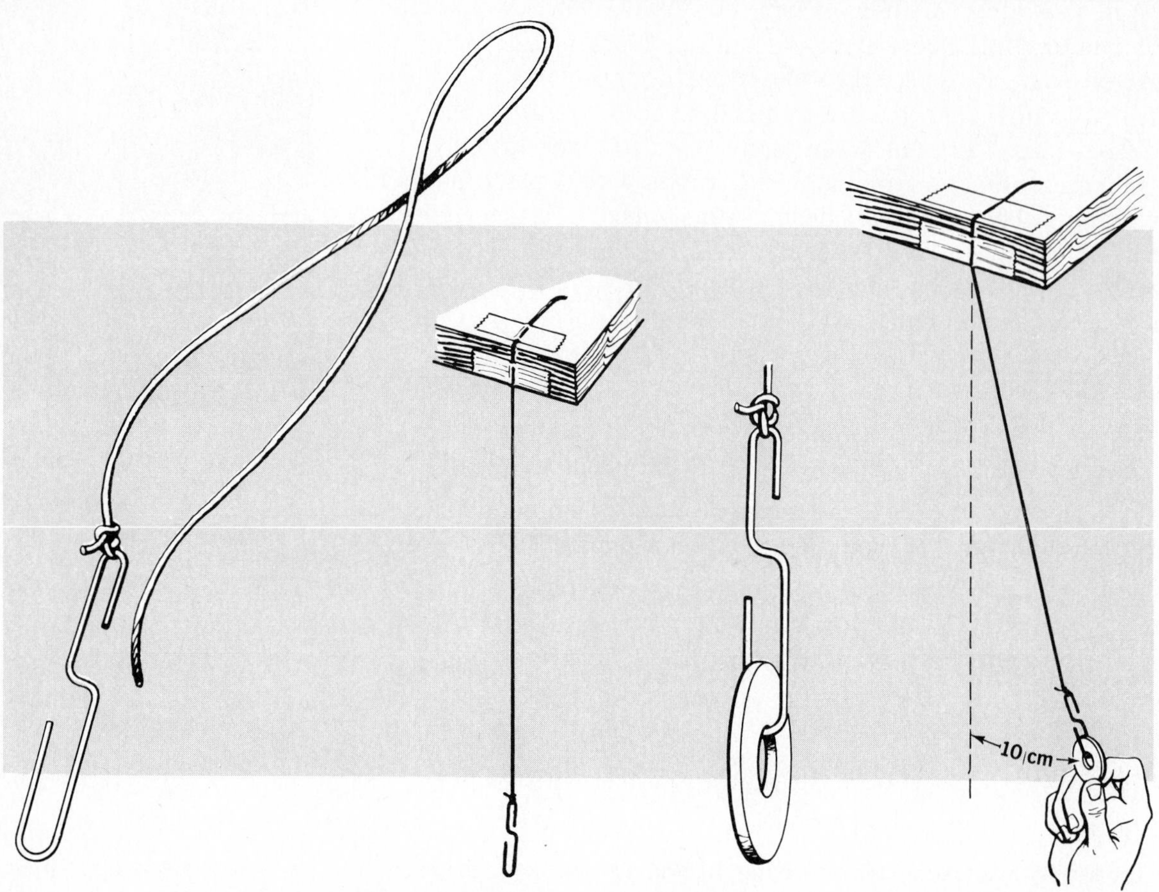

Test nature another way. Follow the directions and the diagram to make a PENDULUM. A pendulum is a weight hung on a string or other light support that is free to swing back and forth. You may have seen a pendulum in an old-fashioned clock.

---

a. Take a piece of string about 60 cm long. Bend a paper clip into a hook. Tie it to one end of the string.
b. Tape the other end of the string to the table.
c. Hang a washer on the hook.
d. Pull the washer sideways about 10 cm (the width of your hand).
e. Let the pendulum go. Count the number of swings (full round trips) it makes in one minute.
f. Pull the pendulum aside 10 cm and let it go again. Count the number of swings for one minute. Repeat this action a third time.
g. Change conditions a little. Pull the washer sideways about 20 cm (two hands). Count the swings in one minute.
h. Have different people start the pendulum and count the swings per minute.

---

13. How many swings did you get per minute the first time?
14. How many swings per minute did you count for the second two trials?
15. How do the first three trials compare.
16. What was your count when you pulled the washer sideways 20 cm?
17. How does this compare with the shorter pull?
18. What was your count of the swings per minute when different people started the pendulum?
19. Does it matter who pulls the washer if nothing else is changed?
20. Do your results show that nature is reliable? Explain your answer.

SUMMARY

dependable consistent gravity pendulum

VOCABULARY

Nature is dependable.

The same set of conditions will produce the same set of results.

The same test today will produce the same results as it did in previous centuries.

KEY FACTS AND CONCEPTS

When scientists ask questions about how nature works, they don't expect any surprises. Any scientist working anywhere will get the same result if the same question is asked in the same way.

CONCLUSION

21. What is the KEY IDEA of this chapter?

CHAPTER

3 Hypothesis

The Educated Guess

3A INTRODUCTION

What will happen if the driver of a car goes through a red light? Of course, you know the answer to this question. But would you be so sure of the answer if you hadn't been around cars and traffic signals most of your life?

When you work on something new, you have no experience to rely on. Like you, scientists have to GUESS their first answer when they explore the unknown. Scientists work on the edge between the known and the unknown. Every new fish from the sea or new particle from nuclear reactions or new kind of star from the edge of space causes questions to be asked.

The scientist will first review everything already known for a guide. **After this review, a reasonable guess about the unknown is made.** Therefore, this is a very special kind of guess. Scientists base their guesses on experience and study.

1. What do scientists do when they explore the unknown?

2. What do scientists do to make sure that their guesses are not just wild guesses?

3B GUESSES, PREDICTIONS, AND HYPOTHESES

There are other words to describe the kind of guess that scientists make. One of these words is PREDICTION. However, instead of using the word *prediction* or *guess,* scientists use the word HYPOTHESIS (plural: hypotheses).

A HYPOTHESIS IS:
a possible solution
a prediction
a suggested explanation
a tentative answer
a game plan
a trial answer
an educated guess

You can form hypotheses for many different kinds of problems, not just scientific ones. Forming a hypothesis can help you to solve problems by giving you a direction in which to work. Even if it is not the final answer, the hypothesis starts you thinking about all the possible solutions to your problem.

What do you predict about this flight?

Scientists use hypotheses as possible solutions to problems.

A hypothesis may be complicated. Scientists use a special kind of hypothesis. When they don't know how something really works, they put together as much as they do know. Then the scientists create a MODEL.

The model is not the real thing. A model is often a mental picture of how something could work. An early model of the atom looked like a tiny solar system. No scientist really thought the atom looked like the solar system. The model was only a good way to organize ideas. When more was learned about atoms, the solar system model of the atom was abandoned.

A model is a kind of hypothesis. For example, an early model of the solar system had the earth at the center. When new facts did not fit with the earth-centered model of the solar system, a new model was developed. The new model correctly placed the sun at the center of the solar system. But the old model was not wasted effort. It had done its job of paving the way for a model that was closer to reality.

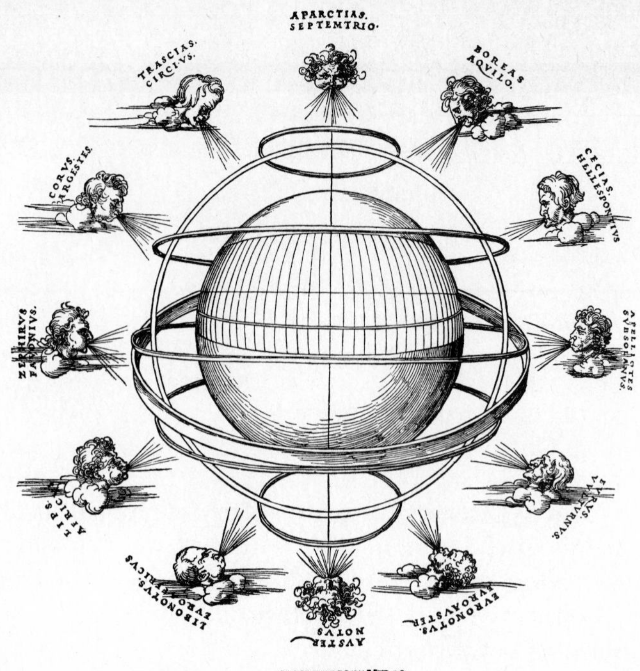

People in ancient times thought that the earth was at the center of the universe. This drawing of a 16th-century woodcut shows the earth at the center, surrounded by the twelve wind gods.

Not every hypothesis you form will be correct either. But by testing each hypothesis, you can arrive at the answer to your problem.

The hypothesis does not have to be correct to be useful in solving problems. For example, early scientists wondered what happens when something burns. Their first hypothesis stated that things that burned contained a gas called phlogiston. Objects burned because they released the phlogiston gas. It wasn't until one hundred years later that new facts proved that there was no gas called phlogiston.

The hypothesis had not been valid, but the questions about burning had been answered. The hypothesis had served its purpose. It had led scientists to further explore the problem of burning.

Scientists must be flexible in their thinking. A hypothesis that has lasted a century is hard to give up. **The mark of a good scientist is the ability to accept the changes that come with new facts.** There is no hypothesis in science that is one hundred percent certain. A new fact can destroy the grandest ideas. Scientists must be prepared to rethink their ideas periodically. The scientist who cannot adapt will be left behind in the search for knowledge.

> The organized and scientific way to attack a problem is to:
>
> THINK: Stop, observe, and think about past solutions.
>
> CONSULT: Check books and ask other people for more information.
>
> HYPOTHESIZE: Make a list of possible solutions.
>
> CHOOSE: Make a choice from the list.

3. What is a hypothesis?
4. How can forming a hypothesis help you solve problems?
5. How is a model used as a hypothesis?
6. Why doesn't a hypothesis have to be right to be useful?

ACTIVITY: Predicting How Balls Bounce

MATERIALS: Balls of different sizes

a. Your team will be given a bag that contains different balls. Look at each ball. Predict which ball will bounce the highest. Answer question 7.

b. Drop the balls two at a time until you can pick out the ball that bounces highest.

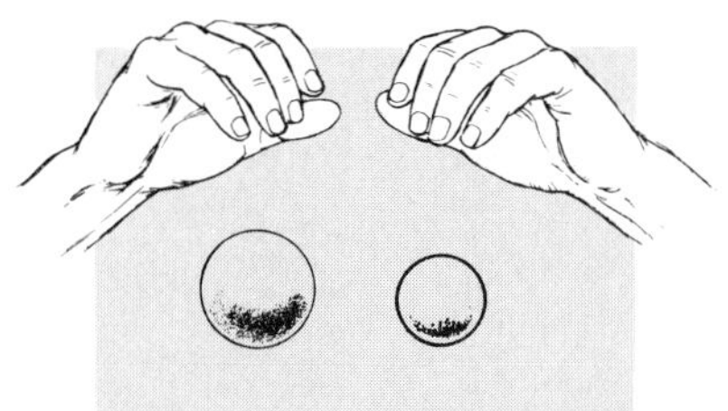

c. Pick out the largest and smallest ball. Predict which will hit the ground first.

d. Drop the two balls at exactly the same time from the same height.

7. Which ball did you predict would bounce the highest?
8. What was the result of bouncing them?
9. Which ball did you predict would hit the ground first?
10. What happened when you dropped the two balls at the same time from the same height?
11. What did you learn from this activity about how balls bounce?
12. How did your prediction affect what you learned?

3C PREDICTORS

The world depends upon predictions. Many people work as predictors. People such as weather forecasters and economists spend much of their time making predictions. They start out the same way. They gather up all the available facts. Then these predictors put the facts together and think about them. Then the predictors are ready to make the best prediction of what will happen.

Farmers, firefighters, crossing guards, and bus drivers count on the accuracy of the weather forecaster. Business people, labor leaders, and politicians depend on the accuracy of economists' predictions. People who work as predictors really have to do their homework!

13. What is the next step after gathering information about a problem?

SUMMARY

VOCABULARY

guess prediction hypothesis model

KEY FACTS AND CONCEPTS

An important step in answering questions or solving problems is using what is already known to make a good guess or hypothesis.

A hypothesis does not have to be right to help solve the problem.

Making a model is one way of forming a hypothesis.

Predictors gather all facts and put them together to make predictions.

CONCLUSION

When scientists work on a problem, they gather as much information as possible. The scientists use this information as a guide to guess the correct answer. This method is called forming a hypothesis.

14. What is the KEY IDEA of this chapter?

CHAPTER

4 Experiments and Controls

Testing the Hypothesis

4A INTRODUCTION

In Chapter 3, you learned that an important step in solving problems is forming a hypothesis. This chapter is all about what happens after the hypothesis is formed. But how do scientists test their hypotheses?

Experiments are used to test the validity of hypotheses.

Scientists use EXPERIMENTS to test hypotheses. A weather forecast can be checked just by looking out the window. But other hypotheses are much harder to test. In every case, scientists rely on experiments to decide whether or not their hypotheses are valid.

1. How do scientists test their hypotheses?

4B EXPERIMENTS PRODUCE DATA

The process of scientific research starts when a scientist sees something that does not fit in with what is already known about nature. This poses a problem about how nature works. To solve the problem, a hypothesis is formed. **The experiment is used to test the hypothesis.**

Scientists enjoy the excitement of testing their hypotheses. The purpose of experiments is to collect DATA, or facts, that will show if the hypotheses are valid (singular: datum). The data scientists collect help them reach their conclusions. So the method of science consists of asking the questions:

What do I want to know? (PROBLEM)
What do I think the answer might be? (HYPOTHESIS)
What must I do to tell if the hypothesis is valid? (EXPERIMENT)
What happened during the experiment? (DATA)
Do the data show if the problem is solved? (CONCLUSION)

2. When does the process of scientific research start?
3. What is the purpose of an experiment?

4C THE SCIENTIFIC PAPER

The scientist reports on the results of the experiment in journals or special magazines. The report is called a SCIENTIFIC PAPER, or research paper. Scientific papers may be long or short, but they are all well-organized pieces of writing.

THE SCIENTIFIC METHOD
State the PROBLEM.
Form a HYPOTHESIS.
Do an EXPERIMENT.
Collect DATA.
State the CONCLUSION.

A scientific paper starts with a PURPOSE. This tells the reader what the paper is all about. It describes the hypothesis being tested and may give some information about how the hypothesis was formed.

The next two parts are PROCEDURE and EQUIPMENT. The equipment is often listed first, but this can vary. **Equipment tells what supplies and instruments were used.** In very delicate experiments, a different brand of chemical may give different results. It is essential that exactly the items that are used be listed.

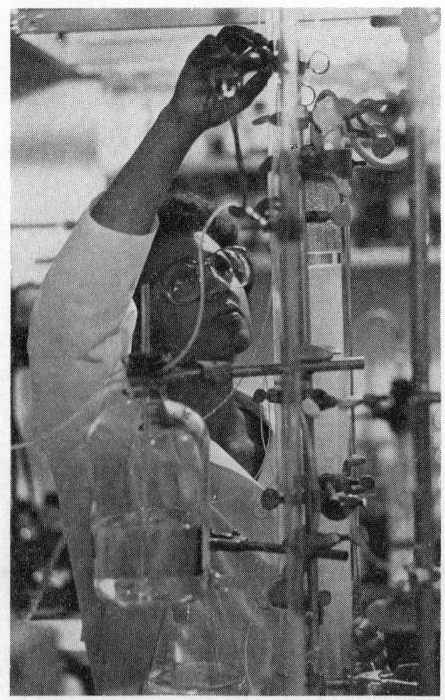

Equipment and supply lists have as much detail as necessary. Any scientist should get exactly the same data by doing the same experiment. It takes complete information to do an experiment the same way twice.

The procedure tells exactly what the scientist did. The procedure is the experiment. The procedure gives enough information so that another scientist could take the same supplies and go through the whole experiment in exactly the same way. The weighings, mixings, heatings, or coolings are all described in detail. Nothing is left out.

The data, or facts, come next. This part tells what happened. Whenever possible, data are presented in tables and graphs. The original numbers are included. These are the amounts, distances, lengths, temperatures, and so on that the scientist measured. Including these numbers prevents errors in arithmetic from going unnoticed.

Following the data is a discussion. The scientist talks about the data and what they may mean. The discussion may include references to other papers and how this data fits in with them.

The last step in a scientific paper is the conclusion. The conclusion tells whether the data support the hypothesis or not. Sometimes, the hypothesis is proven to be completely VALID, that is, the hypothesis was true. Other times, a hypothesis has to be completely rejected. Often, the conclusion shows how the hypothesis may be changed to fit new data. The new hypothesis is tested with other experiments.

THE SCIENTIFIC PAPER

Purpose
Procedure
Equipment
Discussion
Conclusion

4. Where does a scientific paper tell what the experiment is for?
5. What part of the paper gives details about the supplies and instruments?
6. Where does a scientific paper tell what the scientist did?
7. What part of a paper shows what happened?
8. Where does a scientific paper state whether or not the hypothesis was valid?

4D EXPERIMENTS NEED CONTROLS

When an experiment is performed, it must have a CONTROL. The control is used to compare. Controls are used to determine whether or not new factors added to experiments caused the results. Scientists must be able to compare results with and without the factor. So they conduct the experiment with the factor. Then they conduct the same experiment without the factor.

Scientists use a control when performing an experiment. The results of a procedure with a factor are compared with the results of the same procedure without the factor.

It is as if controlled experiments had two parts. In the first part of the experiment, something is observed. In the second part, that same thing is observed with a factor added. Then the two parts of the experiment are compared. In this way, plants without fertilizer are compared to plants with fertilizer. A car without an anti-smog device is compared to a car with an anti-smog device. Life spans of nonsmokers are compared to life spans of smokers. In these examples, the plants without fertilizer, the car without the anti-smog device, and the people who didn't smoke were the controls. The fertilizer, the anti-smog device, and the cigarettes were the factors added.

9. What is the purpose of a control in an experiment?

ACTIVITY: Testing Hypotheses with a Spring and Weights

MATERIALS: Spring, large weight, small weight, string, paper clip, tape

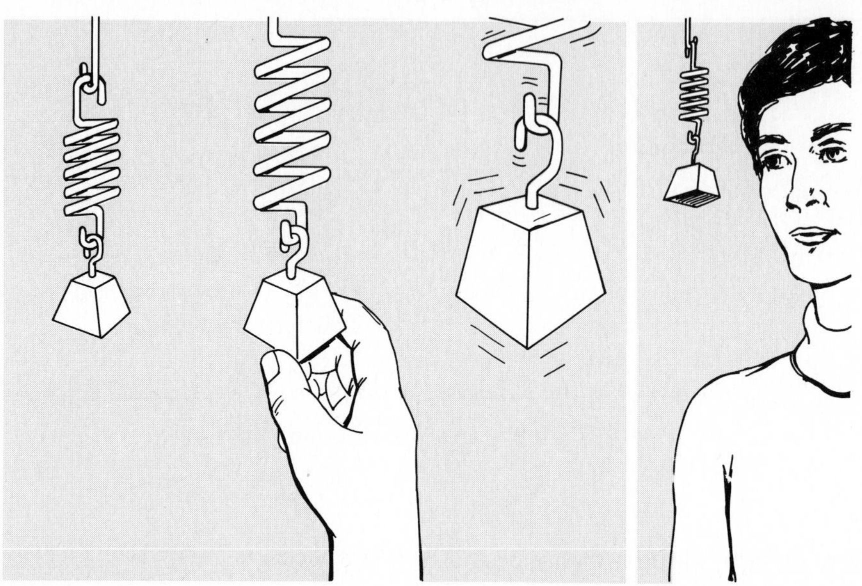

a. Hang the large weight on the end of a spring.
b. Pull the weight down about 1 fingerwidth and let it go.
c. The weight bounces up and down.
d. Count how many times per minute the weight hits the bottom of its bounce. Answer questions 10 and 20.
e. Form a hypothesis about how many times per minute the small weight will bounce. Answer question 11.
f. Hang the small weight on the spring. Pull it down the width of your finger and let it go. Count the bounces carefully for one minute. Answer question 12.
g. Scientists are often unsatisfied with one trial. Answer question 13.
h. Count the bounces per minute again for each weight. Answer questions 14 through 17.
i. Use the large weight and spring again. Form a hypothesis about how fast the large weight will bounce if it were pulled down 3 fingerwidths instead of 1 fingerwidth. Answer questions 18 and 19.
j. Pull the large weight down 3 fingerwidths. Release it and count the bounces for one minute. Answer question 21.

---

10. How many times per minute did the large weight hit the bottom of its bounce when pulled down 1 fingerwidth?
11. What is your hypothesis on how fast the small weight will bounce when pulled down 1 fingerwidth?
12. How many times did the small weight bounce per minute when pulled down 1 fingerwidth?
13. Why not just take one trial with each weight?
14. How many bounces were there per minute for each weight on their second trials?
15. What would happen if you tested the same thing again and again?
16. What did the data show about your hypothesis on the bounce rate of the small weight?
17. Even if you didn't guess right, what did you learn?
18. What is your hypothesis on the bounce rate of the large weight if it were pulled down 3 fingerwidths?
19. What should you do with the hypothesis in question 18?
20. How many times did the larger mass bounce per minute when pulled down one fingerwidth?
21. How many times did the larger mass bounce per minute when pulled down 3 fingerwidths?
22. Look at your answers to questions 20 and 21. Decide the validity of your hypothesis on how fast the mass will bounce when pulled down a longer distance.
23. What is the test of a hypothesis called?
24. Why are hypotheses tested?

4E USING CONTROLS

Here are some examples of how controls add meaning to what you see. Like a scientist, you must compare to be correct.

Look at Picture A at the right.

Picture A

25. How large do you think the flowers are?
26. Check with other students in the class. Do you all have the same answer?

Look at Picture B, page 30.

27. How large do you think the flowers are now?
28. Do your classmates agree with each other this time?
29. What was different about Picture B?

Take a good look at the actors in Picture C.

Picture C

30. How tall would you say they are?
31. How tall do your classmates think they are?

Now look at Picture D, page 30.

32. What size do you think the "actors" are now?
33. How did the people in Picture D change your opinion about the size of the "actors"?
34. Why did the photographer put the coin in Picture E?

Picture E

A student wanted to test a new kind of battery in his radio. He put in the battery and let the radio run until it went dead. Then he recorded how many hours the radio had worked. He decided the battery was pretty good.

35. How well was the student's experiment designed? Defend your answer.
36. What should every experiment include to show the accuracy of the results.

The following ads could appear in a newspaper.

OUR BELTED RADIALS ARE 40% STRONGER.

37. What is missing from this claim?

OUR CIGARETTES CONTAIN 27% LESS COAL TARS.

38. How would you criticize this ad?

Picture B

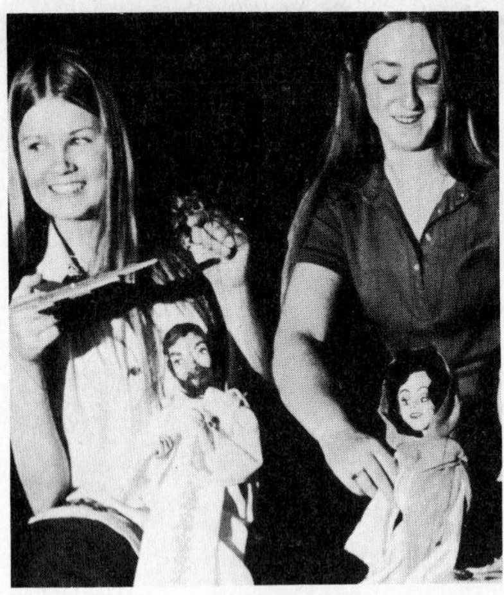

Picture D

ACTIVITY: Comparing Different Antacids

MATERIALS: Beaker, graduated cylinders, glass rod, indicator, acid solution, antacid pill, water

The units on the graduated cylinder are milliliters, abbreviated ml. If you are not familiar with metric units, they are explained in Chapter 6.

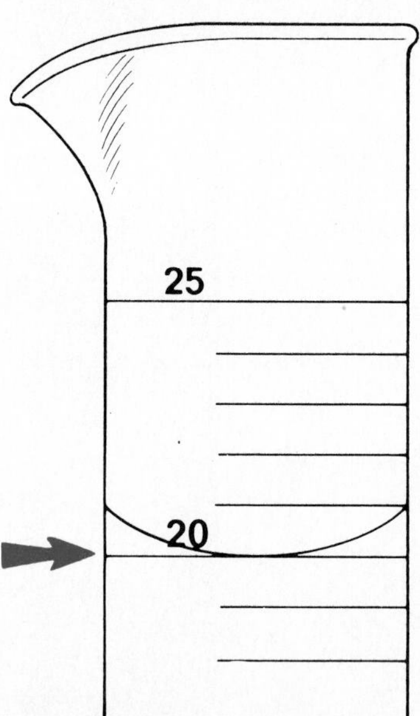

Take the measurement from the bottom of the curve. The graduate contains 20 ml of water, not 21 ml.

a. Your team will be given some brand of antacid in pill form. Crush the pill into a powder by wrapping it in paper and hitting it.

b. Put *all* of the powder in the beaker.

c. Add 20 ml of water.

d. Put in two drops of indicator. An indicator is a substance that tells you if a certain material is present. The indicator will change color when the pill is used up. This means the pill has neutralized that much acid.

e. Use a glass rod to stir the beaker every time you add something. Keep careful track of what you do.

f. Fill a graduated cylinder with acid solution to the 100 ml mark. Be sure everyone uses the same acid.

g. Pour a small amount of the acid into the beaker and stir it. Watch the color.

h. Keep adding acid in small amounts. Stir each time. When the color changes and doesn't change back, stop!

i. Write your results on the board. Put down the brand and the amount of acid you used.

39. What brand of antacid did you use?
40. What did the color of the solution do when you added the acid?
41. How much acid did you add?
42. Which antacid tablet neutralized the most acid?
43. How do you know what brand neutralized the most acid?
44. Why did everyone have to use the same acid solution?

SUMMARY

VOCABULARY

experiment	scientific paper	procedure	valid
data	purpose	equipment	control

KEY FACTS AND CONCEPTS

Hypotheses are tested by experiments.
Experiments are written up as scientific papers.
Scientific papers are divided into the following parts:
purpose, equipment, procedure, data, discussion, and conclusion.
Controlled experiments have two parts.
In experiments, controls are used to set up comparisons to determine the effects of changes.

CONCLUSION

The climax of the scientific way of solving problems is the experiment. The data from an experiment determine if a hypothesis is valid.

An experiment must have a control. The control allows the experimenter to know if an added factor is causing the effects in the experiment.

45. What is the KEY IDEA of this chapter?

CHAPTER

5 Standards

The Need for Comparison

5A INTRODUCTION

You have learned about scientists and how they work. First, scientists observe a fact that doesn't fit in with what they already know. This makes them curious and gives them a problem to solve. Scientists form hypotheses to solve problems. Then they perform experiments to test their hypotheses. The experiments include controls so that they can compare results with what they knew before.

There is a lot of measuring in the average experiment. In previous chapters, you measured volumes of liquid, bounces of balls per second, and swings of a pendulum. MEASUREMENTS are a fact of life.

In fact, you measure things all day. How much soda is left in the bottle? How many baskets did you make in the game? How many cassettes can you buy with your allowance? How many minutes to the end of this class?

Measuring is comparing. When you measure, you are comparing an unknown amount with a known amount. Distances are compared with rulers and tape measures. Liquids are compared with meters on gas station pumps or measuring cups in the kitchen. Weights are compared with scales and balances. The question is, who decides the size of the ruler? This is where STANDARDS come in.

These objects were used as standard weights in England in the 16th century.

Distance is measured by comparing the unknown distance with a length. These lengths do not change. Everyone accepts them. In the English system, the inches, feet, and yards on tape measures and rulers are set by comparison with a standard yard. In the metric system, lengths are compared with a standard meter. **A standard is a value that is accepted by a large number of people.**

1. When you measure with a ruler or tape measure, what are you really doing?

2. What is a standard?

5B STANDARDS ARE UNIVERSAL

This standard weight was used in Babylon when King Nebuchadnezzar II ruled, 605–562 B.C.

People have used standards for many centuries. Some scientists study ancient civilizations. They have found that standard weights were used in all the countries along the eastern Mediterranean Sea. For example, the same size weight was used as a standard throughout Greece and the surrounding islands. The first standard weights were probably made well over 4,000 years ago.

The Romans measured distance in paces. Each standard pace was 5 feet in length. The mile that is still used today is based on how far the Roman soldier marched with 1,000 paces. In fact, the word *mile* comes from the Latin words meaning "1,000 paces."

A standard must always stay the same. The steel measuring tapes used by surveyors have a place to attach a thermometer. The surveyor must make an adjustment for how much the tape expands or contracts with temperature changes. Surveyors do this so that their measurements always stay the same.

Standard meter bars are kept by the National Bureau of Standards. Like the surveyor's measuring tape, the meter bars expand and contract. The lengths marked on them are accurate only when the bars are at the temperature of melting ice.

> A standard is a particular value that is accepted as the official value.

Standards apply to more than lengths and weights. You would be able to plug in a radio and play it almost anywhere in the United States. Similarly, there would be no problem using hair dryers, electric razors, cassette players, or appliances. Even with traffic signals, a red light means stop almost everywhere. It is standard throughout most of the world, even where people drive on the other side of the road.

Standards are needed in industry. For example, one kind of truck part may be made in California. But the body of the truck may be made in Japan. The parts always fit the bodies because they are a standard size.

Most thirty-five millimeter camera film is made in the United States, England, and Japan. Most thirty-five millimeter cameras are made in Japan and Germany. Because of standards, the film always fits the cameras.

3. What would happen to a business that bought lengths of cloth with a short tape and sold them with a long tape?

4. How long have standards been used?

5. Why should standards be the same all over the world?

6. Name some standards other than mass, length, and volume.

7. Why does industry need standards?

ACTIVITY: Making a Standard Ruler

MATERIALS: Stick, masking tape

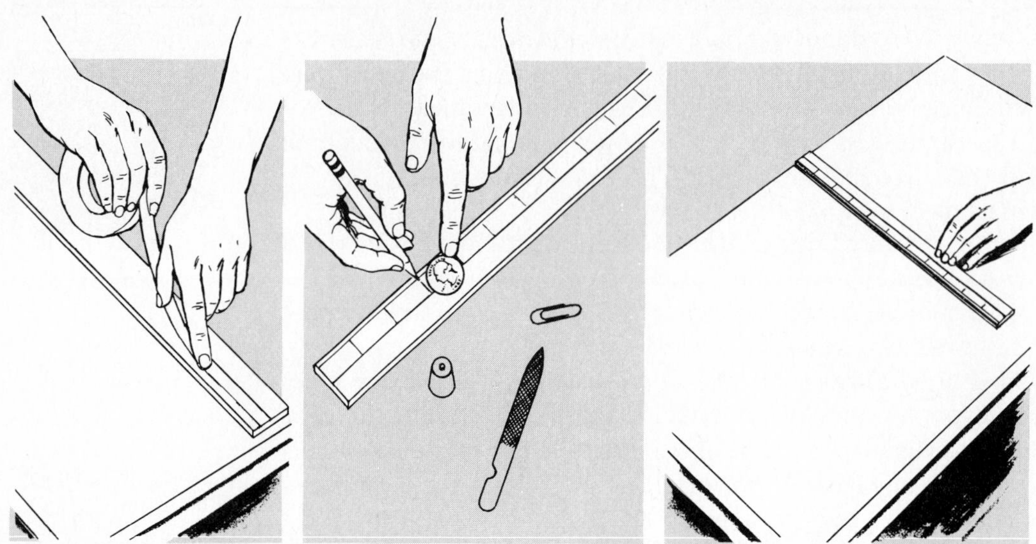

Use these materials to create your own ruler. You may use your finger, a dime, a paper clip, or anything you wish to mark off the spaces. Just be sure to use the same object for the entire ruler.

a. Put a strip of masking tape on the piece of wood or plastic that you have been given.
b. Make it into a ruler by marking off equal spaces.
c. Measure the width of your table as so many marked spaces or units.
d. Write the value you found for width on the chalkboard. Include the unit you used.
e. From the chalkboard, make a list of the values your classmates found for their tables. Include the units they used.

8. What units did you use?
9. What was the width of your table in your own units?
10. Do the data you collected show all the tables have the same width?
11. Do the lab tables all look to be the same size?
12. What is necessary for the answers to questions 10 and 11 to agree?

5C STANDARDS ARE MAINTAINED

Standards are important enough to be controlled by law. The yard still used in the United States is defined by an act of Congress. The yard is a certain part, 0.9144, of a standard meter. **Congress set up the National Bureau of Standards to maintain the standards for the United States.** The Bureau compares such things as the measuring equipment used in factories with the standards for the whole country. Therefore, everyone in this country can speak of measurements in the same terms.

Most state and county governments have departments of weights and measures. If you look at the scales in a market or the pumps in a gas station you may see a sticker. The sticker shows that the equipment has been tested by the local department of weights and measures. The equipment has been compared to a standard.

13. Why should market scales be checked by a department of weights and measures?

14. Why are standards so important?

SUMMARY

VOCABULARY

measurement standard

KEY FACTS AND CONCEPTS

A standard is a unit of length or some other quantity that everyone agrees to use.

People have used standards for many centuries.

Standards are needed in business and industry to be sure everyone knows what the other person means.

The National Bureau of Standards maintains the standards for the United States.

CONCLUSION

Standards are needed in almost every aspect of life and are used around the world. Standards are used to ensure that things fit together, whether it be a cassette in a stereo or an English roll of film in a Japanese camera.

15. What is the KEY IDEA of this chapter?

CHAPTER

6 Metric Measurement

The Most Common System of Measurement

6A INTRODUCTION

A standard provides something for comparison. For example, the length of a football field is the same everywhere football is played. When a football stadium is being built in Utah, the builders know what length their football field has to be. The builders compare the length of their field with the others. The new field will be the same length as fields in New York and California. All football fields are a standard length.

Measurement standards should have certain characteristics. They should be easy to use. Measurement standards should be related to each other. The same standards should be used all over the world.

The metric system meets these requirements better than any other system of measurement. The metric system is easy to use because it has decimal divisions. Like the number system we use, metric divisions are based on the number 10. Larger metric units are multiples of 10. Smaller units are found by dividing by 10. The metric units for length, volume, and mass are related to each other.

The metric system is used throughout the world. The United States is the only industrialized nation that does not presently require metric measurements in trade. Congress adopted the meter back in the 19th century but didn't require that people use it. The United States is slowly changing.

The metric system is a system of measurement with units based on multiples of 10. The units for mass, length, and volume are related.

1. What are some advantages of the metric system?

6B THE UNIT OF LENGTH

The unit of length in the metric system is the METER. To give you an idea of the size of the meter, an average doorway is just over two meters high.

The meter is divided into tenths, hundredths, and thousandths. There are names for these divisions. One tenth of a meter is a decimeter. One hundredth of a meter is a centimeter. One thousandth of a meter is a millimeter.

When naming metric units, the same PREFIXES are used over and over again. These prefixes are the first parts of the unit names. DECI always means one tenth of the unit. CENTI always means one hundredth of the unit. MILLI always means one thousandth of the unit. Deci is seldom used.

There are also standard prefixes for the larger units. DEKA is 10 times the unit, HECTO is 100 times the unit, and KILO means 1,000 times the unit. So ten meters is a dekameter. One hundred meters is a hectometer. One thousand meters is a kilometer. Deka and hecto are seldom used.

meter	(m)	=	1 meter
kilometer	(km)	=	1000 meters
centimeter	(cm)	=	100th part of a meter
millimeter	(mm)	=	1000th part of a meter

Because metric units are usually used in steps of one thousand, dekameters, hectometers, and decimeters are not used very often. Centimeters are an exception. The centimeter is used because it is a convenient size. It is used to measure objects that are more than 100 millimeters long but small enough to pick up and handle.

There are other prefixes as well. MICRO means one millionth of a unit. Therefore, a micrometer is very tiny. This special unit is often called a micron, although micron is not an official metric name. A single bacterial cell is about one micron long. For measuring large amounts or sizes, one prefix that is used is MEGA. Mega means one million times the unit.

To save time and space, the units are abbreviated. To abbreviate kilometers use km, for meters use m, and for millimeters use mm. Centimeters are abbreviated cm.

Bacteria are about one millionth of a meter long.

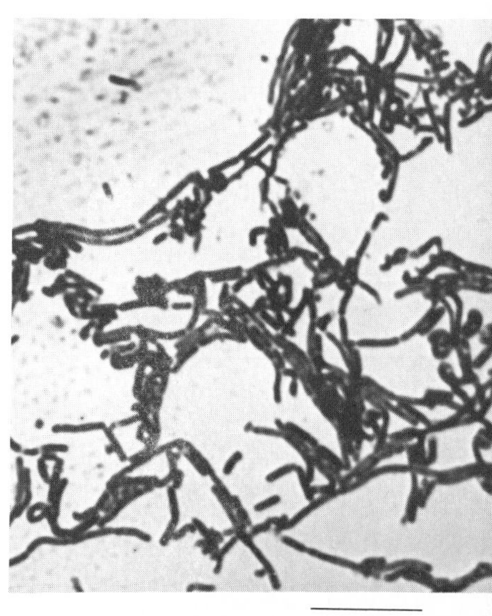

Metric Prefixes and Their Values

Multiplier	Prefix	Symbol
1,000,000	mega	M
1,000	kilo	k
100	hecto	h
10	deka	da
1	—	—
$\frac{1}{10}$	deci	d
$\frac{1}{100}$	centi	c
$\frac{1}{1,000}$	milli	m
$\frac{1}{1,000,000}$	micro	μ

Metric measurements are used in many industries, in international events, and in scientific notation. The width of an eye glass lens is measured in millimeters. The Olympic Games hold such events as the 100-meter dash. Scientists have determined the average distance to the moon to be 384,400 kilometers.

2. What is the unit of length in the metric system?
3. How many meters are in one kilometer?
4. What does mm stand for?
5. Is 100 mm larger or smaller than 1 meter?

6C CONVERTING UNITS

In the metric system, only the decimal moves when the units change.

2600 meters
2.6 kilometers

The decimal moves left when the new unit is larger

1.816 meters
1816 millimeters

The decimal moves right when the new unit is smaller

To convert to larger or smaller divisions of a meter, just move the decimal point. The decimal point moves two places to the right for hundredths and three places to the right for thousandths. If a man is 1.816 meters tall, he is also 181.6 centimeters tall, and 1816 millimeters tall. A distance of 2600 meters is also 2.6 kilometers. **The decimal moves to the right when the new unit is smaller and to the left when the new unit is larger.**

The U.S. Customary, or English, system of yards, feet, and inches is harder to use. With this system, the man measured in the preceding paragraph is 1 yard, 2 feet, 11½ inches tall, or 5 feet, 11½ inches tall, or 71½ inches tall. Changing from one unit to another requires doing more arithmetic in this system. A distance of 13,992 feet becomes 2.65 miles. This is figured by dividing the number of feet in one mile, 5,280, into the total amount of feet, 13,992. You can see that moving a decimal is easier than dividing by 5,280, even with a calculator.

6. Which system uses less arithmetic to change units?

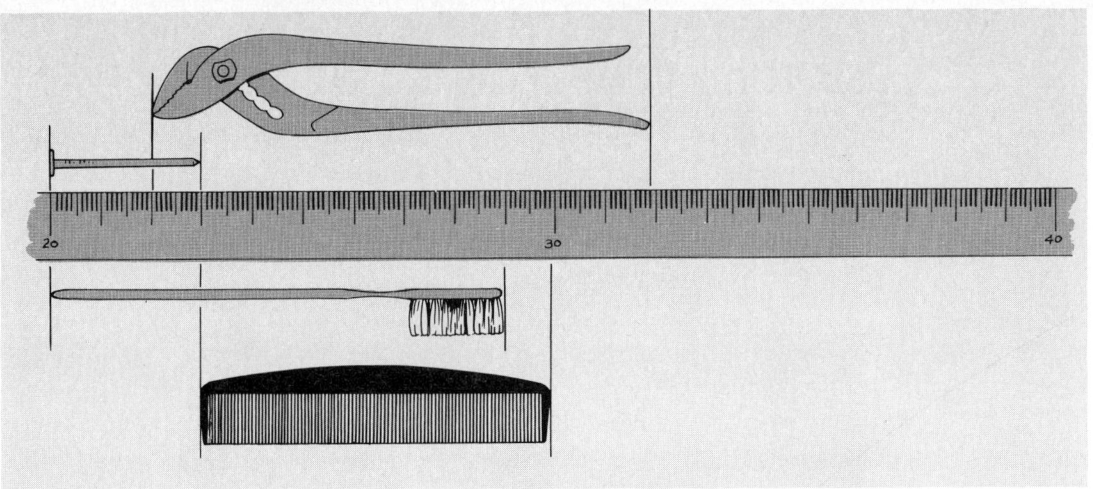

Use the picture of the meter stick above to answer the following questions.

7. What is the length of the nail in millimeters?
8. What is the length of the pliers in centimeters?
9. What is the length of the toothbrush in millimeters?
10. What is the length of the comb in centimeters?
11. What is the length of the toothbrush in meters?

ACTIVITY: The Meter Stick

MATERIALS: Meter stick

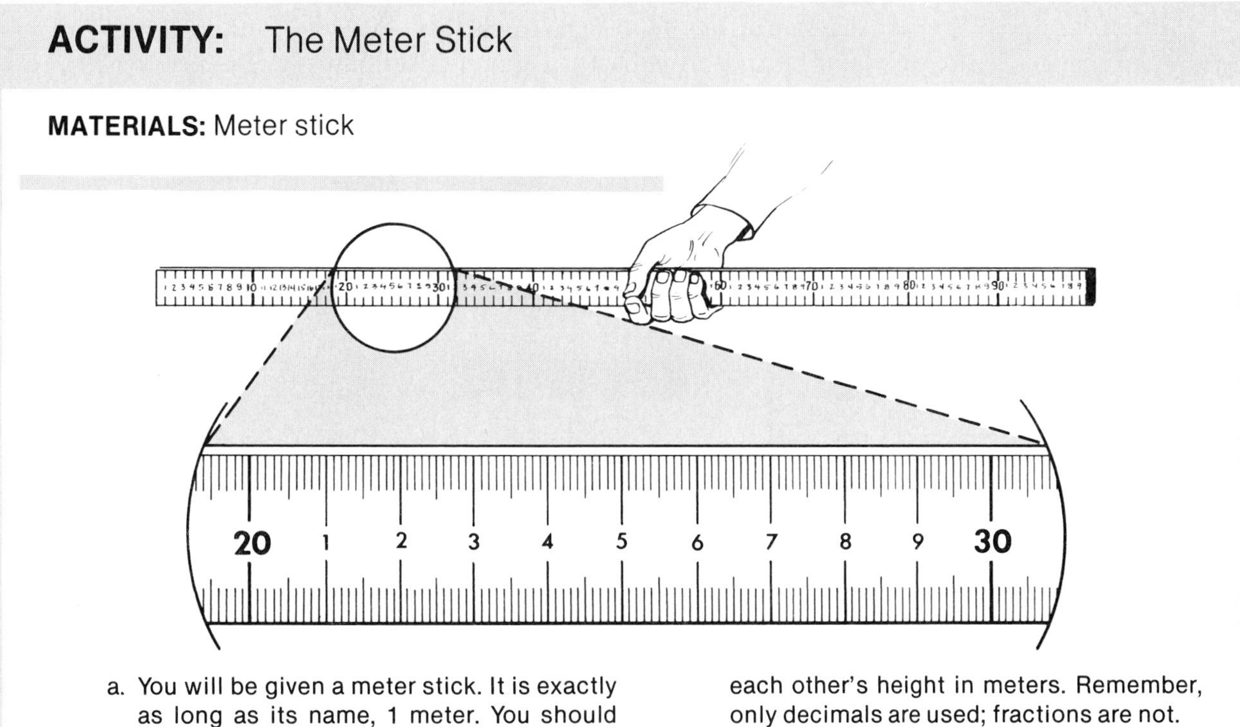

a. You will be given a meter stick. It is exactly as long as its name, 1 meter. You should notice there are 100 numbered divisions. The number 100 itself is usually left off the end.
b. Count how many small spaces there are between number 22 and 23. The numbers are centimeters. The tiny spaces are millimeters.
c. Work with your team partner to measure each other's height in meters. Remember, only decimals are used; fractions are not.

12. How many small spaces did you count?
13. Without counting, tell how many small spaces, or millimeters, are on the whole stick.
14. What is your height in meters?
15. What is your height in centimeters?
16. What is your height in millimeters?

6D THE UNIT OF VOLUME

For big projects, such as the building of a skyscraper, concrete is measured in cubic meters. For daily use, the unit of volume is the LITER. The liter is the unit used in laboratories all over the world. It is the unit you will use to measure VOLUME. **Volume is the amount of space an object occupies.**

The engine volume of a car, expressed in liters, often appears on the car's body.

The liter is related to the meter. The liter is the amount of space taken up by a cube 10 centimeters long by 10 centimeters wide by 10 centimeters high. Volume is found by multiplying length times width times height. In all cubes, these dimensions are always equal. In this cube, 10 times 10 times 10 is 1,000. So a liter holds 1000 cubic centimeters. Cubic centimeters are sometimes used to express volume and are abbreviated cm^3 or cc. You will use cc when you need to abbreviate.

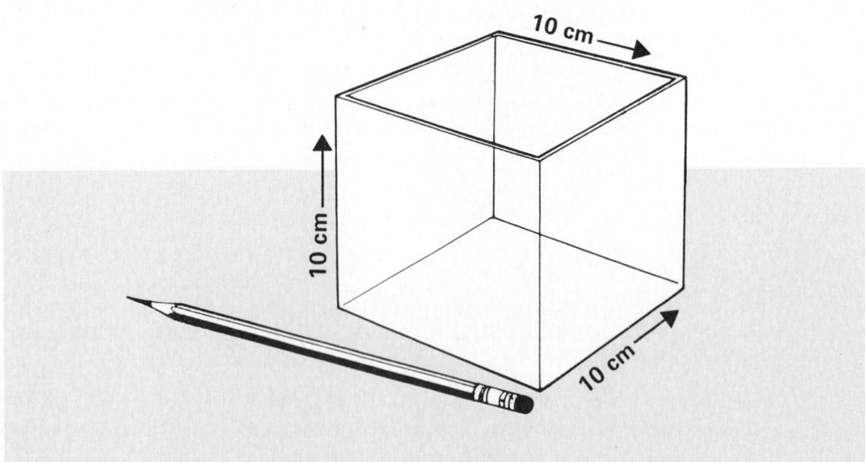

A liter may be divided into 1000 milliliters. *Milli* is the same prefix that is used with the meter. The in-between divisions, deciliter and centiliter, are not used very often in laboratory work. The units for you to remember are liters and milliliters, abbreviated l and ml.

liter	(l)	=	1 liter
milliliter	(ml)	=	1000th part of a liter

If 1000 milliliters and 1000 cubic centimeters both equal 1 liter, then 1 milliliter must equal 1 cubic centimeter. This is another example of how the metric units are related. **Milliliters and cubic centimeters are interchangeable.**

17. What is the metric unit of volume in everyday use?
18. How many milliliters are in a liter?
19. How many cubic centimeters are in a liter?
20. A student poured 875 ml of water into a jar. Then 647 ml were added. How many ml of water were in the jar? How many liters of water were in the jar?
21. A plastic box measured 16 cm long by 12 cm wide by 8 cm high. How many ml of liquid can it hold? How many liters can it hold?

Use the picture of the graduated cylinder at the right to answer the following question.

22. There are three layers of different liquids in the graduated cylinder. How many milliliters are in each layer?

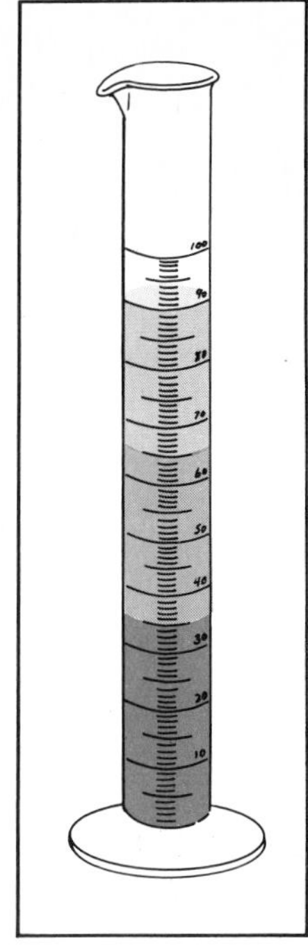

There are three layers of liquid in this graduated cylinder.

ACTIVITY: Measuring Volume in Milliliters

MATERIALS: Graduated cylinder, bottles or containers of various sizes

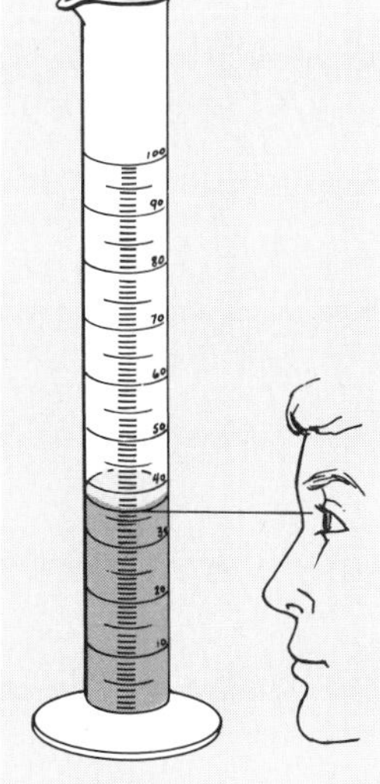

Keep your eye level with the waterline. Take your reading from the bottom of the curve.

a. Liquids are measured in the laboratory with a graduated cylinder. It is named by its shape, a cylinder, and the marks down the sides, called graduations. It is often called a graduate. Inspect the graduate given to your team.

b. Put some water in the graduate. Bend over so your eye is level with the water line. Always use the very bottom of the curved water line as the measuring point. This curved line is called the meniscus.

c. There will be several bottles or other containers in the room. Choose four of them and measure how much water each will hold. You will have to count how many times you fill the graduate for the larger bottles.

23. What units are marked on the graduate?
24. How much would it hold to the top of the graduations?
25. What is the shape of the water line?
• 26. Identify each of the bottles or other containers you measured and list their volumes.

SUMMARY

VOCABULARY

meter	centi	hecto	mega
prefix	milli	kilo	liter
deci	deka	micro	volume

KEY FACTS AND CONCEPTS

The metric unit of length is the meter.
The unit of volume is the liter.
The units of the metric system are multiplied or divided by 10's, 100's, 1,000's, and so on.
The metric system is a decimal system. Fractions are not used.
Metric units are related. One cubic centimeter is equal to one milliliter.

CONCLUSION

There are less than a dozen countries in the whole world that do not use the metric system. The system is easier to use than any other system of measurement known today. Its units are related and require less arithmetic to handle. Countries, such as the United States, that do not use the metric system are handicapped in international trade.

27. What is the KEY IDEA of this chapter?

CHAPTER

7 The Unit of Mass

The Amount of Matter

7A INTRODUCTION

Lengths are measured in meters, and volumes are measured in liters. If you cross the United States, you make a journey of well over 4000 kilometers. If you drink a glass of milk, you consume about 200 or 300 milliliters of liquid. Meters and liters take care of two of the big three measurements you make daily. The third big measurement is involved when you step on a scale. But the metric system does not use pounds because it does not measure weight in the same way as the US system.

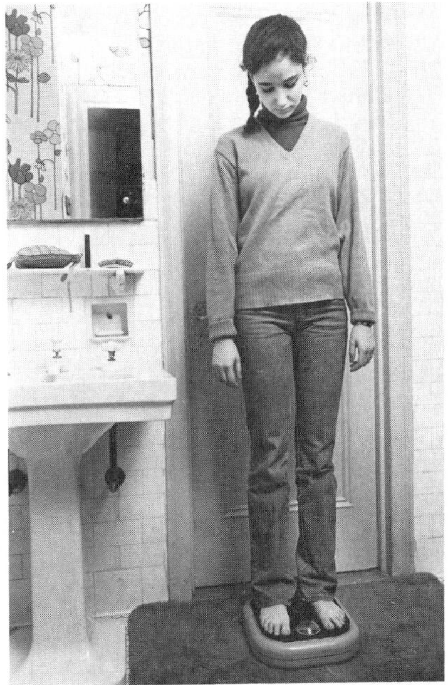

1. In the metric system, what units are used to measure lengths?
2. In the metric system, what units are used to measure volumes?

7B THE KILOGRAM

The metric unit of mass is the KILOGRAM. In metric countries, bathroom scales and butcher's scales are in kilograms. The device you will use to measure mass is marked in grams.

Once again, you will notice the prefix *kilo* in the word *kilogram. Kilo* means 1,000 times the unit. **So there are 1000 grams in a kilogram.** Kilograms, abbreviated kg, are used for expressing the mass of people, potatoes, and other large amounts. GRAMS, abbreviated g, are used for smaller amounts. The milligram, mg, is used to measure really tiny amounts. The meat in a hamburger or the things in your purse or pockets would be measured in grams. The dose of medicine in a capsule is measured in milligrams.

gram	(g)	=	1 gram
kilogram	(kg)	=	1000 grams
milligram	(mg)	=	1000th part of a gram

You will use a BALANCE to weigh objects in class. But there is a complication. **Mass and weight are not the same thing.** MASS is a measurement of the amount of matter in an object. MATTER is the material that things are made of. You will learn more about matter in Chapter 12.

WEIGHT is the pull of gravity on matter. GRAVITY is the pull between the earth and all other objects. When you weigh an object on a balance, you are comparing pulls. The balance tells you when the pull on an object is equal to the pull on a known mass. **It is the two pulls, or forces, that balance.** That is why the device is called a balance.

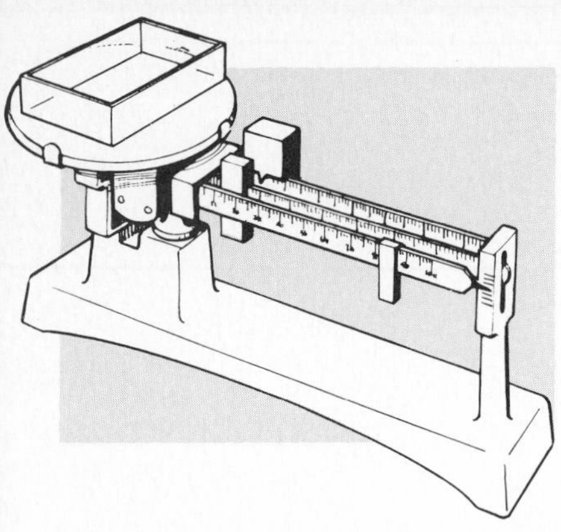

This is one type of balance. To use this balance, you would move the riders along the arms, or beams, until the pointer stopped at the zero point. The mass of the object on the pan is equal to the sum of the readings on the three beams. This is called a triple-beam balance.

Scales don't balance; they work with springs. The pull of gravity stretches the springs. If gravity changes, the pull changes and, therefore, the weight changes.

Mass, on the other hand, does not change. A kilogram of mass will be a kilogram anywhere. Only weight will change with location. For example, the moon exerts a much weaker gravitational pull on objects than the earth does. So while 1 kilogram of mass weighs about 2.2 pounds on earth, it will weigh only about one sixth of that on the moon. But it is still 1 kilogram of mass whether it is on the moon or on earth.

> WEIGHT is a measure of the pull of gravity between two objects. This measure does change.
>
> MASS is the amount of material in an object. This amount does not change.

Scientists use mass because it is more reliable than weight. When scientists do experiments, mass is what they use to express their findings and calculations. This book will also use mass. It is more dependable because it does not change.

3. What is the metric unit of mass?
4. What does weight measure?
5. How does a balance work?
6. Why do scientists use mass rather than weight when they work?

7C METERS, LITERS, AND MASS

Meters and liters are related. A cube with a length, width, and height of 10 centimeters, holds 1 liter of water. Water is the liquid used to show the relationship between mass, volume, and length.

One liter of water has a mass of 1 kilogram. A liter can be broken down into 1000 milliliters. One thousand milliliters equals 1000 cubic centimeters. A kilogram can be broken down into 1000 grams. One milliliter of water and 1 cubic centimeter of water both have masses of 1 gram. A cubic meter of water is 1000 liters. It has a mass of 1000 kilograms.

Compare this with the units now used in the United States. A gallon of water has a volume of 231 cubic inches. That much water weighs 8.33 pounds. None of these units is related to the other. Multiplying or dividing them is not easy.

7. What is the mass of 50 cubic centimeters of water?
8. What is the volume of 100 grams of water?
9. How many grams are in 2 kilograms?

ACTIVITY: The Mass of Water

MATERIALS: Balance, graduated cylinder

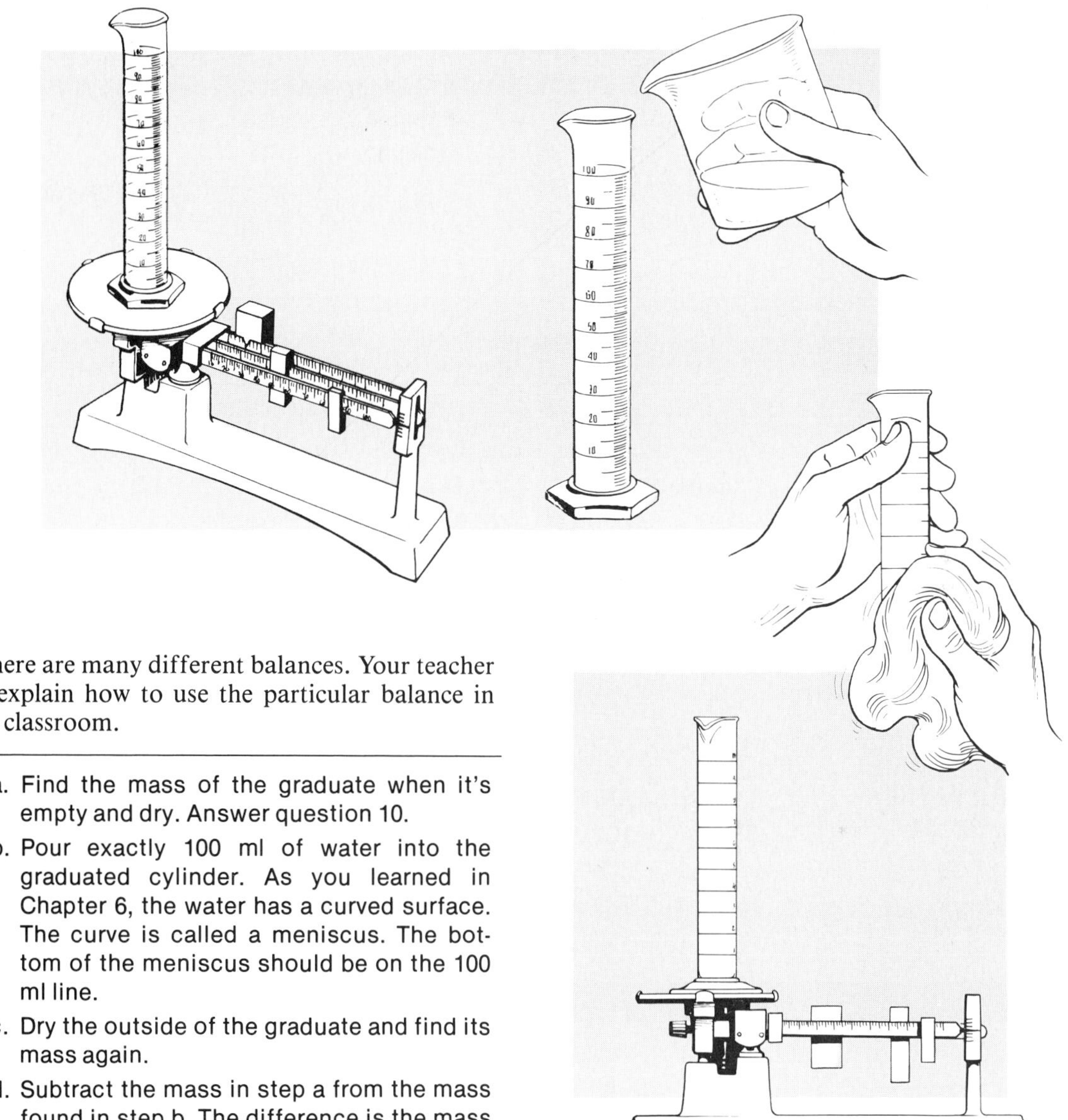

There are many different balances. Your teacher will explain how to use the particular balance in your classroom.

a. Find the mass of the graduate when it's empty and dry. Answer question 10.
b. Pour exactly 100 ml of water into the graduated cylinder. As you learned in Chapter 6, the water has a curved surface. The curve is called a meniscus. The bottom of the meniscus should be on the 100 ml line.
c. Dry the outside of the graduate and find its mass again.
d. Subtract the mass in step a from the mass found in step b. The difference is the mass of the water. Answer question 11.
e. Pour off the 100 ml of water and try some other amount. Put in 50 ml or 75 ml. Dry the outside and find the mass of the graduate again. Answer question 13.
f. Subtract the mass of the empty graduate from the mass of the partly filled graduate. Answer question 14.

10. What is the mass of the dry graduate?
11. What is the mass of the 100 ml of water?
12. How close is the mass of water in grams to its volume in milliliters? What does this show?
13. What volume of water did you use the second time?
14. What is the mass this time?
15. When you subtracted the mass of the empty graduate from the mass of the partly filled graduate, what did you find was the mass of the water?
16. How close is the mass of the water in grams to its volume in milliliters? What does this show?

7D REVIEWING METRIC UNITS

SUMMARY OF THE METRIC SYSTEM UNITS AND TOOLS

MEASUREMENT	UNITS		TOOL
Length	kilometer	(km)	Meter stick
	meter	(m)	Metric ruler
	centimeter	(cm)	
	millimeter	(mm)	
Volume	liter	(l)	Graduated cylinder
	milliliter	(ml)	
Mass	kilogram	(kg)	Balance
	gram	(g)	
	milligram	(mg)	

If necessary, turn back to Chapter 6 to answer the following questions.

17. What metric unit would you use to measure each of the following?
    a. the height of a table
    b. the length of an automobile
    c. a sack of rice
    d. the milk in a carton
    e. gasoline or diesel fuel
    f. the distance from San Francisco to New York
    g. the width of a postage stamp
    h. a dose of penicillin

18. Convert these values.
    100 ml to l
    2000 ml to l
    1.5 l to ml

19. What do the following abbreviations stand for?
    g ml
    l kg
    mm cm
    km m

20. Fill in the missing labels.
    5.0 cm = 50 ____
    200 mm = 20.0 ____
    1500 mm = 1.500 ____

21. Find the missing amounts.
    30 mm = ____ cm = ____ m
    ____ mm = ____ cm = 1 m
    ____ mm = 55 cm = ____ m

22. Convert these values.
    1500 g = ______ kg
    300 g = ______ kg
    ______ g = 0.83 kg

23. What instrument would you use to measure the mass of a hot dog? The length of a living room? The volume of a soda bottle?

24. A plastic shoe box is 30 cm long, 15 cm wide, and 12 cm deep. The box is filled with water. Answer the following questions about it.

a. What is its volume in cubic centimeters?
b. What is its volume in milliliters?
c. What is the mass of the water in grams?
d. What is the mass of the water in kilograms?

SUMMARY

VOCABULARY

kilogram	balance	matter	gravity
gram	mass	weight	

KEY FACTS AND CONCEPTS

The kilogram is the unit of mass in the metric system.

There are 1000 grams in a kilogram.

Grams are used for small amounts of mass.

A liter of water has a mass of one kilogram. A milliliter of water has a mass of one gram. A cubic centimeter of water also has a mass of one gram.

Mass and weight are not the same thing.

Mass is an amount of matter in an object. Weight is the pull of gravity on matter.

Scientists use mass in their work.

CONCLUSION

Water relates the kilogram of mass to volume and length. Water was chosen to show the relationship because it is used so often for so many purposes.

A unit in the metric system may be converted into a larger or smaller unit by multiplying or dividing by 10, 100, or 1,000. This can be done simply by moving the decimal point. To convert from one unit to another in the system used in the United States requires much more work.

25. What is the KEY IDEA of this chapter?

CHAPTER

8 Data Tables

Organizing Information

8A INTRODUCTION

As you have learned, experiments produce data that support or reject hypotheses. The word *data* is just the scientific term for information. **Scientists usually collect data in the form of numbers because most of their activities require measurements.** Scientists feel that when they can measure an effect, they know more about it.

Scientists not only have to use the right numbers. They must also use the right UNITS to describe the numbers. A number like "10" doesn't mean much by itself. But using "10 minutes" indicates a very exact period of time. All numbers must be identified by the correct unit.

Recording data and measurements means writing down many numbers. But numbers must be organized to be meaningful.

Data must be organized to be useful.

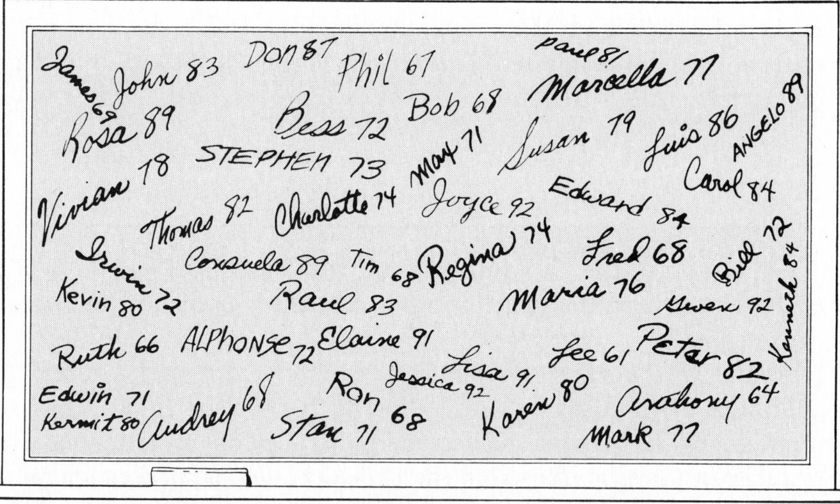

The drawing above shows you what can happen when numbers are recorded in a disorganized way. In this case, there is no way your eye can go smoothly from number to number. The numbers do not form a pattern, and it is difficult to match up a figure with a name. Reading this information is confusing and time consuming.

1. Why do scientists collect data in numerical form?

8B DATA TABLES

Data is organized in DATA TABLES. A data table is a chart that organizes numbers in ROWS and COLUMNS. Your eye can run down a column of figures quickly. You can pick out important numbers and see patterns easily. Less time is lost hunting for the largest or smallest number. **Scientists use data tables to communicate their findings simply and clearly.**

WHY A DATA TABLE IS HELPFUL AND USEFUL

It is well organized.

It contains only the facts.

Facts can be found rapidly.

Look at Table 1 below. This is a data table about the polluting chemicals from cars. Notice that only the facts are listed in a data table. Data tables generally have the following characteristics.

A. Tables are numbered in the order in which they appear.
B. The TITLE tells what information is in the table.
C. The table often has a box rule drawn around it. The table is usually divided into rows and columns.
D. The rows and columns have HEADINGS, and sometimes subheadings, to explain their information.
E. The units used in the table are shown in either the headings or the title.

Table 1. Motor Vehicle Pollutant Emission per Vehicle-Mile Traveled 1970-1981. (grams per mile)

Pollutant	1970	1974	1975	1976	1977	1978	1979	1980	1981
Carbon Monoxide	86.9	79.0	77.0	74.3	71.4	68.3	65.2	60.6	55.5
Hydro-carbons	12.1	9.9	9.4	8.9	8.4	7.9	7.3	6.6	5.8
Oxides of Nitrogen	4.7	4.7	4.6	4.4	4.1	3.9	3.8	3.6	3.4

THE FIVE MAIN PARTS OF A DATA TABLE

Number — Columns
Title — Rows
Box

2. What information is in Table 1?
3. Which pollutant shows the least change?
4. What units are used to describe the numbers in this table?
5. What years are missing from the table?

ACTIVITY: Measuring Bounces

MATERIALS: Set of balls, meter stick

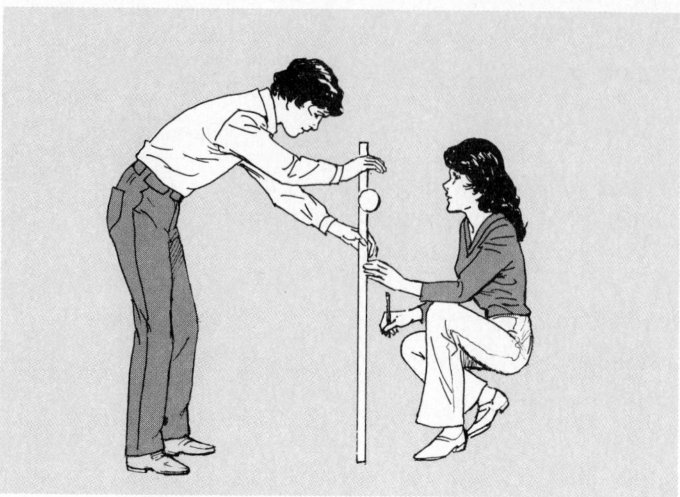

a. Drop the balls onto the floor. Notice that each ball bounces to a different height. If you were asked to choose the ball that would bounce the highest, which would you choose: a solid ball, a hollow ball, a light ball, a heavy ball, a large ball, a small ball?

b. Work in pairs. One person should hold the meter stick and drop the ball. The other person should read how high the ball bounces and catch it.

c. Before you begin, you must decide on the procedure of the experiment. To keep this experiment controlled, all balls must be dropped from the same height. To allow for errors, each ball should be dropped several times.

• d. All of your data will go in a table. Draw a table. Remember the five important parts of a table. The table should be numbered. The title tells what the information in the table is all about. The data is boxed in rows and columns.

e. Remember to have enough rows and columns to record all the trials of each ball. Include space to record the height from which they are dropped. The columns and rows need headings to identify them.

f. Don't forget the units you will use to measure the heights of the bounces. Finally, include a column to show the average height each ball bounced.

g. Do the experiment. Enter your data in the table.

h. Find the average height bounced for each ball and enter it in the table. If you don't remember how to average, do it this way. Add up all the bounce heights for one ball. Divide that number by the number of trials.

---

6. What was your hypothesis about which ball would bounce the highest?
7. Which unit did you use to measure height—meters, centimeters, or millimeters?
8. Run your eye down the column that shows the average height each ball bounced. Which ball bounced highest?

8C CONSTRUCTING YOUR OWN TABLES

Tables are not just used by scientists in laboratories. You probably see or use tables yourself everyday. Tables appear in newspapers, in magazines, and on TV. Credit card and utility bills are in table form. Tables are used so much because they help people understand numbers easily.

Table 3. World Series Players' Bonuses

Year	Winning Team	Bonus $	Losing Team	Bonus $
1961	Yankees	7,389	Reds	5,356
1962	Yankees	9,882	Giants	7,291
1963	Dodgers	12,794	Yankees	7,874
1964	Cardinals	8,622	Yankees	5,309
1965	Dodgers	10,297	Twins	6,634
1966	Orioles	11,683	Dodgers	8,189
1967	Cardinals	8,314	Red Sox	5,115
1968	Tigers	10,936	Cardinals	7,078
1969	Mets	18,338	Orioles	14,904
1970	Orioles	18,216	Reds	13,688
1971	Pirates	18,465	Orioles	13,905
1972	A's	20,705	Reds	15,080
1973	A's	24,617	Mets	14,950
1974	A's	22,219	Dodgers	15,704
1975	Reds	19,060	Red Sox	13,326
1976	Reds	26,366	Yankees	19,935
1977	Yankees	27,758	Dodgers	20,899
1978	Yankees	31,236	Dodgers	25,483
1979	Pirates	28,236	Orioles	22,113
1980	Phillies	34,693	Royals	32,211

Use Table 3 above to answer the following questions.

9. In what year did the Orioles make the most money?
10. How many times were the Yankees in the playoffs?
11. What is noticeable about players' bonuses starting in 1969?

Practice making another table. Be sure to include all five parts of a table. The five parts are the number, title, columns and rows, headings, and units. The following paragraph contains the data.

In 1974, the average motor vehicle emitted 79.0 grams of carbon monoxide for each kilometer traveled. In 1975, the amount of carbon monoxide emitted was 77.0 grams per kilometer. The 1976 value was 74.3 grams per kilometer. In 1977, carbon monoxide emission was 71.4 grams per kilometer. In 1978, cars emitted 68.3 grams per kilometer. In 1979, the value was 65.2 grams. The values for 1980 and 1981 were 60.6 grams per kilometer and 55.5 grams per kilometer respectively.

12. When did the greatest reduction in carbon monoxide emission take place?

Table 4. The Population of the United States

Year	1920	1930	1940	1950	1960	1970	1980
Population in Millions	106	123	132	151	179	203	226

Use Table 4 above to answer the following questions.

13. Which DECADE, or ten-year period, had the greatest population growth?

14. People tend to have fewer children during economic depressions. By looking at the table, in which decade did a depression probably occur?

Construct a table with the data in the next paragraph. Look back through the chapter if you need help, but first see how many of the five parts of a table you can remember by yourself.

In 1972, the United States imported 811 million barrels of oil. In 1973, 1,184 million barrels came in. In 1974, the number was 1,296 million. There were 1,498 million barrels in 1975, 1,983 million in 1976, 2,414 million in 1977, 2,320 million in 1978, and 2,332 million barrels in 1979.

15. Look at your table to decide which year had the greatest single increase.

16. Judging from the number of barrels imported from year to year, when did conservation practices begin to have an effect?

8D HOW TO READ DATA TABLES

You have learned why data tables are important and how they are constructed. You have even had practice making some tables. The knowledge about data tables can be applied to your life as a useful life skill.

You use data tables every day of your life. The quality of your life can depend on how well you can read a data table. Some examples of data tables include: weather reports, stock reports, phone bills, recipes, sales receipts, and bank statements.

The best way to learn about data tables is to look at one and use it.

A CHECKING ACCOUNT STATEMENT

EASTERN
SAVINGS BANK

ACCOUNT NUMBER
5275-450412-1
DATE
09/08/83
PAGE
1

SUNNYVALE 12-74
1200 SOUTHVALE AVE.
SUNNYVALE, CA. 95088
288/632-8464

DR WILLIAM S. BURNE
MRS WILLIAM S. BURNE
18 1432 RIVERSIDE
36 SUNNYVALE CA 95088
7

CHECKING STATEMENT SUMMARY.......................................

PREVIOUS STATEMENT 8-06-83, BALANCE OF...	367.69
2 DEPOSITS AND OTHER CREDITS TOTALING	1,203.50
CONSISTING OF 1 DEPOSIT ITEMS	
7 CHECKS AND OTHER DEBITS TOTALING...	396.68
SERVICE CHARGE AMOUNT	.00
CURRENT BALANCE AS OF STATEMENT DATE.....	1,174.51

CHECKING ACCOUNT TRANSACTIONS....................................

DATE	AMOUNT	TRANSACTION DESCRIPTION
08/26	1,200.00+	DEPOSIT CHECK
09/08	3.50+	NOW INTEREST CREDIT

DATE..	CHECK NO.........	AMOUNT	DATE..	CHECK NO........	AMOUNT
09/01	150	35.00	08/27	154	170.38
08/16	151	13.90	09/02	155	50.24
08/23	152	15.75	09/07	156	50.59
08/23	153	60.82			

DAILY BALANCE SUMMARY..

DATE.....	BALANCE	DATE.....	BALANCE.....	DATE....	BALANCE
08/16	353.79	08/27	1,306.84	09/07	1,170.01
08/23	277.22	09/01	1,271.84	09/08	1,174.51
08/26	1,477.22	09/02	1,221.60		

*** FOR CHECKING CONVENIENCE...INTEREST-EARNING CHECKING, ***
*** WELCOME CHECK, MASTERCARD/VISA ASK US FOR DETAILS! ***

17. What was the period of the statement?
18. How many checks were written?
19. How much money was deposited?
20. What was the beginning and ending balance?
21. Was there any interest paid? How much?

SUMMARY

VOCABULARY

units	row	title	decade
data table	column	heading	

KEY FACTS AND CONCEPTS

Experiments produce data.
Data are often presented in numerical form.
All numbers must be identified by the correct unit.
Data tables organize information to make it easier to understand.
Tables are divided into columns and rows, with the title, headings, and units clearly shown.
Tables are used by everyone every day.

CONCLUSION

Just as words must be organized into sentences to have meaning, numbers must be organized into tables. Data tables make numbers much easier to understand. Tables allow you to pick out the facts you need without wasting time. That's why scientists use them. But you see tables all the time. For example, the family phone bill is in table form. Income tax statements involve tables. You will be using tables throughout your life.

22. What is the KEY IDEA of this chapter?

CHAPTER

9 Graphing Data

Presenting Data in Picture Form

9A INTRODUCTION

If one of your teachers put test results on the chalkboard in a random way, it would take you a while to understand them. First, you would have to find your score. Then, you would have to find other scores so you could compare your score with them.

In Chapter 8, you learned a better way to present data. Data can be organized in a data table.

Table 1 below shows how much clearer test scores become when they are organized. Your eye can go up and down the columns easily. You can quickly see what the highest and lowest grades are. You can also see how each person's score fits in.

There is still a faster way to understand data. Data can be put in a GRAPH. **A graph is data shown in the form of a picture.** A picture can tell you a story fast. With a graph, it is not necessary to read each number to know what's happening. The numbers form a pattern that you can recognize.

Many people use graphs in their work. Scientists use graphs to report the data from their experiments. Business executives use graphs in large meetings to illustrate what they are saying. Disc jockeys use graphs to determine the top twenty hits. Graphs are a popular way of making information clear. They are used all over the world by all kinds of people.

1. What is a graph?
2. Why is a graph easy to read?

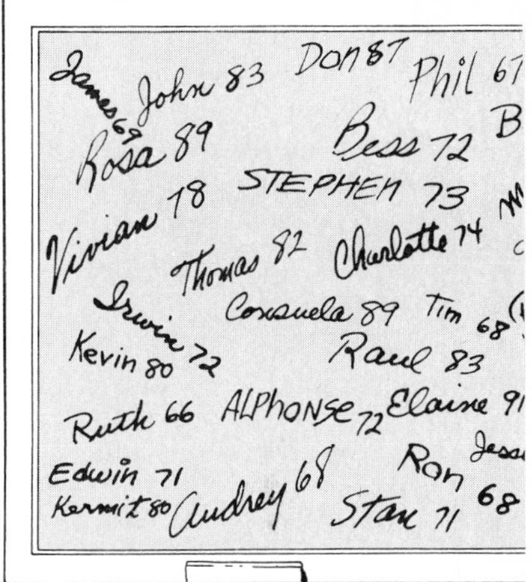

Table 1. Grades of Students

Student's Name	Grade
Joyce	92
Lisa	91
Angelo	89
Luis	86
Paul	81
Marcella	77
Bill	72
Fred	68
Anthony	64
Lee	61

9B BAR GRAPHS

You will learn how to draw two kinds of graphs: BAR GRAPHS and LINE GRAPHS. These are the kinds of graphs that best fit the things you will be doing. There are other kinds of graphs. But if you understand how to use bar and line graphs, understanding other kinds of graphs will not be a problem.

Look at the bar graph, Graph 1, on page 56 to see how data are organized in a graph. **The graph is identified by a number and a title, just like a table.** Each bar is labeled to show which group it represents. There is a SCALE of values running across the top of the graph. **The length of the bar is compared with the scale.** Comparing the bar against the scale tells what the bar represents.

Graph 1. Dollar Income of Household by Education of the Head of the Household.

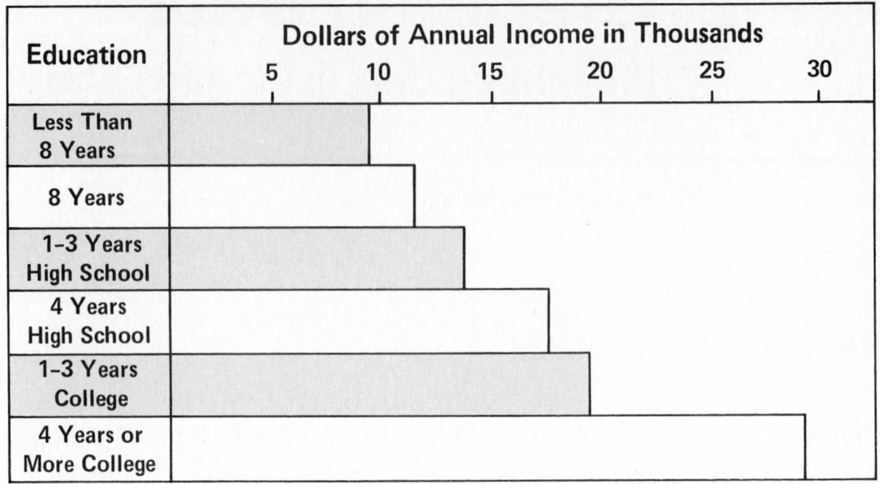

Scales are usually drawn so that equal distances represent equal amounts. In the scale on Graph 1 above, the distance from $5,000 to $10,000 is the same as the distance from $20,000 to $25,000. Equal spaces for equal amounts is an important rule in graph making. Follow the rule of equal spaces for equal amounts unless you are instructed to use a different system.

> Scales in graphs should be linear. Use equal amounts of space for equal changes in value.

Bar graphs may be drawn across the page. These are HORIZONTAL graphs. Graphs running up and down the page are VERTICAL graphs. Whether to use a horizontal or a vertical graph depends upon the size of the page, the number of bars, the lengths of the bars, the size of the labels, and the scale being used. If the name for each bar is long, then there may not be enough room for the name under the bar in a vertical graph. If the scale is long, the paper may be too narrow for a horizontal graph. You will often just have to see which style will best fit your data.

3. According to Graph 1, which group has the highest income?

4. How carefully did you have to read the numbers in Graph 1 to answer the first question?

9C LINE GRAPHS

Look at Graph 2 at the top of page 57. This is a line graph. **In a line graph, two factors are compared.** Statements can then be made about the relationship between the two factors. **The position of the line compares the two factors.** In Graph 2, the year is compared with the number of children born.

The line graph is useful for telling when a change is taking place. The point where the line starts up or down is important. It marks the

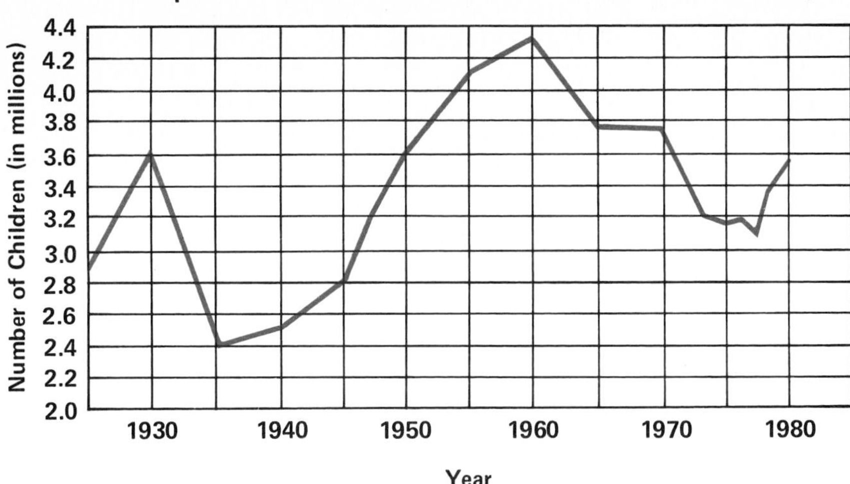

beginning of the change shown by the line. Conclusions can be drawn from whether the line goes up or down.

Like bar graphs, line graphs have numbers, titles, and accurate labeling. The bottom and left sides of the graph are called its AXES (singular: axis). The axes are labeled to show what each side of the graph represents.

The axes are also marked to show the scale. The scale on line graphs follows the same rule as the scale on bar graphs, that is, equal amounts of space for equal values. For example, in Graph 2, the distance from 2.2 million children to 2.6 million children is the same as the distance from 3.6 million children to 4.0 million children.

Graphs are usually drawn on paper ruled in squares. **The squares are called a grid, but the paper is called graph paper.** Different kinds of graph paper have different grids. The grids range in size from tiny one-millimeter squares on up. Typical grids measure about five or six millimeters square.

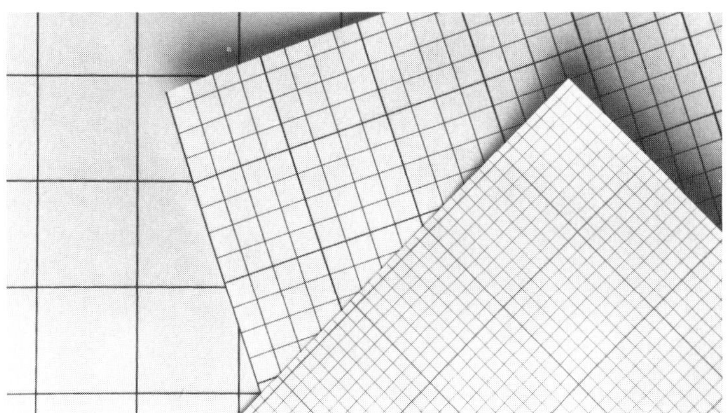

5. Look at Graph 2. In what year did the birth rate start climbing after a sharp five-year drop?

6. Look at Graph 2 again. In what year did the increase in birth rate stop and the birth rate start falling again?

7. What tells you what a graph is all about?

8. If one square on a bar graph is equal to $100, how many squares longer is an $800 bar than a $500 bar?

ACTIVITY: Drawing Bar and Line Graphs

MATERIALS: Graph paper

Table 2. Average Monthly Rainfall in Tonka City

Month	Jan.	Feb.	Mar.	Apr.	May	June	July	Aug.	Sept.	Oct.	Nov.	Dec.
Rainfall in cm	4.5	3.5	7.3	7.0	9.2	10.5	6.8	8.0	8.0	6.5	5.8	5.0

a. Use the data in Table 2 to draw a horizontal bar graph. There are data for 12 months, so you will need 12 bars. The greatest amount of rainfall is 10.5 cm. Allow for 15 cm in your scale.

• b. You will be given a sheet of graph paper. Draw a vertical line near the left edge of your paper. Leave enough space at the left of the line for labeling the bars.

c. Mark off two spaces for each bar. Leave a space between bars.

d. Write the month, in abbreviated form, to the left of each bar.

e. Use two squares to represent each centimeter of rainfall. Draw a line across the bottom of the page, one space below the lowest bar.

f. Where your vertical and horizontal lines cross, put a dot for the zero rainfall point.

g. Now put a dot on every other line across the bottom. Number the dots, starting with 0 at the left and going to 15.

Graph 3. Average Monthly Rainfall in Tonka City

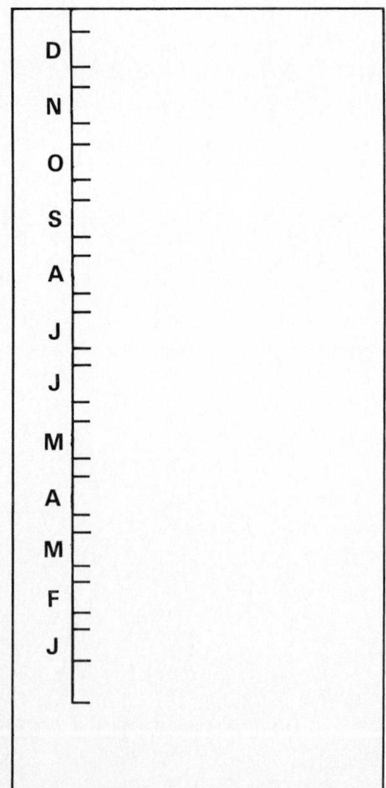

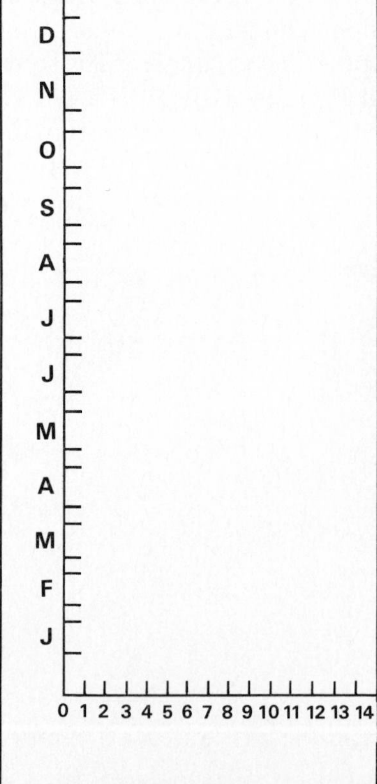

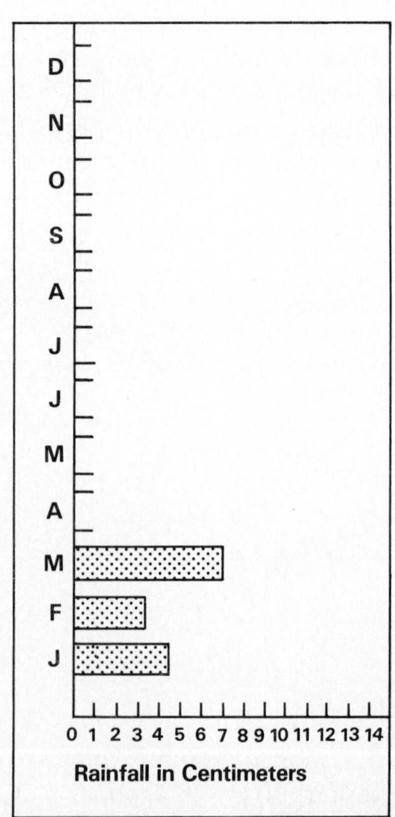

h. Write "Rainfall in Centimeters" across the bottom of your graph. Put the number and title at the top. Use the same title as the table because it is the same information. This is the third graph in Chapter 9, so make it Graph 3.

i. Measure off each bar. For January, the rainfall is 4.5 cm. You can measure off the bar in two ways. Count the squares. At 2 squares per centimeter, 4.5 cm takes 9 squares. Or, look at where the 4 cm and 5 cm lines are. You know that 4.5 cm must be halfway in-between them. Mark the end of the bar at 9 squares and darken the bar to the left end.

j. Do this for the other 11 months the same way. You will have to estimate where the divisions come for numbers like 7.3 cm. Seven is 14 squares and 7.5 is 15 squares, so you know 7.3 must be in-between.

• k. Use the same data about rainfall to produce a line graph. First, draw your axes on the graph paper you are given.

l. In line graphs, it is customary to put time across the bottom. Put a dot for each month on every other line starting where the axes cross at the left. Write the first letter of the month under each dot.

m. Write the rainfall scale up the axis on the left side. Start with 0 where the axes cross, then dot every other line. Number the dots from 0 to 15.

n. Don't forget to write "Rainfall in Centimeters" along the side. Put the number and title across the top. This is the fourth graph in Chapter 9.

o. Follow the January month line up from the bottom to where it reaches the 4.5 cm line coming across. This is 9 squares up. Put a dot there.

p. Put a dot on the February line at 3.5 cm. That is 7 squares up. Mark the rest of the month lines with a dot at the point showing their rainfalls.

q. Connect the dots with a line going from month to month in order through the year.

---

9. Using the bar graph, what month has the highest rainfall?

10. Using the bar graph and without looking at numbers, what is the dryest season in Tonka City?

11. Using the line graph, which season is wetter, spring or summer?

Graph 4. Average Monthly Rainfall in Tonka City

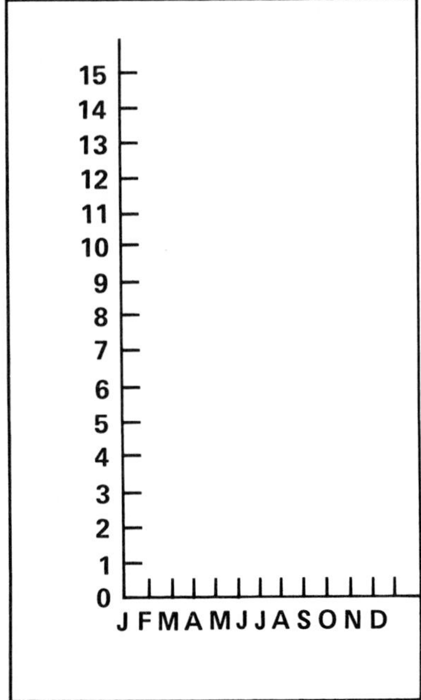

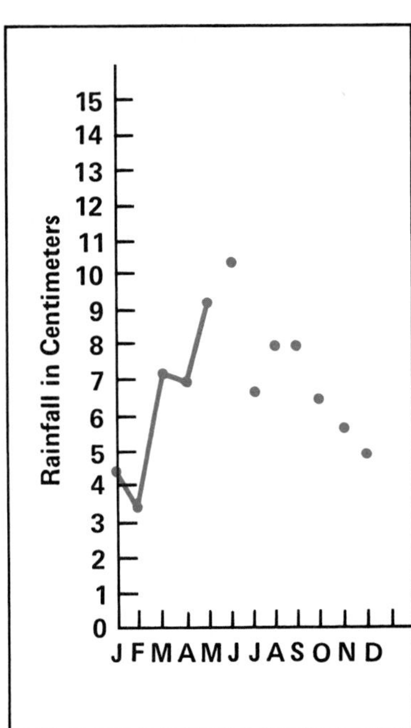

9D IMPORTANCE OF GRAPHS

TABLE 3 THE NUMBER OF PEOPLE IN THE WORLD

(past and projected)

Year	Billions of People
1900	1.5
1925	1.9
1950	2.5
1975	4.0
2000	6.3

Graphs do more than present data. Graphs can help predict the future by showing TRENDS. **A trend is the general direction in which a factor is moving.** Graphs show trends clearly. You can easily see if a line or bar is going up or down.

Look at Table 3 at the left. It tells how fast world population grew during the 20th century. Now look below at the same information as it would be shown in a graph.

In Graph 5 you can really see how fast the population of the world is changing. People in government use graphs like this one. They use graphs to help them determine if such things as food production and construction should be increased or decreased.

Graph 5. The Number of People in the World

People in World (in billions)

10
9
8
7
6
5
4
3
2
1

1900 1925 1950 1975 2000 2025

Year

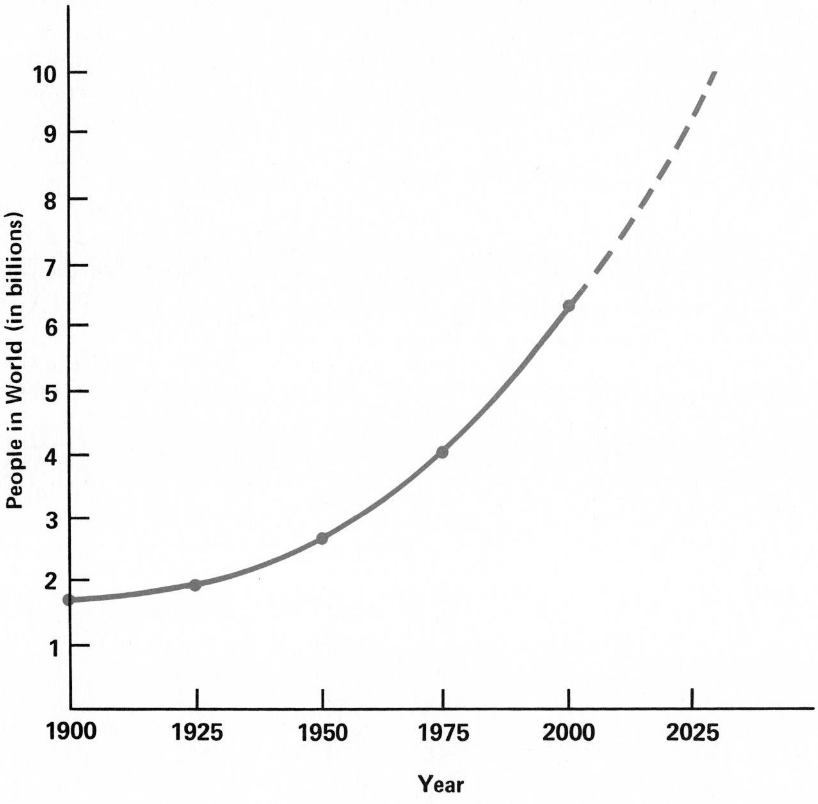

Look at Graph 5. What do you think should happen to food production and construction to meet people's needs?

Business people use graphs. For example, the marketing director of a camera company might look at a graph like Graph 6 on page 61 before deciding what to do next. The company might decide to stock more 35 millimeter cameras if instant camera sales keep slipping down. This decision would be based on the trend shown in the graph.

This book is about science. **Scientists use graphs all the time to illustrate experimental results.** To give an example of how important graphs are to scientists, notice that in Graph 7 scientists are studying attendance at their own meetings. The initials APS stand for The American Physical Society. Scientists even use graphs to study themselves.

12. How do graphs help predict the future?

13. What form of presentation seems to be the easiest way to understand data?

Graph 6. Sales of Instant Cameras in the U.S.

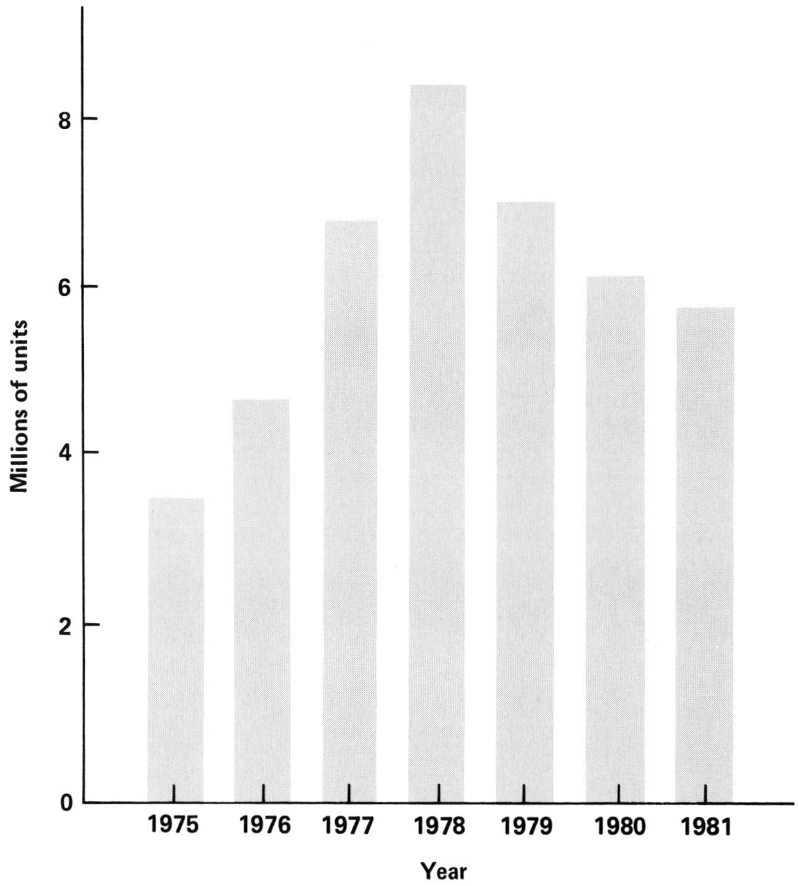

Millions of units: 0, 2, 4, 6, 8

1975 1976 1977 1978 1979 1980 1981

Year

Graph 7. Registration at APS General Meetings

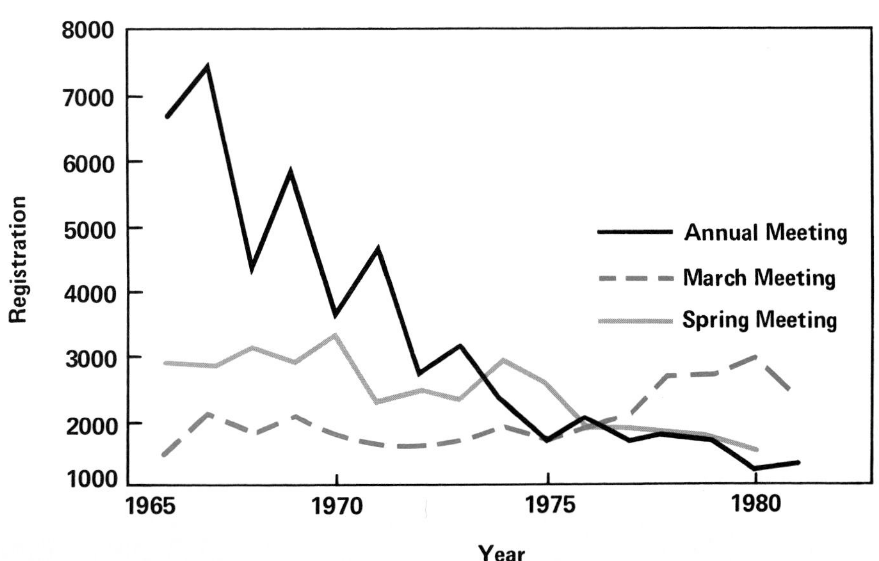

SUMMARY

VOCABULARY

graph	line graph	horizontal	axes
bar graph	scale	vertical	trend

KEY FACTS AND CONCEPTS

The picture used to present data is called a graph.

A graph allows you to understand data fast.

A graph should have a number, title, and enough information along the axes to tell what values the lines and bars represent.

Scales on graphs are usually drawn so that equal distances represent equal amounts.

Graphs show trends; they can help predict the future.

CONCLUSION

Graphs can improve your understanding of facts. It is easier to communicate with pictures than with words or numbers alone. The direction of a line or the length of a bar on a graph gives you a picture of what's happening. Graphs prove that "one picture is worth a thousand words."

14. What is the KEY IDEA of this chapter?

CHAPTER

10 Using Data

Conclusions Are Drawn from Data

10A INTRODUCTION

You have been learning the method of science. You have learned to observe, to depend upon nature to be consistent, to form hypotheses, to test hypotheses with experiments, to use metric standards of measurement, and to present data in tables and graphs. The next step is to decide if the hypothesis being tested is valid.

The data are the proof of whether a hypothesis describes what is really happening in nature. Experimental data will often disprove both popular opinion and centuries-old beliefs. For example, people believed for centuries that highly intelligent children died younger, were smaller or weaker physically, and had more personal problems when they grew up. A research project that has been going on since the 1930's has disproved this.

Several hundred children who were above average in intelligence have been studied. The study followed them from elementary-school age until late middle age. It has been found that these children are physically above average, have had a lower death rate, and have had fewer personal problems than people of average intelligence. The popular belief has been destroyed by carefully collected data.

> The data, the hard facts, are what scientists use to test their beliefs.

1. What is the proof that a hypothesis is valid?

10B DATA IN RESEARCH PAPERS

Data are analyzed to see whether they support the hypotheses. For example, is a new metal really stronger than steel? To find the answer, data on the force needed to bend the new metal are compared to the control data on steel. In every experiment, the facts are compared to see whether they support the hypothesis. If they do, the hypothesis is valid. **Data are of primary importance because data are the deciding factor in experiments.**

ACTIVITY: The Weight of a Pendulum

MATERIALS: String, tape, paper clip, washer

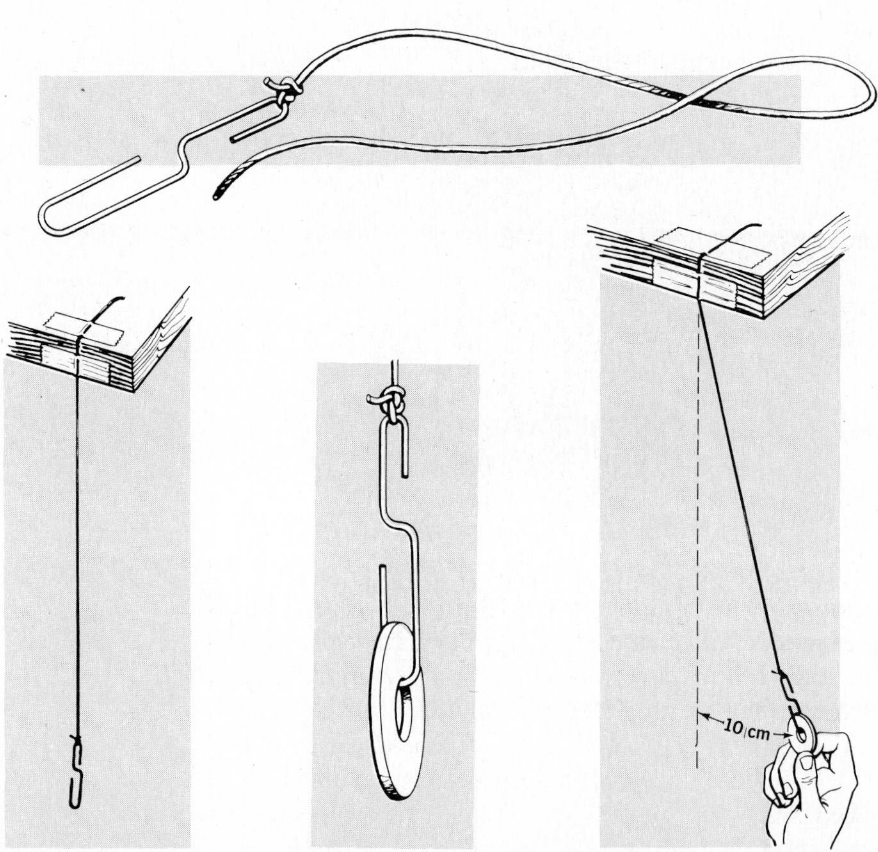

In this Activity, you will decide what effect mass has on how fast a pendulum swings. Will more mass cause more swings per minute or fewer swings per minute?

a. Take a piece of string about 60 cm long. Bend a paper clip into a hook. Tie it to one end of the string.
b. Tape the other end of the string to a table.
c. Hang a washer on the hook.
d. Pull the washer sideways about 10 cm (the width of your hand).
• e. Draw a table in which to record data. You need space for two trials each of pendulums with one, two, and three washers. Do not change the length of the pendulum once you have started taking data.
f. Count the number of swings for one minute. Do this twice with one washer, two washers, and three washers. Record the number of swings in your table.

2. What was your hypothesis about whether more mass causes more or fewer swings per minute?
3. What did the data show about the number of swings with different masses?

Scientists write research papers to report their findings. Research papers are filled with experimental data. These papers are printed in SCIENTIFIC JOURNALS where everyone can read what was done. Another scientist can read the research paper, duplicate the experiment, and come up with the same data. Even if the two scientists argue about conclusions, they should still get the same data from the same experiment. If other scientists cannot duplicate an experiment and get the same data, the original paper will lose credibility.

New discoveries can result from retesting old experiments. A chemistry professor used to repeat a test for a certain chemical in front of his class every year. If the chemical was in the liquid he was testing, the liquid would change color when another chemical was added. One year the test didn't work. The scientist investigated. He discovered that his assistant had replaced the natural plant product he usually used with a SYNTHETIC, or manufactured, chemical. When the plant product was carefully analyzed, new chemicals were discovered. It was these chemicals in the natural plant product that had been causing the color change all along.

Scientific journals are the storehouse of science. The journals hold all the information that has been collected about how nature works. Some journals were written hundreds of years ago. Often, the original copies are still in libraries. Scientific historians read ancient journals to discover what scientists in the past believed and how they worked. Most scientists set aside time every week to read the current journals in their field of work.

The data in scientific journals may be used by other scientists. **Scientists can use published data to support their own hypotheses.** Usually, the scientists also do more experiments after their hypothesis is developed. Scientists must verify their findings many times before their work is accepted.

The PROCEDURE of Science	**The PRODUCT of Science**
Thinking	Information
A method	Data
Questioning	Observations
Testing	Facts
Problem solving	Reports

Sometimes the papers that are published are hypotheses. Other papers may follow to support or reject the published hypotheses. Einstein once published a paper with a hypothesis about light and matter. Several years later, other scientists did experiments that tested his hypothesis. The data supported Einstein's hypothesis. Einstein was awarded the Nobel Prize when his work was proved valid.

The number of scientific journals is growing. **As new areas of science open up, new journals are started.** It is hard for a scientist to keep up with even one narrow specialty. There are journals that just list the papers published each month. The lists are arranged by subjects so scientists can save time by going directly to the subject that interests them. Scientific organizations are working on computer systems to store information. The computer is the only device fast enough to keep up with the hundreds of pages of research papers published daily.

Scientists read their journals carefully. They study the new data. **When the data and the hypotheses don't agree, new discoveries are made.** It is the possibility of finding something new that attracts men and women to scientific work. It is the data that decides which hypotheses will be remembered and which will not.

4. What is used to decide if a hypothesis is valid?
5. How do scientists learn of each other's work?
6. Where do scientists publish their research papers?

SUMMARY

VOCABULARY

scientific journal

synthetic

KEY FACTS AND CONCEPTS

The data in an experiment decide whether the hypothesis is valid. Data have the highest priority.

Experiments are written up as research papers. These papers are published in scientific journals.

Journals are available for everyone to read.

A scientist's data must stand up to testing by other scientists. The same results must be seen each time an experiment is performed.

CONCLUSION

Scientists publish reports of what they have done. They may report on their hypotheses, experiments, and data. They publish the results for other scientists to challenge and to use. The data, which can be reproduced by any scientist, decide scientific questions.

7. What is the KEY IDEA of this chapter?

CHAPTER

11 Applying the Scientific Method

Using Scientific Knowledge

11A INTRODUCTION

In the first ten chapters of this book, you learned about the method of science. You will use this information as you proceed through this course. But students have always asked the question, ''What do we have to know that for?'' It is a question worth answering. There are two main reasons for studying the method of science.

The first reason is that the scientific method of problem solving can be used to solve ordinary problems. The second reason is that scientific discoveries, which have been made by using this method, have changed the way people live. You will look at each of these reasons more closely in this chapter.

1. Give two reasons why it is important to study the scientific method.

11B SOLVING PROBLEMS

Choosing a career is an example of a problem that can be solved by using the scientific method. The problem is what vocation, or profession, should you choose. **To form your hypothesis, gather information first.** Pamphlets in the library can tell you what duties people perform in different jobs, how much they are paid, and how much training they need. Your guidance counselor at school may have aptitude tests that you can take. These tests can often tell you more about yourself by highlighting your particular abilities. Use all the information you can get to form your hypothesis about what field would be best for you.

> The scientific method of problem solving can be applied to problems in everyday life.

To test your hypothesis, take a part-time or summer job in the field you have chosen to try. After you have been working awhile, ask yourself some questions. How do you like what you are doing? Do you want to stay in school long enough to learn what is needed for a full-time position in this field? Is the salary what you want? Are working conditions and hours satisfactory? The answers you get to these questions are the data you need to make a decision.

For example, suppose a student thought that health care work would be a valid hypothesis. After a part-time job in a hospital, the data showed that the student felt too uncomfortable with sick people to work well. The student chose a different career. Forming and testing this hypothesis saved the student years of training that would have been wasted.

2. How can the scientific method of problem solving help you?

11C SCIENCE, ENGINEERING, AND TECHNOLOGY

The scientist's task is finding out how nature works. Scientists study a range of subjects—from what matter is made of to how the human body fights off viruses. Science is broken down into many separate branches, or divisions. Even in one branch, there is too much for any one person to learn. **Of course, dividing science into branches was done by scientists to make studying science easier.** There are no divisions in nature. In fact, many scientists find themselves working across the divisions to solve their problems.

The information discovered by scientists is used by ENGINEERS. **Engineers are the people who find ways to use what scientists have discovered.** Jets, radar, lasers, space shuttles, home video systems, and computers were all developed by engineers. They used what scientists had discovered about electricity, magnetism, light, gravity, and energy to build these devices.

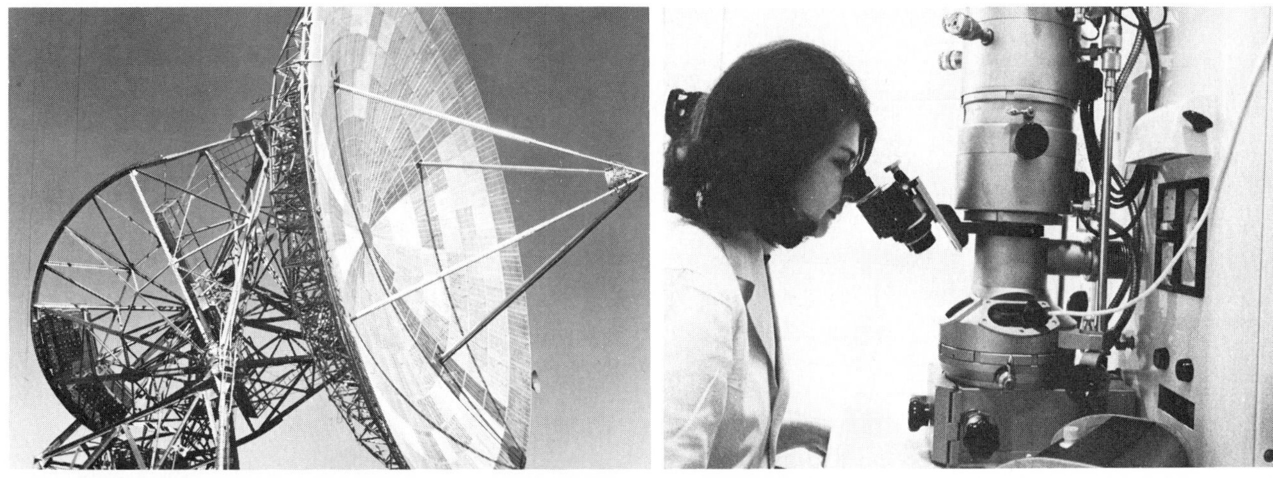

Scientists and engineers have worked hand in hand to produce the radar dish, the electron microscope, and the supersonic transport shown here.

Using scientific information to produce the things that people use is called TECHNOLOGY. **Modern technology has changed the way people live.** Before modern technology, people had to do most things for themselves. Hundreds of years ago, each family grew or caught its own food, built its own shelter, and made its own clothes. Small communities banded together to defend themselves against wild animals and invaders. In the past, there was little people could do to cure diseases or heal injuries. LIFE SPANS were much shorter than they are today. **A life span is the length of time a person lives.**

> The growth of technology, based upon the discoveries of science, has changed the way people live.

Industrial technology has changed life very dramatically in the last two centuries. In the last 200 years, factories have sprung up, and the use of machines has become widespread. Also, the assembly line has increased the amount of manufactured goods available. The invention of the airplane and the automobile have given people greater freedom to move around. The telephone has made communication easier. Radio and television have brought the world into people's living rooms. Advances in medical technology have led to the control of such diseases as polio and smallpox. Rocket ships have made the dream of space travel a reality.

Industrial technology has brought about a modern society. Remember that only 200 years separates the covered wagon from the lunar rover driven by the astronauts on the moon.

SCIENTISTS study	ENGINEERS produce
Electricity	Jets
Magnetism	Radar
Light	Lasers
Gravity	Space shuttles
Energy	Computers

Science and technology work together. Engineers use information from science about electricity and magnetism to build such things as electron microscopes. Then scientists can use the electron microscope to discover more about viruses or how the crystals in magnets fit together. Perhaps some day an engineer will use this information to build a better magnet.

3. What did scientists do to make the study of science easier?

4. What does an engineer do?

5. What is technology?

6. How does technology affect your life?

7. Where does the information engineers use come from?

8. How do scientists depend upon engineers for help in studying nature?

9. In what two ways are the method of science important?

SUMMARY

VOCABULARY

engineer technology life span

KEY FACTS AND CONCEPTS

The scientific method works for solving everyday problems.

Information gathered by scientists is used by engineers to build modern devices.

Technology is the process of using scientific information to design new machines or ways of doing things to satisfy people's wants and needs.

Industrial technology has changed life dramatically in the last 200 years.

CONCLUSION

Scientists keep adding to what is already known about nature. Engineers use scientific information to build new and different devices to improve society. The whole process of discovery and invention depends upon the method of science. A method that has changed the world so much must be a powerful tool to use to solve problems.

10. What is the KEY IDEA of this chapter?

UNIT TWO

Matter

SCIENCE COMPETENCIES

Unit 2 will help you to master one LIFE SKILL:

USING MATERIALS AND ENERGY—How to Use Matter and Energy Wisely

CHAPTER

12 Properties of Matter

Describing an Object

12A INTRODUCTION

What is everything made of? Are things on earth made of the same material as things out in space? What makes one substance different from another? These are questions that have puzzled people for centuries. With the development of the scientific method, some of the questions have been answered.

The word used to describe what things are made of is MATTER. **Almost everything in the universe is made of matter.** This unit will concentrate on what is known about matter, how it is put together, and why it acts the way it does.

The astronaut in this photograph is taking samples of matter from the moon's surface.

Matter is anything that has mass and occupies space.

1. What is matter?

12B DESCRIBING MATTER

Scientists start by observing. They have observed the different forms of matter and have described them. Describing matter means listing its PROPERTIES, or characteristics. Is a particular rock hard or soft? Is it rough or smooth? What is its color? Does the rock burn, melt, or resist heat? Does it crumble or crack into neat pieces? The answers to these questions are examples of some of the properties to look for in a rock. The different kinds of matter can be identified by their unique properties. **A particular set of properties can tell you what kind of matter you are working with.**

You use the properties of matter to tell things apart all the time. For example, look at a piece of cheese and a pat of margarine. The margarine is softer, it spreads easily on toast. Cheese is a different color. Cheese may have holes in it. Margarine and cheese have two different tastes and smells. Even if you just had two different kinds of cheese, you would have no trouble telling a soft, white cream cheese from a firm, yellow cheddar.

Metals are forms of matter known for their useful properties. Metals are MALLEABLE. They can be forced into different shapes by heat, pressure, or pounding. Metals are good conductors of heat and electricity. They are easily identified by their hard, shiny surfaces. Gold, silver, copper, iron, tin, lead, aluminum, and zinc are all metals.

PROPERTIES OF METALS

Metals are:

Malleable

Good conductors

Hard

Shiny

There are two properties common to all matter. All matter has mass. All matter has volume; that is, matter takes up space. Although there are tremendous differences in properties among the countless kinds of matter, the properties of mass and volume are always present.

ALL MATTER HAS

Mass

Volume

2. List as many different properties of jam and peanut butter as you can think of.

3. What difference in properties helps you tell a piece of chalk from a candle?

4. What are the two properties common to all matter?

Air has mass and takes up space.

12C ALL MATTER HAS MASS

Air is matter, therefore, air has mass. An air tank, like the kind scuba divers use, will feel heavier when it is filled with air. This is because the tank weighs more when it is full of air. In Chapter 7, you learned that weight and mass are not the same thing, but they are related. In this example, the fact that the air tank weighs more when it is full of air proves that the air has mass.

The most popular way to find the mass of an object is to weigh it. The famous scientist Sir Isaac Newton found that all pieces of matter pull on each other. This is Newton's Law of Universal Gravitation. **Every two objects have a force of attraction between them.** This force is called GRAVITY. As you recall from Chapter 7, weight is the force of gravity on an object. Mass is the amount of matter in an object. **Mass is related to the force of gravity in that the greater the mass, the greater the force of gravity exerted on it.** The relationship between weight and mass is why weighing can be used to find mass.

The LAW OF UNIVERSAL GRAVITATION states that every two objects have a force of attraction between them.

Kilograms are units of mass. When you weigh something and express your answer in kilograms, you are mentally translating the force of gravity into mass in kilograms.

All gases have mass because all gases consist of matter. Nitrogen, oxygen, argon, and carbon dioxide are the most common gases in air. The gases have different properties. Oxygen must be present when things burn. It is difficult to combine nitrogen with other substances. Argon won't combine with anything. Carbon dioxide is necessary to plants. In another form, it also puts out fires. These gases turn to liquids at certain temperatures and will become solids at certain lower temperatures. In any one of these forms, these gases still have mass.

Weighing is not the only method of finding mass. But other methods are more complicated. Finding mass without weighing uses a property of matter called INERTIA. **Inertia is the property of matter that causes an object to resist a change in motion or direction.** When a car speeds up, the engine has to work to overcome inertia. When a car slows down, the brakes have to work to overcome inertia. Inertia explains why a fast-moving car travelling on a straight road will skid on a sharp turn. Inertia causes the car to continue in a straight line. **Inertia also explains why you should wear a seat belt when you ride in a car.** If you were not wearing a seat belt, inertia would keep your body moving forward if the car stopped suddenly.

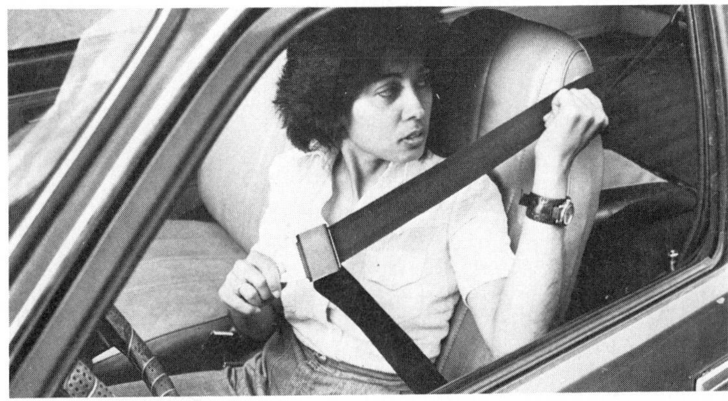

Because it is much harder to measure mass by using inertia, this book will measure mass by weighing.

5. What does weight measure?
6. What is inertia?
7. What is gravity?

12D ALL MATTER TAKES UP SPACE

VOLUME is the measurement of the amount of space an object occupies. In metric units, big spaces are measured in cubic meters. For smaller volumes, liters, milliliters, and cubic centimeters are used. These measurement units are used all the time by many people. The engineer planning a tunnel has to estimate the cost of digging out the many cubic meters of rock that are in the space where the tunnel will go. The engineer designing a motorcycle must decide how many cubic centimeters of space are in the engine's cylinders.

The volume of a block is equal to its length times its width times its height.

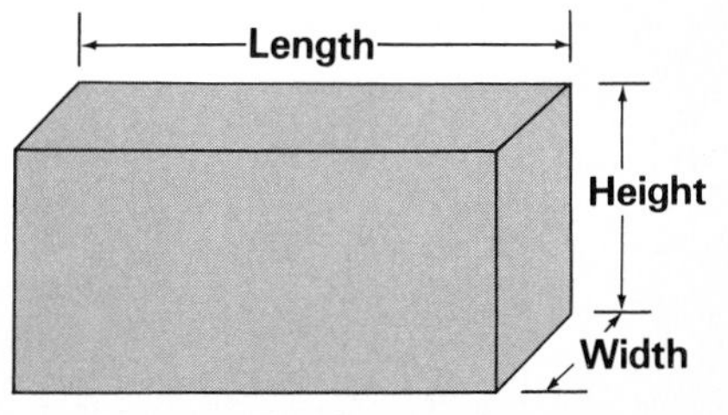

Finding the volume of something shaped like a brick or a cracker box requires measuring and computing. **To find volume, you would measure the length, width, and height, and then multiply the three measurements together.** Remember, your answer would be expressed in cubic units.

VOLUME = length × width × height

Measuring the volume of a liquid requires a graduated cylinder. To find the volume of a liquid, you would pour it into the graduate. You would see where the bottom of the meniscus curve was located on the graduations. The number at the bottom of the curve would be the volume. However, other shapes, such as balls and irregular objects, are harder to measure.

There are mathematical equations that can be used to find some volumes. For instance, a sphere's, or ball's, volume can be found by measuring the sphere's diameter and applying a mathematical equation. There are other equations for finding the volume of cones, pyramids, and cylinders.

An easier way to find the volume of hard-to-measure shapes is by using water. In Chapter 6, you found the volumes of bottles and jars by measuring how much water they would hold. Now to find the volumes of objects you can do the opposite—put them in water. Since all matter takes up space, then an object will take up its own space in water. The object will move, or displace, the water to make room for itself. **The amount the water moves will equal the volume of the object.** This is called DISPLACEMENT.

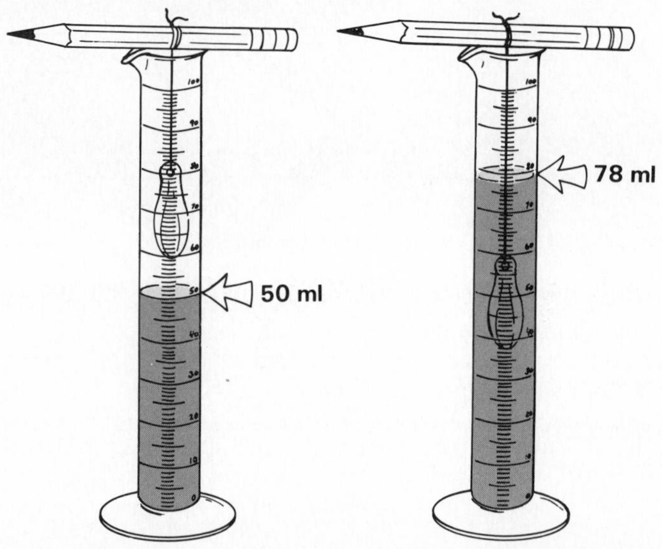

To measure an object using the displacement method, start with a graduated cylinder partly filled with water. Record the volume of water in the graduate. Carefully lower the object into the water with a thread. Dropping the object in will cause water to splash out of the graduate and will give a false reading. Record the volume of water containing the object. Subtract the old volume from the new volume. **The difference between the old and new volumes is the volume of the object.**

8. What does volume measure?

9. What unit would you use to measure the volume of all the water in a lake?

10. What unit would you use to measure the volume of a liquid in a soda bottle?

ACTIVITY: Determining the Properties of Matter

MATERIALS: Balance, graduated cylinder, ruler, assortment of objects

- a. Make a list of your assortment of objects. Leave space next to each object on the list for that object's properties.

b. Then write as many properties as you can think of for each object.

c. Weigh each object.

d. Find each object's volume. You may find the volume either by measuring and multiplying or by using the displacement method.

11. Explain how you tell one kind of matter from another by the properties you have listed.

SUMMARY

VOCABULARY

matter
properties
malleable
gravity
inertia
volume
displacement

KEY FACTS AND CONCEPTS

Matter is anything that takes up space and has mass.

A description of an object is a list of its properties.

Matter makes up all of the objects in the universe.

Inertia is the property of matter that causes an object to resist a change in motion or direction.

Sir Isaac Newton found that all pieces of matter have a force of attraction between them. This is stated in his Law of Universal Gravitation.

Gravity is the force of attraction between all the pieces of matter in the universe.

The displacement method is used to find the volume of hard-to-measure objects.

CONCLUSION

Everything is made up of matter. All forms of matter have mass and occupy space. The quantity of matter in an object is usually determined by measuring the force of gravity on it. Every time you weigh something, you are measuring the pull of the earth's gravity.

12. What is the KEY IDEA of this chapter?

CHAPTER

13 Density

The Amount of Matter in a Unit Volume

13A INTRODUCTION

In the preceding chapter, you learned to describe an object by its properties. There are two special properties, mass and volume, that apply to all matter. Every bit of matter in the universe, regardless of how unusual it is, has some mass and takes up some space. Matter may take any form. Mount Everest, a koala bear, and a soap bubble are all made of matter. **Regardless of its form, matter will still have mass and volume.**

A liter of water has a mass of one kilogram. A liter of mercury, a silvery, poisonous liquid used in thermometers, has a mass of 13.6 kilograms. There is much more mass in mercury than in the same volume of water. Differences like these are measured by an important property of matter called DENSITY. **Density is the mass per unit volume of a substance.** This means that the property of density tells how tightly matter is packed in a substance.

1. What is density?

13B FINDING DENSITY

Density is found by dividing the mass of an object by its volume. Density can be measured in grams per cubic centimeter or kilograms per cubic meter. A cubic meter of water has a mass of 1,000 kilograms. That is a metric ton and is much too big to handle. You will use grams per cubic centimeter, abbreviated g/cc.

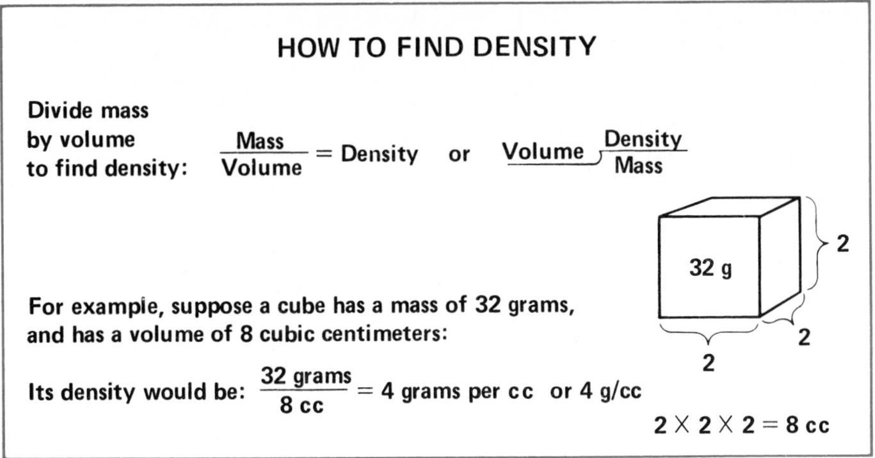

Density is used to identify substances. Different materials have different densities. Gold has a density of 19.32 grams per cubic centimeter. Lead has a density of 11.35 grams per cubic centimeter. Copper has a density of 8.9 grams per cubic centimeter. Gold is too soft to use alone in the making of jewelry. It is often mixed with copper. Gold is worth several dollars a gram. If gold is mixed with copper or lead, the density of the mixture, called an ALLOY, will be less than pure gold. The gold alloy will not be worth as much as pure gold.

Density can be used to tell how much copper is in the gold alloy. First, the piece of jewelry is weighed to find its mass. Then, the volume of the jewelry is measured, usually by the displacement of water method. The mass is divided by the volume. This will give the density. If a piece of jewelry is fifty per cent copper and fifty per cent gold, its density would be 12.22 grams per cubic centimeter.

When old jewelry or coins are sold just for the gold in them, the objects are weighed. The mass found is multiplied by the percent of gold. This gives the amount of gold the objects contain. The buyer pays for the value of the gold. Knowing the densities of the different metals makes the transaction possible.

DENSITIES OF VARIOUS MATERIALS

Material	Density
Gold	19.32 g/cc
Lead	11.35 g/cc
Copper	8.9 g/cc
Ether	0.736 g/cc
Water	1 g/cc
Sulfuric acid	1.8 g/cc
Mercury	13.6 g/cc
Steel	7.8 g/cc

A carton of milk shows the milk's butterfat, or milkfat, content. Milkfat is not as dense as water.

Density applies to all forms of matter. Sea water is denser than fresh water. Cold air is denser than warm air. Mercury, a liquid, is denser than steel, a hard, tough solid. Ether, at 0.736 grams per cubic centimeter, is one of the least dense liquids.

VISCOSITY is a property of liquids that is often confused with density. **Viscosity measures how fast a liquid will flow.** A thick whipping cream moves slowly. Its viscosity is high. Milk pours quickly. Milk's viscosity is low. People call whipping cream heavy cream. But the density of cream is less than that of milk. This is because cream has more butterfat, and butterfat has a much lower density than milk. A liter of heavy cream has less mass than a liter of milk. If heavy cream were called thick cream, it would be more accurate.

2. How is the density of a substance determined?
3. If 15 cubic centimeters of silver has a mass of 157.5 grams, what is its density?
4. What is viscosity?

ACTIVITY: Finding the Density of Solids

MATERIALS: Ruler, balance, set of blocks

- a. You are going to find the densities of a set of numbered blocks. Start by drawing a table for your data. It should have columns for the block number, the length, width, and height of each block, the volume of each block, the mass of each block, and the density of each block.
- b. Measure the length, width, and height of each block in centimeters. Be accurate to the nearest tenth of a centimeter. Record the measurements in the table.
- c. Find the volume of each block by multiplying the length, width, and height of each block together. Round off your answer to the nearest tenth of a cubic centimeter.
- d. Weigh each block. Record its mass in the table.
- e. Divide the mass of each block by its volume to find the density. Put the result in the table. Do not carry your answer beyond three digits.

5. How do the densities of the blocks compare?
6. Why not just look at the blocks to decide how dense they are?

13C USING DENSITY

Density can be used to identify some kinds of matter. The densest substance known on earth is the metal osmium. Its density is 22.48 grams per cubic centimeter. Because nothing else is as dense as osmium, the property of density would be enough to tell if a specimen of metal was osmium.

The densities of liquids can show how much other matter is dissolved in them. Pure water has a density of 1 gram per cubic centimeter. The liquid in an automobile battery is a mixture of water and sulfuric acid. Sulfuric acid is much denser than water. Its density is about 1.8 grams per cubic centimeter. When the two liquids, water and sulfuric acid, are mixed, the density will be between 1.0 and 1.8 grams per cubic centimeter. The exact number depends on the proportions of the liquids.

The hydrometer in this photograph is being used to measure the density of battery acid.

The density of the liquid in an automobile battery is usually about 1.3 grams per cubic centimeter. When an automobile battery is in good condition, the liquid is at its highest density. As the battery ages and loses its ability to produce electricity, the density of the liquid drops. The condition of the battery can be determined by measuring the liquid density. The higher the density, the better the condition of the battery.

Service stations have a tube with a float in it. This device is called a HYDROMETER. **The hydrometer measures the density of the battery liquid.** There is a rubber bulb on one end of the tube. The attendant squeezes the rubber bulb to draw battery liquid into the hydrometer. The float floats in the liquid. In denser liquids, more of the float remains above the surface. The float rides deeper in less dense liquids. Marks on the float tell what the liquid density is. Some hydrometers are marked with words that describe the condition of the battery.

Other hydrometers are made for different liquids. The densities of these liquids can show how much milk sugar, grape sugar, alcohol, or pollutants may be in them.

Densities also show which objects will float in various liquids. An object in water takes up space and pushes away, or displaces, the water. **The water will push up with a force equal to the downward pull of gravity on the mass of water displaced.** This upward force is called BUOYANCY. Gravity also pulls down on the mass of the object in the water. If the buoyant force of the water is greater than the weight of the object, the object floats. If the object has more mass than the water displaced, the object sinks. **The rule is: objects of lower density float on liquids of higher density.**

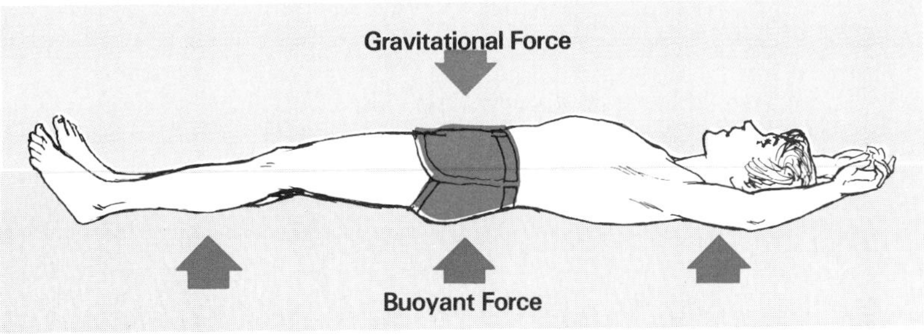

The downward force of gravity is balanced by the upward force of the water.

7. How is density used to identify some kinds of matter?
8. What is a hydrometer used for?
9. Using the table on page 79, determine which of the materials would float on mercury.

SUMMARY

VOCABULARY

density, viscosity, buoyancy, alloy, hydrometer

KEY FACTS AND CONCEPTS

Density is the mass per unit volume of a substance.

Density is found by dividing the mass of an object by its volume.

Density is used to identify substances. It is used to tell how much material is dissolved in a liquid. It is also used to find which objects will float in which liquids.

Viscosity is the measurement of how easily a liquid will flow.

Buoyancy is the upward force exerted by a liquid on an object immersed in it.

CONCLUSION

Density is a useful property. It can be used to make the best choices of materials for different jobs. High density materials make good fishing sinkers, anchors, and foundations. Low density materials are best for airplanes, backpacks, and spacecraft.

10. What is the KEY IDEA of this chapter?

CHAPTER

14 Change of State

Solids, Liquids, and Gases

14A INTRODUCTION

Solids and liquids have mass, volume, and density. They also have color, texture, hardness, a freezing point, and a melting point, to name a few more properties. These properties may be used to tell different kinds of matter apart.

Most of the matter you see around you takes one of three forms. **Matter is either a solid, a liquid, or a gas.**

Ice has a lower density than water.

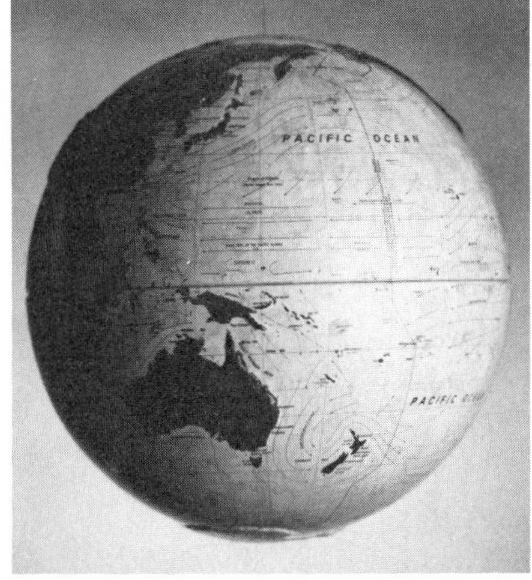

The surface of the earth is seventy percent water.

THREE FORMS OF MATTER
Solid
Liquid
Gas

Air is a mixture of gases.

Since you will be studying these three forms of matter, you should know their special properties. A solid has a constant shape and volume. A liquid keeps a constant volume but takes the shape of its container. A gas takes both the shape and volume of its container.

Matter does not stay in the same form all the time. When water is frozen to make ice cubes, it changes from a liquid to a solid. If the ice cubes are left out of the freezer for very long they change from solid to liquid. When a pot of water is boiling, liquid is turning to gas. These changes of form are important. Changing from one of these forms to another is called a CHANGE OF STATE.

Form of Matter	Property
Solid	Constant shape and volume
Liquid	Constant volume; takes the shape of its container
Gas	Takes both the shape and volume of its container

1. What are the three forms of matter?
2. What is the difference between a solid, a liquid, and a gas?
3. What happens when matter changes its state?

14B CONSERVATION OF MATTER

A question arises when matter changes state. Does the amount of matter, the mass, remain constant when matter changes state? Take a glass of ice cubes and let it stand until the ice melts. Is there the same amount of matter in the glass after melting as there was before melting?

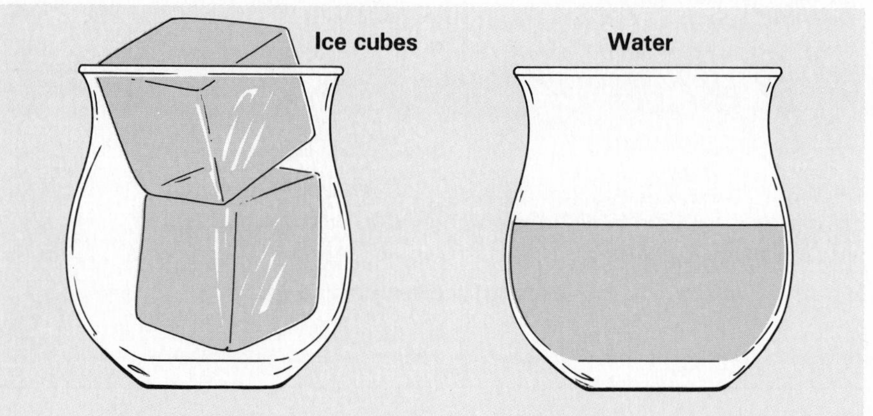

The amount of matter in the glass did not change when the ice melted.

The scientist's answer is a great big yes! The answer is important enough to have its own law. It is called the LAW OF CONSERVATION OF MATTER. **The law states that the amount of matter present will always remain the same.** For everyday situations this is very true. However, there are some important exceptions that will be discussed in Unit 3.

> No matter how many times a substance changes state, the amount of matter will stay the same. Matter is conserved.

4. If 350 grams of ice melts, what is the mass of the water?

ACTIVITY: The Masses of Liquids and Solids

MATERIALS: Test tube, balance, crushed ice, rubber stopper, beaker or jar, hot water, wax, balloon

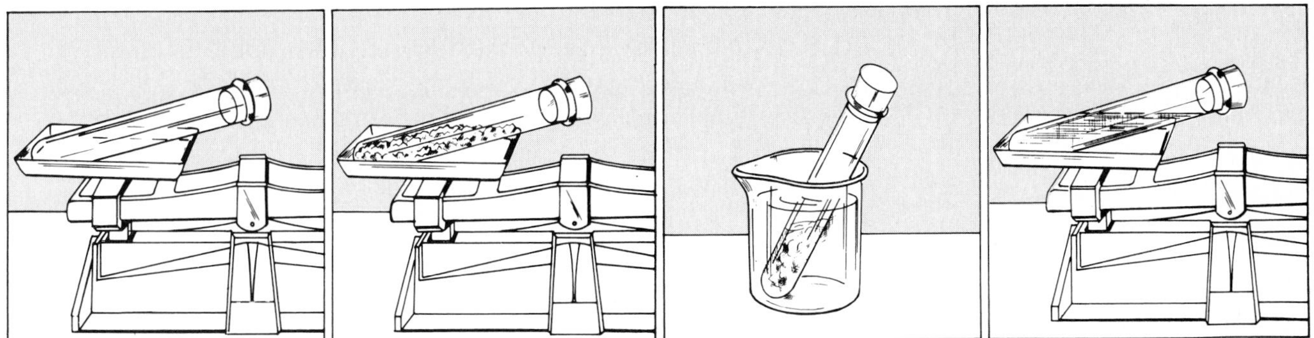

You are going to compare the mass of ice with the mass of water when the ice melts. Draw a table to record your data and label it Table 1. The table should contain space for the following information:

the mass of the stoppered test tube
the mass of the stoppered test tube plus ice
the mass of the stoppered test tube plus water
the mass of the ice
the mass of the water
the change in mass, if any

There should be two columns for data as you will take two trials.

- a. Weigh a clean, dry, empty stoppered test tube. Record its mass in Table 1.

b. Fill the test tube about two thirds full of ice. Stopper, dry, and weigh it again. Record its mass in Table 1.

c. Place the stoppered test tube in hot water until all the ice has melted.

d. Dry the outside of the test tube and weigh it again. Record the mass in Table 1.

e. After you have weighed the test tube with water and recorded the mass, empty the tube.

f. Dry the test tube and stopper, weigh them again and repeat steps a through d for Trial 2. Remember, you subtract the mass of the empty tube from the mass of the tube with ice to find the mass of the ice.

g. Do the subtractions to find the mass of ice and the mass of water. Find the difference between them and record the difference of mass in the table.

h. If the mass increased, mark the number with a plus sign (+). If the mass decreased, mark the number with a minus sign (−).

i. Average your two trials and write the result on the chalkboard.

j. Average the change in mass for the whole class. Use the data on the board.

5. What was your average mass change?
6. What was the class average mass change?

- k. Do a similar activity using wax. Draw another table to record the data and label it Table 2. You will need three spaces for the mass of the test tube, balloon, and wax. They will be weighed together three times, with the wax cold and solid, warm and liquid, then cold and solid again. You will also need two spaces to record any change of mass.

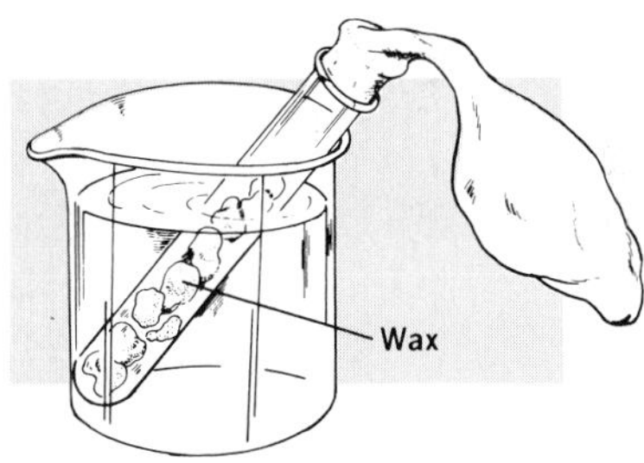

l. First, find the mass of the balloon, test tube, and wax while the wax is cold and solid. Record this in the table.

m. Stand the test tube in a beaker of hot water. Do not remove the balloon.

n. As soon as the wax melts, dry the test tube and find the mass again. Record the mass in the table.

o. Let the wax cool and harden. Find the mass and record it once more.

p. Find the change of mass, if any. Record this in your table and write it on the board.

7. What change of mass did you find?
8. What was the class average change of mass?
9. How well does the data support the hypothesis that there is no change of mass with a change of state?

Boiling water is a common example of evaporation.

14C CHANGES OF STATE

When a solid becomes a liquid, the process is called MELTING. Examples of melting are ice turning to water, heated wax turning to liquid, solder flowing when a hot soldering iron touches it, and butter running in a hot frying pan. In each case, the amount of matter stayed the same.

FREEZING is the change of state from liquid to solid. Examples of freezing are wax cooling and hardening, water forming ice, and solder cooling until it hardens. In each case, the masses did not change. A change from a liquid to a gas is called EVAPORATION. Examples of evaporation are water boiling and spilled gasoline drying up.

It is harder to prove that the mass of gas is equal to the mass of the liquid it came from, but it can be done. When a gas changes state to a liquid, the process is called CONDENSATION. The water that collects on cold soda bottles was a gas just before it touched the bottle. The mass of the liquid equals the mass of the gas that condensed.

Finally, there is a change you don't see as often as the others. A change from a solid directly to a gas is called SUBLIMATION. The same term is used to describe matter going directly from gas to solid. An example of sublimation is dry ice (solid carbon dioxide) disappearing. The dry ice turned into gas. Another example is the frost that forms on refrigerator coils. The frost is water that changed directly from gas in the atmosphere to solid ice. A piece of solid iodine will gradually vanish, as will some kinds of mothballs. The iodine and mothballs went from solid to gas. Once again, if you measured the different gases and solids, you would find that the masses remained the same.

CHANGES OF STATE

- Melting
- Freezing
- Evaporation
- Condensation
- Sublimation

10. Which process is taking place when you dry off after a swim?

11. Will the freezer cold packs used in picnic baskets change mass as they freeze and melt? Explain your answer.

14D USING CONSERVATION LAWS

The Law of Conservation of Matter is used in many ways. It is used by steel makers to determine how much metal they can extract from a batch of iron ore. It is used by chemists to determine how much plastic they can make with a vat of chemicals. Refinery operators can measure how much gasoline they are producing and decide if any expensive crude oil is being wasted. Both science and technology rely heavily on conservation laws.

12. How will the mass of popsicles you made in the freezer compare with the mass of the mixture you put in the molds?

13. An ice cube tray that has been in the freezer a long time has very small ice cubes. Which change of state has gone on?

14. Sulfur is shipped from one place to another as a hot liquid in an insulated tank. If the tank cools off too much and the sulfur freezes, what will happen to the amount of mass of the sulfur in the tank?

15. When water is heated and turns to steam, it becomes a gas with over 1,500 times as much volume as the original liquid. What happens to its mass?

SUMMARY

VOCABULARY

change of state
Law of Conservation of Matter
melting
freezing
evaporation
condensation
sublimation

KEY FACTS AND CONCEPTS

Matter is either a solid, a liquid, or a gas.

When matter changes from one form to another, it is known as a change of state.

The amount of matter present stays the same during a change of state.

The process of a solid changing to a liquid is called melting.

The process of a liquid changing to a solid is called freezing.

The process of a liquid changing to a gas is called evaporation.

The process of a gas changing to a liquid is called condensation.

The process of a solid changing to a gas is called sublimation.

CONCLUSION

Scientists communicate well because they are careful about the meaning of words. A scientist means something very specific by the word *freeze*. For example, when liquid lead freezes, it becomes solid at 327.4° Celsius. Liquid nitrogen evaporates to a gas when it boils at 195.8° Celsius. In each case, the mass of matter stays the same as it goes through its different changes.

16. What is the KEY IDEA of this chapter?

CHAPTER

15 Chemical Change

How Materials Are Formed

Baking a cake is a chemical change. Slicing it is a physical change.

15A INTRODUCTION

Ice, steam, and water are three forms of the same substance. When ice changes to water it is called a change of state. A change of state is a PHYSICAL CHANGE.

There is another kind of change, CHEMICAL CHANGE. Chemical changes are taking place all the time. You caused a chemical change if you fried some bacon for breakfast this morning.

Chemical changes raise a new question. Does the amount of matter change when the substances themselves change? For instance, if you mix two chemicals to form a new chemical, do you still have the same amount of matter?

Once again, the scientists say the amount of matter does not change. **The Law of Conservation of Matter applies to chemical changes as well as physical changes.** The mass of gasoline and air going into an engine equals the mass of exhaust coming out. No mass is added; no mass is taken away.

> The LAW OF CONSERVATION OF MATTER applies to chemical changes. The total mass of reacting materials will equal the total mass of the final products.

The mass of the car's exhaust equals the mass of the gasoline plus the mass of the air in the engine.

1. What law applies to both physical and chemical changes?

15B CHEMICAL CHANGES

A physical change takes place when matter changes state. Melting, freezing, evaporating, and condensing are physical changes. Breaking glass is a physical change. Other physical changes are tearing paper, chopping logs, or mixing powdered sulfur and powdered zinc. A physical change does not change the properties of a substance. The small pieces of broken glass are still glass. Splinters are still wood.

A chemical change takes place when the properties of the remaining materials are different after the change from the original materials. Burning paper is a chemical change. Other examples of chemical changes are burning logs, heating a sulfur and zinc mixture until it flares up, or etching glass with acid to make stained glass.

Chemical changes cause changes in properties. When iron or steel rusts, a chemical change takes place. Steel is silvery and shiny; rust is red-brown and dull. Steel is hard and strong; rust is soft and crumbly.

Steel is affected by magnetism. Most rust is not affected by magnetism. The properties of rust are very different from the properties of steel.

Chemical changes can take many forms. One kind of chemical change takes place when different substances combine. If hydrogen and oxygen are mixed and a spark is added, they combine with an explosion to form something new, water. Water has properties different from either hydrogen or oxygen, which are gases under normal conditions.

In other chemical reactions, materials combine then break apart again to form new combinations. They can form more than one new material. Sugar in your body combines with oxygen. The new materials formed are water and carbon dioxide. Sugar and oxygen are very different from water and carbon dioxide.

Burning causes a chemical change.

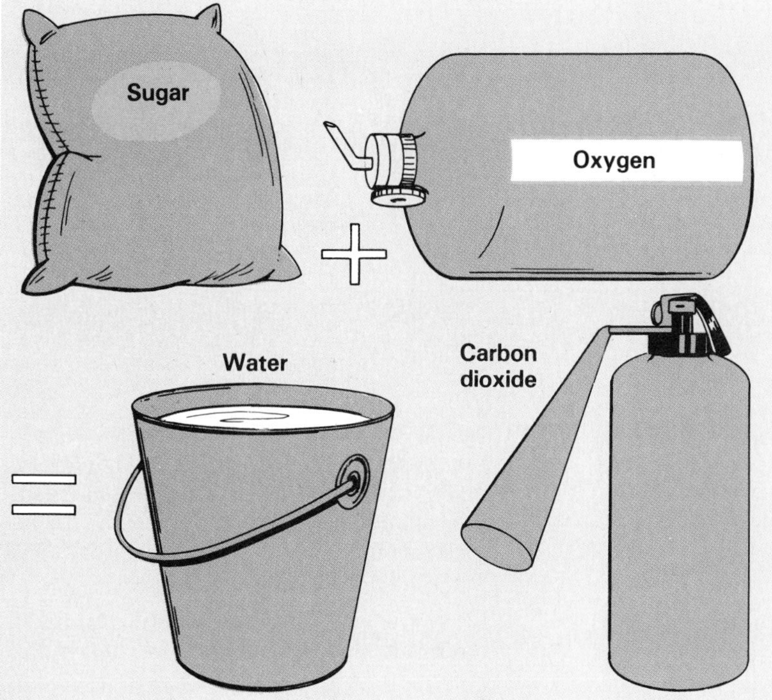

Sugar and oxygen combine to form carbon dioxide and water.

Physical Changes
Breaking glass
Tearing paper
Chopping wood
Slicing meat
Bending iron

Another important chemical change occurs when a substance changes because of heating. For example, many foods change when they are cooked. When cooked, the larger chemicals in food break down into smaller ones that can be digested more easily.

The different kinds of chemical changes, also called CHEMICAL REACTIONS, are endless. Some are hard to stop, like iron rusting. Others are hard to start, like nitrogen combining with hydrogen. But all the changes are part of your environment, and you depend upon them to live.

Chemical Changes
Etching glass with acid
Burning paper
Burning wood
Cooking meat
Causing iron to rust

2. Tell which of the following changes are chemical and which are physical.

a. chopping wood
b. cooking hamburgers
c. baking a cake
d. slicing tomatoes
e. squeezing oranges
f. changing a tire
g. roasting a turkey
h. lighting fireworks
i. digesting dinner
j. drying your hair
k. building a snowman
l. steaming rice

ACTIVITY: Measuring Chemical Changes

MATERIALS: Erlenmeyer flask, small test tube, Liquid 1, rubber stopper, graduated cylinder, Liquid 2, balance, Liquid 3, Liquid 4

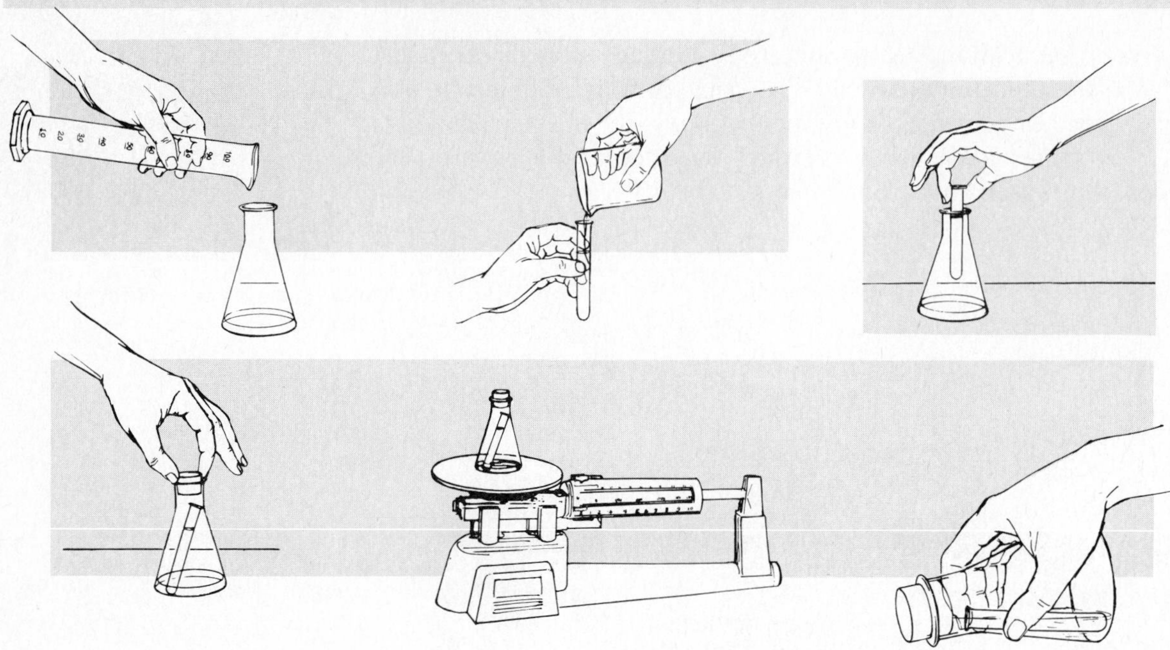

Always follow these instructions when you handle chemicals:

Never put anything in your mouth.

Always wash your hands after working with chemicals.

Wear safety glasses or other eye protection.

Look out for your neighbors.

- a. Draw your data tables first. You need three columns. Label the first column Mass of the Glassware and Chemicals Before Mixing. Label the second column Mass after Mixing. Label the third column Change in Mass. Draw Table 1 and Table 2 with three columns each. There will be one table for each pair of solutions.

b. Put about 10 ml of Liquid 1 in the flask.

c. Fill the test tube about two thirds full with Liquid 2. After filling, dry the outside of the test tube.

d. With no spilling or splashing, very carefully lower the test tube into the flask.

e. Place the stopper tightly in the flask.

f. Weigh the flask and its contents. Record the mass in the first column of Table 1.

g. Tip the flask over so that the two liquids mix. Answer question 3.

h. Weigh the flask and its contents. Record the mass in Table 1. Record the change of mass in Table 1. Write on the chalkboard the change of mass your team found. Answer question 4.

i. Find the class average change of mass.

j. Rinse out your glassware carefully. Don't forget the stopper.

k. Use Liquid 3 and Liquid 4 to repeat steps b through g.

l. Weigh the flask and its contents after mixing. Record the mass in Table 2. Clean the glassware. Answer question 7.

m. Write on the chalkboard the change of mass your team found. Find the class average change of mass.

---

3. What happened when you mixed Liquid 1 and Liquid 2?
4. What change of mass did you find?
5. What did the class data show about Conservation of Matter after Liquids 1 and 2 were mixed?
6. What happened when Liquids 3 and 4 were mixed?
7. What change of mass did you find when you mixed Liquids 3 and 4?
8. What does the class data show about Conservation of Matter during a chemical change?

15C CHEMICAL CHANGES ARE COMMON

Frying an egg causes a chemical change.

Life is a series of chemical changes. The oxygen you breathe combines with your food. This releases energy to run your body machinery. The process of making polyester for clothing is a series of chemical changes. Other chemical changes are frying an egg, cooking a potato, and making cheese. If chemical changes suddenly stopped, all life on earth would stop.

Scientists have good reason to study chemical changes. Most of the things you see around you in your classroom are manufactured, not natural. It took chemical changes to produce them. **The Law of Conservation of Matter helps scientists understand chemical changes.**

If there are so many chemical changes going on, who studies them? The answer is CHEMISTS and CHEMICAL ENGINEERS. **They want to know why chemical changes take place and how they can be controlled.** Chemists specialize in everything from the cells in the human body to the silicon transistors in stereo equipment. They develop catalytic converters to be put in cars to reduce air pollution. They also make artificial skin for burn victims. As you can see, chemists are involved in a wide variety of activities.

WHO STUDIES CHEMICAL CHANGES?

Chemists

Chemical engineers

When chemists study reactions, they use the conservation law continuously. If the masses of the new products of a reaction do not equal the masses of the original substances, then the chemists have missed something. This gives them a method of testing their understanding of what is happening. It is also a way of testing to see if something is leaking out of the equipment into the environment.

Chemists and chemical engineers often study chemical changes in laboratories like this one.

9. Go through your purse or pockets. How many things are natural and how many must have gone through at least one chemical change?

10. What do chemists and chemical engineers want to know?

11. If, after a fire, the ashes do not have the same mass as the original wood, does this upset the Law of Conservation of Matter? Explain your answer.

SUMMARY

VOCABULARY

physical change, chemical change, chemical reaction, chemist, chemical engineer

KEY FACTS AND CONCEPTS

A physical change does not change the properties of a substance.

A chemical change does change the properties of a substance by either combining it with something else or breaking it down into simpler parts.

Chemical changes can take many forms.

In a chemical change, the amount of matter stays the same.

CONCLUSION

Chemical changes are taking place in you and around you all the time. You couldn't survive without them. In every one of these chemical changes, the total amount of matter involved always remains constant.

12. What is the KEY IDEA of this chapter?

CHAPTER

16 Particles

The Building Blocks of Matter

16A INTRODUCTION

So far in this book you have learned that almost everything is made of matter. All matter has the properties of mass and volume. Just how much mass in relation to volume is in a sample of matter is found by determining density. The mass of a sample of matter remains constant during both physical and chemical changes. Knowing these facts about matter will help you understand some of the things you experience in the world around you.

These facts about matter are important, but a big question still remains to be answered. The big question about matter is, "What is matter made of?" After studying the data about matter, scientists have gradually come to believe that matter is a collection of PARTICLES.

1. State three facts about matter.

16B PARTICLES OF MATTER

Scientists believe that matter is made of particles, which are very tiny pieces. Each of the substances known in the universe can be broken down into its smallest pieces. A substance, such as sugar for example, can be broken down into smaller and smaller pieces. But there is a point at which a piece cannot be broken down any further. At this point, if the piece is made any smaller, the particles will no longer be sugar. **Therefore, every substance has a smallest size limit.**

Sugar is made of molecules.

SOME FACTS ABOUT MATTER

Everything is made of matter.
All matter has mass and volume.
Matter's mass remains constant.
Matter is made of particles.

The smallest possible piece of a substance is called a MOLECULE. **This is referred to as the molecular hypothesis.** Molecules stick together to form substances large enough to see. These substances are all the objects you see around you. Molecules of cellulose make the pages of this book. Molecules of protein make the muscles of your body. Molecules of gasoline go into the fuel tank of your car.

Molecules are small. Simple substances such as water or sugar have molecules that are unbelievably small. A carbon dioxide molecule has a diameter of 0.000000038 centimeter. A single object that small will not reflect light. This is why no one can see molecules directly, even with a light microscope.

The smallest piece of a substance that still keeps its properties is a molecule.

The molecules in different substances have different sizes and shapes. Molecules vary in size from slightly smaller than the carbon dioxide molecule mentioned above to protein molecules many times larger. Even a molecule 100 times wider than a carbon dioxide molecule would be small. Multiplying 0.000000038 by 100 still produces 5 zeros after the decimal point.

Molecules of different gases can mix together. DIFFUSION is the intermingling, or mixing together, of molecules. **The process of diffusion explains how odors spread.** If an open bottle of ammonia is placed in a closed room, the smell of ammonia very quickly fills the room. This is because molecules of ammonia have escaped from the bottle and mingled with the air molecules in the room.

Scientists have measured the rates of diffusion of various gases. **The rate of diffusion is how long it takes the molecules of different gases to mix with each other.** The data can be used to estimate the sizes of molecules. This is possible because the smaller the molecule, the faster it diffuses.

Diffusion is one reason scientists believe matter is made of particles. Both gases and liquids diffuse readily. Even solids will gradually mix with each other.

Suppose you placed a bar of gold and a bar of lead next to and touching each other. You let the bars remain in the same position for several months. At the end of that time, you separate the bars and analyze them. You would find that some gold had diffused into the lead, and some lead had diffused into the gold. Scientists find the molecular hypothesis the simplest way to explain these data.

2. What is a molecule?
3. Why can't you see a single molecule?
4. What is diffusion?

16C MOLECULES IN MOTION

The three states of matter can be explained in terms of how their molecules behave. This is possible because of two characteristics that molecules have. **First, molecules are always moving. Second, the molecules within a substance have special attractions for each other.** These special attractions are different from the attractions of the molecules for other kinds of molecules.

In a gas, molecules are moving too fast to attract each other. When two gas molecules collide, they bounce away from one another. The

ACTIVITY: Mixing and Measuring Liquids

MATERIALS: Two 100-ml graduated cylinders, water, alcohol

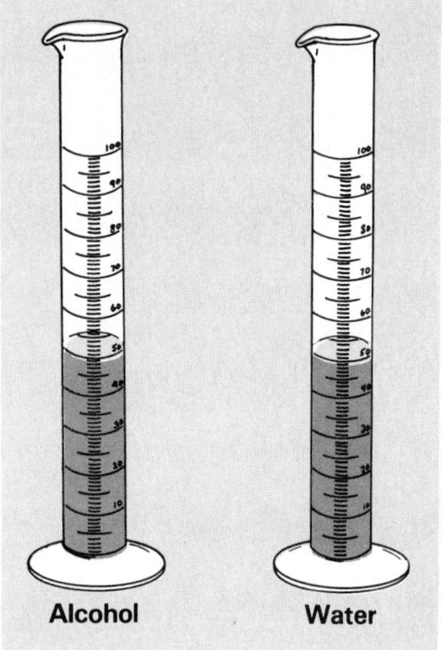

a. Fill one graduated cylinder to the 50 ml mark with water. Fill the second graduated cylinder to the 50 ml mark with alcohol. Measure very carefully each time.
b. *Without spilling one drop,* half the class will pour all the water into the alcohol. The other half of the class will pour the alcohol into the water.
c. Measure the volume of the mixture.

---

5. What is the volume of the mixture?
6. Explain your results. Remember that alcohol and water are made of particles of different sizes and shapes.

hotter the gas, the faster the molecules move. The faster the molecules move, the harder they hit each other and the walls of their container. In a tire, when the molecules move faster, the pressure inside the tire increases. This is why drivers have more tire trouble on hot days. The pressure can build up inside the tire until it eventually causes a blowout.

When a gas is cooled, its molecules slow down. Condensation takes place when molecules slow down enough to attract each other. The molecules move just enough to stay close together but not to stick tightly. This results in a liquid being formed. This is why a cold soda bottle collects water. The water molecules in the air hit the cold soda bottle. They slow down enough so the attractions between all the molecules can take effect. The water molecules stick to the glass and to each other. Water collects on the bottle.

Evaporation takes place when some of the molecules in a liquid escape into the air. As a liquid warms up, the molecules speed up. The faster the molecules move, the more easily they can overcome the attraction of the other molecules that hold them. The more easily they can overcome this attraction, the more easily they can escape. When the liquid is warm enough, the molecules are escaping very fast. The liquid is boiling.

State of Matter	Behavior of Molecules
Gas	Molecules move too fast to attract each other.
Liquid	Molecules move just enough to stay close together but not to stick.
Solid	Molecules lock together and vibrate in place.

Freezing takes place when the molecules in a liquid slow down enough to lock together. In solids, the molecules vibrate in place but do not change places very often. In warmer solids, the molecules vibrate harder. Most solids expand when they are heated, probably because of the increased vibration.

As a solid is heated, the molecules vibrate hard enough to pull apart. The solid melts. Molecules of different substances have different attractions. This is why ice melts at 0° Celsius, lead melts at 324.7° Celsius, and tungsten, which is the wire in light bulbs, melts at 3370° Celsius.

Some molecules attract different molecules as much as they attract each other. Water molecules have this quality. **This is why water can wet so many things.** However, the attraction between water and wax is low. For example, water on a freshly polished car forms little beads instead of spreading out. The water molecules in this case are more attracted to each other than to the molecules in the wax.

7. Use the concept of molecules to explain condensation.
8. Use the concept of molecules to explain melting.
9. Use the concept of molecules to explain why water wets other substances.

SUMMARY

VOCABULARY

particle molecule diffusion

KEY FACTS AND CONCEPTS

Matter is made of tiny particles called molecules.
Each substance is made of a different kind of molecule.
Molecules are always in motion. The hotter a substance is, the faster its molecules move.
Molecules attract each other.
Changes of state can be explained in terms of moving molecules.

CONCLUSION

The theory that all matter is made of molecules is used to explain many events in nature. The theory has been widely accepted by scientists, even though no one has ever seen a molecule with the unaided eye.

10. What is the KEY IDEA of this chapter?

CHAPTER

17 Composition of Molecules

The Law of Constant Composition

17A INTRODUCTION

As you learned in Chapter 16, matter is made of tiny particles called molecules. Each kind of matter, each substance in the universe, is made of different molecules. **Molecules come in different sizes and shapes, but all the molecules of any one substance are exactly alike.**

A wall seen from a distance looks like one piece of material. Up close, however, you will see that the wall is made up of many pieces.

The theory that molecules make up every substance has been widely accepted by scientists. Scientists accept the theory because so many properties of matter match the properties they would expect tiny particles to have. Scientists use the term molecular THEORY because the molecular hypothesis has been tested and proved valid so many times. **A theory is a hypothesis that has been tested many times and has always produced the same results.**

Once scientists realized that everything is made of molecules, they began working on molecules to discover what was in them. The result of their research is now known as the LAW OF CONSTANT COMPOSITION. **The law states that the molecules in each substance always have the same parts.**

The scientists analyzed molecules in different reactions. They learned that in some reactions molecules combined. In other reactions, molecules broke apart into smaller molecules. Molecules also reacted by exchanging parts. When all the molecular parts were accounted for, scientists found that the molecules of any one substance always had the same parts.

The data from their experiments were so consistent that their hypothesis became a theory and is now considered a LAW. **A theory becomes a law when there are no exceptions and the law covers a wide range of facts.**

> The LAW OF CONSTANT COMPOSITION states that the molecules of a given substance are always composed of the same parts.

1. What is a theory?
2. When does a theory become a law?
3. What does the Law of Constant Composition tell you about molecules?

17B MOLECULAR PARTS

Molecules always produce the same parts when broken down. To break down a molecule into its parts is to DECOMPOSE it. Table salt always decomposes to sodium, which is a metal, and chlorine, which is a green, poisonous gas. Water always decomposes to the gases hydrogen and oxygen.

Salt always decomposes to sodium and chlorine.

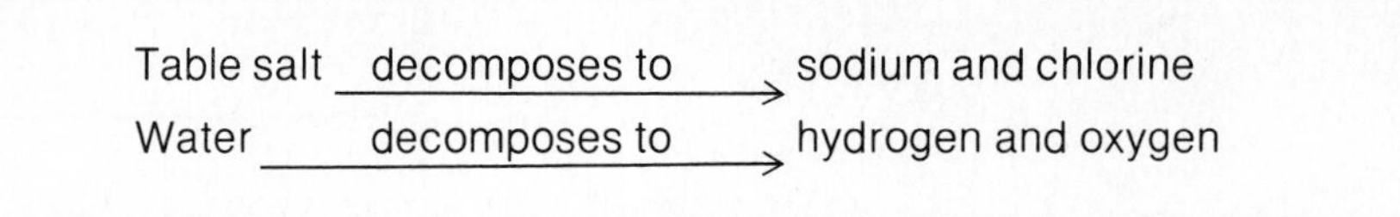

Table salt —decomposes to→ sodium and chlorine
Water —decomposes to→ hydrogen and oxygen

The process of breaking down a substance to identify its parts is called ANALYSIS. Many substances have been analyzed. Each substance always has the same composition every time it is tested.

During chemical reactions, molecules behave according to the Law of Constant Composition. Their behavior is predictable for the substances involved. **Molecules react in constant proportions. Molecules decompose in constant proportions.**

Oxygen and hydrogen always combine in the same ratio.

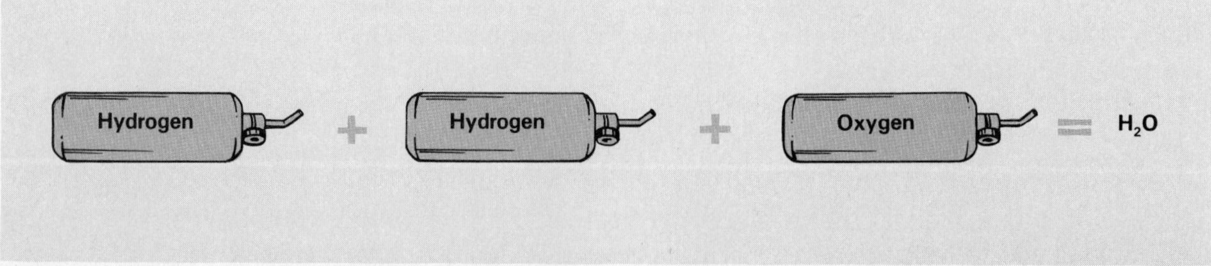

For example, when the gases oxygen and hydrogen combine, the ratio is always 2 parts hydrogen to 1 part oxygen. It may be 2 milliliters of hydrogen to 1 milliliter of oxygen, but the ratio is always 2 to 1.

If 100 grams of table salt are decomposed, 39.34 grams of sodium and 60.66 grams of chlorine gas will be recovered. If 1,000 grams of salt are decomposed, 393.4 grams of sodium and 606.6 grams of chlorine are recovered. It does not matter whether the salt came out of the Indian Ocean, a Siberian salt mine, or from the salt beds of San Francisco Bay, the ratio of sodium to chlorine is always the same.

4. What is decomposition?
5. What is analysis?
6. In what ways are molecules predictable?

ACTIVITY: Combining Acid and Carbonate

MATERIALS: Graduated cylinder, acetic acid (vinegar) beaker, sodium carbonate solution, stirring rod, indicator (phenolphthalein)

Sodium carbonate solution is irritating to the eyes and skin. Handle it carefully. If you spill any, wipe it up promptly. The indicator can make you sick. When you finish using these chemicals, WASH YOUR HANDS! Follow these procedures carefully. Spilling acid or carbonate solution will make your data unreliable.

- a. Prepare a table with three columns. Label the columns as follows:
  Volume of Acid (each team will be different)
  Volume of Sodium Carbonate Solution Used
  Volume of Acid Divided by Volume of Carbonate Solution Used
- b. Measure your volume of acid and put ALL of it into the beaker. Record the volume in Table 1.
- c. If indicator has not been added to your acid, add two or three DROPS now.
- d. Rinse your graduated cylinder. Fill the graduate to the 100 ml mark with sodium carbonate solution.
- e. Pour a SMALL amount of carbonate solution into the acid. Observe what happens.
- f. Pour small amounts of carbonate solution into the acid. Stir each time and watch for a color change.
- g. When the solution changes color and does not fade away, STOP adding carbonate.
- h. Look at the graduated cylinder and measure how much sodium carbonate solution you have used. Record this amount in Table 1.
- i. Divide the volume of acid you used by the volume of sodium carbonate solution added to it. Record this number in Table 1. Write this number on the board.

7. Look at the ratios of acid to carbonate solution found by the different teams. How do they compare?
8. How well does the class data support the concept that molecules react in constant proportions?

17C USING CONSTANT COMPOSITION

The Law of Constant Composition is an important research tool. **To understand how a reaction takes place, scientists must know which reacting material provided the different parts of the new molecule.** The parts of the starting molecules are all known. Their compositions will not change. When the new molecule is analyzed, its parts are identified. The original molecules that had these parts must be the molecules that took part in the reaction.

Substances combine in constant proportions. The same ratio of hydrogen always combines with chlorine. In the gaseous state, their volumes are in a one-to-one ratio. When the gases hydrogen and nitrogen combine, the ratio is one to three. By studying these ratios, scientists find clues to understanding how matter is put together.

Finding that substances react in constant proportions and that each substance always had the same composition changed the way people thought. If predictable products resulted from a chemical reaction, then magic or a supernatural factor was not involved. Starting with the right substances was the way to chemical success, not knowing the right charms, spells, or incantations. **The laws of nature began to replace superstition.**

The Law of Constant Composition is also necessary in technology. A common chemical used in making other chemicals is sodium carbonate. To make sodium carbonate, an important starting ingredient is often salt. The chemical engineer knows that each ton of salt will yield 393.4 kilograms of sodium. The process is efficient because molecules decompose in constant proportions. The engineer always knows how much raw material is needed at each step to make a new product.

A widely used plastic is made of the substances urea and formaldehyde. The plastics manufacturer must know the proportion of urea to formaldehyde. If the right amount of each substance is not added every time, the plastic will be defective and raw materials will be wasted.

Automobile batteries work with lead and sulfuric acid. There is a constant proportion of lead to sulfuric acid used by the battery in the reaction. The battery must be designed with room for enough sulfuric acid to react with the correct amount of lead. If the battery case cannot hold enough acid for the lead, the battery will run down too soon.

In an automobile battery, lead and sulfuric acid react in constant proportions.

9. How does a chemical engineer depend upon the Law of Constant Composition?

10. A red, heavy substance called cinnabar is found in California. The composition of cinnabar is mercury and sulfur. What is the composition of a piece of cinnabar found in Brazil?

11. The usual proportions for a concrete sidewalk are five parts sand and gravel to one part cement. What would happen to the sidewalk if the proportions were changed to ten parts sand and gravel to one part cement?

SUMMARY

VOCABULARY

theory
law
analysis
Law of Constant Composition
decompose

KEY FACTS AND CONCEPTS

Molecules always have the same parts.
Molecules react in constant proportions.
Molecules decompose in constant proportions.
The Law of Constant Composition is important to both scientists and technologists.

CONCLUSION

Science and technology depend upon the Law of Constant Composition. The scientist can trace molecular parts through complex chemical reactions. This increases scientific understanding. The technologist can measure the ingredients in the manufacturing process. This increases industrial efficiency. Thus, many people are dependent upon this law of nature.

12. What is the KEY IDEA of this chapter?

CHAPTER

18 The Building Blocks of Matter Atoms, Elements, and Compounds

18A INTRODUCTION

About twenty-five hundred years ago, the Greek philosophers decided that all matter on earth was made of four elements. The elements were fire, air, earth, and water. They believed that different combinations of these four elements could produce every known kind of matter. This idea of matter lasted about two thousand years.

When early scientists reviewed the data, they could not accept the four-element hypothesis. Today, scientists analyze matter to see why it has certain properties. The way in which matter is studied has changed completely since the time of the ancient Greeks. **The four-element hypothesis disappeared with the change in scientific thinking.**

Scientists now believe that all matter is made of molecules. All molecules are composed of the same basic parts, or components. When a molecule decomposes, it always breaks down into the same parts.

Scientists began to analyze molecules in the early 18th century. When molecules of many different substances were first analyzed, scientists realized that the data they were collecting were telling them something. **They found that the same parts kept appearing over and over again in the molecules.**

These recurring parts were the same no matter what kind of molecule was being analyzed. The scientists named these components the chemical ELEMENTS.

1. What was the ancient Greeks' idea of matter?
2. When did the four-element hypothesis disappear?

18B ELEMENTS AND ATOMS

This rock sample taken from the moon is made up of the same elements that make up matter on the earth.

A 17th century scientist, Robert Boyle, defined elements. **Elements are substances that cannot be broken down into simpler substances.** The chemical elements make up all molecules. It took years for scientists to identify all the elements known today. In the early 1700's, only 30 substances had been identified as elements. Today, there are 108 elements known. The methods of molecular analysis had to be worked out as more substances were tested.

Today, modern technology allows chemists to analyze samples of matter efficiently. When the amounts of each element add up to the mass of the sample being analyzed, chemists know that there can be no other elements in that sample of matter. In this way, all matter can be analyzed for new elements.

At present, scientists believe there is very little chance of finding new elements in nature. All the different materials analyzed so far have been composed of known elements. For example, the samples from the moon were analyzed very carefully. Even the elements in the moon rocks were the same as those already known on earth. In later chapters of this unit, you will learn why scientists do not expect any surprises from nature when they analyze matter.

Elements are forms of matter that cannot be decomposed to anything simpler by chemical methods. Scientists use chemical methods on a specimen of matter to see if it is an element. The methods include heating, treating with acids, passing electrical current through the specimen, and treating the specimen with other substances. If the specimen doesn't decompose to something simpler, then it is an element.

The smallest particle of an element is an ATOM. The atoms of a certain element are different from the atoms of every other element. **All the atoms of an element have exactly the same chemical characteristics.** At first, scientists thought that all the atoms of any one element were exactly alike. Now scientists believe that the atoms have variations in mass. However, the differences in mass have no effect on chemical properties.

Atoms of different elements unite to form molecules. These molecules are called COMPOUNDS. **A compound is a substance that is made up of more than one element.** For example, oxygen and hydrogen are elements. Two hydrogen atoms and one oxygen atom unite to form a molecule of water. Therefore, water is a compound.

Not all molecules are compounds. Many elements form molecules of two or more atoms. **The difference is that a molecule of a compound contains more than one kind of atom. The molecules of an element contain just one kind of atom.** Oxygen, hydrogen, and nitrogen are all elements that have two-atom molecules. Their molecules are called DIATOMIC. An example of an element that has more than two atoms per molecule is sulfur. The sulfur molecule has eight atoms.

3. What are elements?
4. What is an atom?
5. How are the atoms of an element alike?
6. How may atoms of a single element be different from one another?
7. What are compounds?
8. How are the molecules of an element different from the molecules of a compound?

18C ATOMIC SYMBOLS

Each element has a one- or two-letter SYMBOL. Only the first letter is capitalized when two letters are used. **The symbol is used to represent an atom of the element.** Notice how the symbols are used in the following table of Working Atomic Masses. You will learn more about this kind of table in Chapter 21.

WORKING ATOMIC MASSES

NAME	SYMBOL	ATOMIC NUMBER	ATOMIC MASS	NAME	SYMBOL	ATOMIC NUMBER	ATOMIC MASS
Actinium	Ac	89	(227)	Erbium	Er	68	167.3
Aluminum	Al	13	27.0	Europium	Eu	63	152.0
Americium	Am	95	(243)	Fermium	Fm	100	(257)
Antimony	Sb	51	121.8	Fluorine	F	9	19.0
Argon	Ar	18	39.9	Francium	Fr	87	(223)
Arsenic	As	33	74.9	Gadolinium	Gd	64	157.2
Astatine	At	85	(210)	Gallium	Ga	31	69.7
Barium	Ba	56	137.3	Germanium	Ge	32	72.6
Berkelium	Bk	97	(247)	Gold	Au	79	197.0
Beryllium	Be	4	9.01	Hafnium	Hf	72	178.5
Bismuth	Bi	83	209.0	Helium	He	2	4.00
Boron	B	5	10.8	Holmium	Ho	67	164.9
Bromine	Br	35	79.9	Hydrogen	H	1	1.008
Cadmium	Cd	48	112.4	Indium	In	49	114.8
Calcium	Ca	20	40.1	Iodine	I	53	126.9
Californium	Cf	98	(251)	Iridium	Ir	77	192.2
Carbon	C	6	12.01	Iron	Fe	26	55.8
Cerium	Ce	58	140.1	Krypton	Kr	36	83.8
Cesium	Cs	55	132.9	Lanthanum	La	57	138.9
Chlorine	Cl	17	35.5	Lawrencium	Lr	103	(260)
Chromium	Cr	24	52.0	Lead	Pb	82	207.2
Cobalt	Co	27	58.9	Lithium	Li	3	6.94
Copper	Cu	29	63.5	Lutetium	Lu	71	175.0
Curium	Cm	96	(247)	Magnesium	Mg	12	24.3
Dysprosium	Dy	66	162.5	Manganese	Mn	25	54.9
Einsteinium	Es	99	(254)	Mendelevium	Md	101	(258)

The symbols are used to write FORMULAS. **A formula tells which elements are in a molecule. It also tells how many atoms of each element are present in the molecule.** The formula representing a water molecule is H_2O. This formula shows that a water molecule has two hydrogen atoms and one oxygen atom. The number follows the symbol it applies to. The number 1 is never written. The 2 in this formula applies to the H, which stands for hydrogen.

In $Ca(OH)_2$, the number 2 applies to the elements inside the parentheses—O and H. This formula means that there are two oxygen atoms and two hydrogen atoms with one atom of calcium. The substance represented by the formula is calcium hydroxide.

Symbols are agreed upon by chemists throughout the world. No matter what country they are in or what alphabet they use, all chemists use the same chemical symbols. Chemists have an organization, the International Union of Pure and Applied Chemistry (IUPAC). The IUPAC is responsible for standardizing chemical symbols for all the scientists in the world.

Substance	**Formula**	**Number of Atoms**
Water	H_2O	2 hydrogen atoms 1 oxygen atom
Calcium hydroxide	$Ca(OH)_2$	1 calcium atom 2 oxygen atoms 2 hydrogen atoms
Sodium sulfate	Na_2SO_4	2 sodium atoms 1 sulfur atom 4 oxygen atoms
Copper chloride	$CuCl_2$	1 copper atom 2 chlorine atoms

ANCIENT GREEK	LATIN	CHEROKEE	CHEMICAL ELEMENTS
Α	A	Ꭳ o Ꭺ go	K
Β	B	Ꮀ ho Ꮆ lo	Ca
Γ	C	Ꮌ mo Ꮓ no	Sc
Δ	D	Ꮙ quo	Ti
Ε	E	Ꮠ so Ꮩ to	V
Ϝ	F	Ꮰ tlo Ꮶ tso	Cr
Ι, Ζ	Z	Ꮼ wo Ᏺ yo	Mn
⊟	H	Ꭴ u Ꭻ gu	Fe
⊗	–	Ꮁ hu	Co
ϟ	I	Ꮇ lu Ꮍ mu	Ni
Κ	K	Ꮔ nu Ꮚ quu	Cu
Λ	L	Ꮡ su Ꮪ du	Zn

The symbols in every alphabet have meaning. Like the letters in an alphabet, the chemical symbols mean something to many people. The same chemical symbols are used everywhere in the world.

Notice that not all the letters used as symbols come from the English names of the elements. For example, the symbol for iron is Fe because the Latin name for iron is *ferrum*. Elements that have been recognized for centuries have been given symbols that come from their original Latin names. Among the elements with symbols from Latin are gold, Au from *aurum*, and silver, Ag from *argentum*.

There is one element with a symbol from the German language. That element is tungsten. The symbol for tungsten is W from the German word *wolfram*. The word *wolfram* is used in many countries in Europe.

The glowing wire in a light bulb is made of tungsten.

9. What is a chemical symbol?
10. How many atoms of oxygen are in CrO_2Cl_2?
11. How many atoms of chlorine are in CrO_2Cl_2?
12. How many atoms of chromium are in CrO_2Cl_2?

ACTIVITY: Formulas of Common Substances

MATERIALS: None

Following are the formulas of some common substances. Make a list of the names of the substances. Next to each name, write the elements it contains. Include the number of atoms of each element that are in the molecule.

Table sugar: $C_{12}H_{22}O_{11}$
Table salt: NaCl
Lye: NaOH
Iodine: I_2
Grain alcohol: C_2H_6O
Bleach: NaClO
Peroxide: H_2O_2
Baking soda: $NaHCO_3$
Vinegar: C_2H_4O
Ammonia gas: NH_3

SUMMARY

VOCABULARY

element, atom, compound, diatomic, symbol, formula

KEY FACTS AND CONCEPTS

All matter is made of the same substances, the chemical elements.
The smallest unit of an element is an atom.
Elements cannot be decomposed by chemical means.
Molecules are made up of atoms.
Molecules of elements have only one kind of atom.
Molecules of compounds have two or more kinds of atoms.
Symbols are used to represent atoms of elements.
The symbols and numbers in a formula show how many atoms of each element are in the molecule.

CONCLUSION

Elements are basic parts of all matter. Atoms of the elements unite to form molecules. The symbols of the elements are used to write molecular formulas. The symbols are recognized throughout the world. A chemist from any country can look at a formula and understand it.

13. What is the KEY IDEA of this chapter?

CHAPTER

19 Families of Elements

The Periodic Table

19A INTRODUCTION

Different elements have atoms of different masses. Because of the particular properties of gases, chemists can compare the masses of atoms in gas molecules especially easily. The mass ratios of several atoms were determined by using gases. These atoms were used to study mass ratios of atoms in molecules of liquids and solids. While comparing the masses of different atoms, scientists noticed that different elements share similar properties.

The relative atomic masses of the elements have been worked out. When the elements were first listed by their atomic masses, a pattern emerged. **Elements with similar properties appeared at regular intervals.** The early lists started with hydrogen and continued with as many elements as were known at the time. Scientists tried arranging the elements in different ways, based on their properties. **Although some elements have similar properties, no two elements are exactly alike.**

1. When the elements were first listed by their atomic masses, what pattern emerged?
2. What did scientists use to try to arrange the elements?

19B THE PERIODIC TABLE OF THE ELEMENTS

When the elements were listed in order of increasing atomic mass, it became apparent that elements with similar properties appeared at regular intervals. But all of the elements had not yet been discovered. Therefore, it was difficult to decide how often the properties really repeated. After all, there might be more elements in-between elements with similar properties.

The need for order among the elements led the Russian chemist Dmitri Mendeleev to arrange the elements in a table. Mendeleev's table, known as the Periodic Table of the Elements, or PERIODIC TABLE, was introduced in 1869. It was seen as a valuable guide to understanding the similarities and differences in the properties of various elements.

Mendeleev used both the atomic masses and the properties of the elements to construct his table. The elements in each column resemble each other. The atomic masses increase from top to bottom and from left to right. **The group of elements in any given column of the table is called a family of elements.** The elements in a family have many similarities.

Dmitri Mendeleev

ПЕРИОДИЧЕСКАЯ СИСТЕМА ЭЛЕМЕНТОВ

Периоды	Ряды	ГРУППЫ ЭЛЕМЕНТОВ I	II	III	IV	V	VI	VII	VIII			0
1	I	H 1 1,008										He 2 4,003
2	II	Li 3 6,940	Be 4 9,02	5 B 10,82	6 C 12,010	7 N 14,008	8 O 16,000	9 F 19,00				Ne 10 20,183
3	III	Na 11 22,997	Mg 12 24,32	13 Al 26,97	14 Si 28,06	15 P 30,98	16 S 32,06	17 Cl 35,457				Ar 18 39,944
4	IV	K 19 39,096	Ca 20 40,08	Sc 21 45,10	Ti 22 47,90	V 23 50,95	Cr 24 52,01	Mn 25 54,93	Fe 26 55,85	Co 27 58,94	Ni 28 58,69	
	V	29 Cu 63,57	30 Zn 65,38	31 Ga 69,72	32 Ge 72,60	33 As 74,91	34 Se 78,96	35 Br 79,916				Kr 36 83,7
5	VI	Rb 37 85,48	Sr 38 87,63	Y 39 88,92	Zr 40 91,22	Nb 41 92,91	Mo 42 95,95	Ma 43 —	Ru 44 101,7	Rh 45 102,91	Pd 46 106,7	
	VII	47 Ag 107,88	48 Cd 112,41	49 In 114,76	50 Sn 118,70	51 Sb 121,76	52 Te 127,61	53 J 126,92				Xe 54 131,3
6	VIII	Cs 55 132,91	Ba 56 137,36	La 57 * 138,92	Hf 72 178,6	Ta 73 180,88	W 74 183,92	Re 75 186,31	Os 76 190,2	Ir 77 193,1	Pt 78 195,23	
	IX	79 Au 197,2	80 Hg 200,61	81 Tl 204,39	82 Pb 207,21	83 Bi 209,00	84 Po 210	85 —				Rn 86 222
7	X	87 —	Ra 88 226,05	Ac 89 227	Th 90 232,12	Pa 91 231	U 92 238,07					

* ЛАНТАНИДЫ 58-71

Ce 58 140,13	Pr 59 140,92	Nd 60 144,27	61 —	Sm 62 150,43	Eu 63 152,0	Gd 64 156,9
Tb 65 [illegible]	Dy 66 162,46	Ho 67 164,94	Er 68 167,2	Tu 69 169,4	Yb 70 173,04	Cp 71 174,99

This is the way the Periodic Table of the Elements looked in 1900, thirty-one years after Dmitri Mendeleev introduced it.

When Mendeleev first worked out the periodic table, he believed that not all the elements that existed in nature had been discovered. But by studying the known elements, Mendeleev was able to predict where the unknown elements would fit into his table. He even predicted what the properties of the missing elements would be.

In the years after the periodic table was published, more elements were discovered. **The gaps in Mendeleev's table began to be filled in according to his predictions.** The newly discovered elements had just the masses and properties that he had anticipated. As more and more of his predictions turned out to be accurate, Mendeleev's work was accepted by chemists all over the world.

Of course, as more was learned about atomic structure, Mendeleev's table was modified and improved. The current periodic table is more useful than Mendeleev's original. A modern version of the periodic table is shown on pages 110-111. The next three chapters will help you understand the terms used in the Key on page 110.

3. Why did Mendeleev arrange the elements in a table? What is this table called?

4. What did Mendeleev use to construct his table?

5. What does the term "family of elements" refer to?

6. What happened to the periodic table as more was learned about atomic structure?

19C THE ALKALI METALS

The name of the periodic table comes from the way properties of the elements repeat. When something happens over and over again the event is said to occur *periodically.* The way a similar set of properties keeps appearing after a given number of elements is considered a periodic occurrence. **The periodic table was organized to illustrate the recurrence of these properties.**

Vertical columns in the periodic table are groups of elements with similar properties. Some of these groups have been named.

The first column on the left contains the ALKALI METALS. The elements of this group are lithium, sodium, potassium, rubidium, cesium, and francium. Francium is very rare and has not been studied as closely as the other elements in the group.

Hydrogen is listed in the first column, although it is not an alkali metal. Hydrogen is listed in this column because it combines with other elements in the same ratios as the alkali metals. **Hydrogen does not share enough important properties with the alkali metals to be considered one of them.**

The alkali metals share properties that make them easily recognizable. One of their common properties is shininess, or LUSTER. Another property of alkali metals is that heat and electricity move through them easily. This means they are good CONDUCTORS. A third property of alkali metals is low density; half of them are less dense than water. The alkali metals are soft. Except for lithium, they can be easily cut with a knife. These metals also have low MELTING POINTS. Most of them melt at temperatures below 100 ° Celsius.

All of these elements are highly REACTIVE. This means that they react easily with other elements. **In fact, the alkali metals are so highly reactive that they are never found as elements.** They are always found combined with other substances to make compounds.

PROPERTIES OF THE ALKALI METALS

They have luster.

They are good conductors.

They are soft.

They have low melting points.

They are highly reactive.

Alkali metals react with both air and water. In fact, these elements react violently with water. A dangerous chemical, lye, is made from sodium and water. Lye is highly CORROSIVE; that is, it eats away at whatever it comes in contact with. Many drain cleaners contain lye to clean out clogged plumbing.

7. What is the name of the first column on the left in the periodic table?

8. List the properties of the alkali metals.

9. Why are the alkali metals never found as elements, only as compounds?

19D THE HALOGENS

The second column from the right in the periodic table contains the HALOGENS. The halogens are fluorine, chlorine, bromine, iodine, and astatine. Astatine wasn't discovered until 1940 and is so rare that its properties are not well known.

Periodic Table of

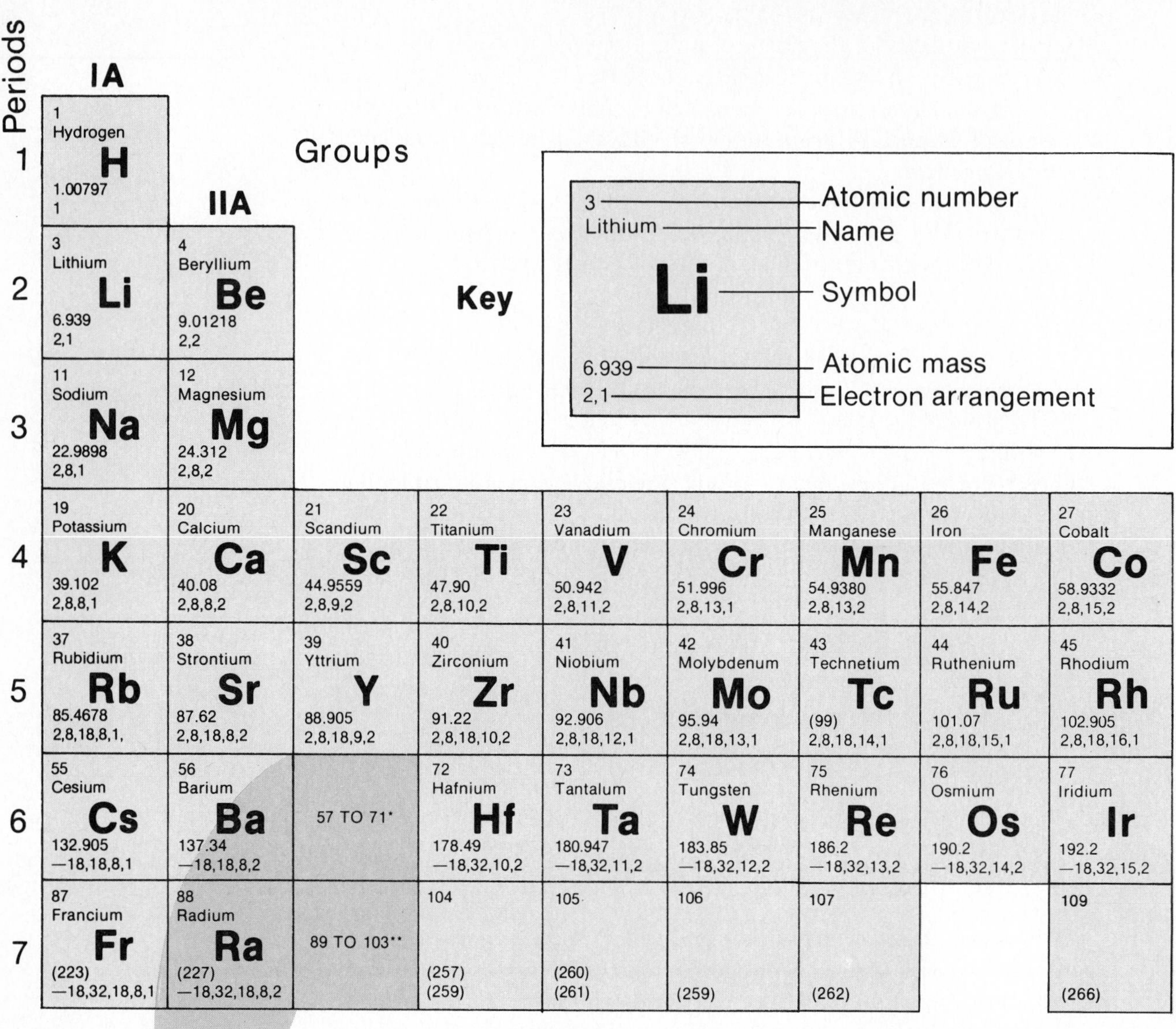

Groups

Key

3 Lithium **Li** 6.939 2,1	
3	Atomic number
Lithium	Name
Li	Symbol
6.939	Atomic mass
2,1	Electron arrangement

Periods	IA	IIA							
1	1 Hydrogen **H** 1.00797 1								
2	3 Lithium **Li** 6.939 2,1	4 Beryllium **Be** 9.01218 2,2							
3	11 Sodium **Na** 22.9898 2,8,1	12 Magnesium **Mg** 24.312 2,8,2							
4	19 Potassium **K** 39.102 2,8,8,1	20 Calcium **Ca** 40.08 2,8,8,2	21 Scandium **Sc** 44.9559 2,8,9,2	22 Titanium **Ti** 47.90 2,8,10,2	23 Vanadium **V** 50.942 2,8,11,2	24 Chromium **Cr** 51.996 2,8,13,1	25 Manganese **Mn** 54.9380 2,8,13,2	26 Iron **Fe** 55.847 2,8,14,2	27 Cobalt **Co** 58.9332 2,8,15,2
5	37 Rubidium **Rb** 85.4678 2,8,18,8,1,	38 Strontium **Sr** 87.62 2,8,18,8,2	39 Yttrium **Y** 88.905 2,8,18,9,2	40 Zirconium **Zr** 91.22 2,8,18,10,2	41 Niobium **Nb** 92.906 2,8,18,12,1	42 Molybdenum **Mo** 95.94 2,8,18,13,1	43 Technetium **Tc** (99) 2,8,18,14,1	44 Ruthenium **Ru** 101.07 2,8,18,15,1	45 Rhodium **Rh** 102.905 2,8,18,16,1
6	55 Cesium **Cs** 132.905 —18,18,8,1	56 Barium **Ba** 137.34 —18,18,8,2	57 TO 71*	72 Hafnium **Hf** 178.49 —18,32,10,2	73 Tantalum **Ta** 180.947 —18,32,11,2	74 Tungsten **W** 183.85 —18,32,12,2	75 Rhenium **Re** 186.2 —18,32,13,2	76 Osmium **Os** 190.2 —18,32,14,2	77 Iridium **Ir** 192.2 —18,32,15,2
7	87 Francium **Fr** (223) —18,32,18,8,1	88 Radium **Ra** (227) —18,32,18,8,2	89 TO 103**	104 (257) (259)	105 (260) (261)	106 (259)	107 (262)		109 (266)

6	57 Lanthanum **La** 138.91 —18,18,9,2	58 Cerium **Ce** 140.12 —18,20,8,2	59 Praseodymium **Pr** 140.907 —18,21,8,2	60 Neodymium **Nd** 144.24 —18,22,8,2	61 Promethium **Pm** (145) —18,23,8,2	62 Samarium **Sm** 150.4 —18,24,8,2
7	89 Actinium **Ac** (227) —18,32,18,9,2	90 Thorium **Th** 232.038 —18,32,18,10,2	91 Protactinium **Pa** (231) —18,32,20,9,2	92 Uranium **U** 238.03 —18,32,21,9,2	93 Neptunium **Np** (237) —18,32,22,9,2	94 Plutonium **Pu** (242) —18,32,24,8,2

the Elements

Groups

			IIIA	IV A	V A	VI A	VII A	VIII A
								2 Helium **He** 4.0026 2
			5 Boron **B** 10.81 2,3	6 Carbon **C** 12.011 2,4	7 Nitrogen **N** 14.0067 2,5	8 Oxygen **O** 15.9994 2,6	9 Fluorine **F** 18.9984 2,7	10 Neon **Ne** 20.183 2,8
			13 Aluminum **Al** 26.9815 2,8,3	14 Silicon **Si** 28.086 2,8,4	15 Phosphorus **P** 30.9738 2,8,5	16 Sulfur **S** 32.064 2,8,6	17 Chlorine **Cl** 35.453 2,8,7	18 Argon **Ar** 39.948 2,8,8
28 Nickel **Ni** 58.71 —2,8,16,2	29 Copper **Cu** 63.54 2,8,18,1	30 Zinc **Zn** 65.37 2,8,18,2	31 Gallium **Ga** 69.72 2,8,18,3	32 Germanium **Ge** 72.59 2,8,18,4	33 Arsenic **As** 74.9216 2,8,18,5	34 Selenium **Se** 78.96 2,8,18,6	35 Bromine **Br** 79.909 2,8,18,7	36 Krypton **Kr** 83.80 2,8,18,8
46 Palladium **Pd** 106.4 2,8,18,18	47 Silver **Ag** 107.870 2,8,18,18,1	48 Cadmium **Cd** 112.40 2,8,18,18,2	49 Indium **In** 114.82 2,8,18,18,3	50 Tin **Sn** 118.69 2,8,18,18,4	51 Antimony **Sb** 121.75 2,8,18,18,5	52 Tellurium **Te** 127.60 2,8,18,18,6	53 Iodine **I** 126.9044 2,8,18,18,7	54 Xenon **Xe** 131.30 2,8,18,18,8
78 Platinum **Pt** 195.09 —18,32,17,1	79 Gold **Au** 196.967 —18,32,18,1	80 Mercury **Hg** 200.59 —18,32,18,2	81 Thallium **Tl** 204.37 —18,32,18,3	82 Lead **Pb** 207.19 —18,32,18,4	83 Bismuth **Bi** 208.980 —18,32,18,5	84 Polonium **Po** (210) —18,32,18,6	85 Astatine **At** (210) —18,32,18,7	86 Radon **Rn** (222) —18,32,18,8

63 Europium **Eu** 151.96 —18,25,8,2	64 Gadolinium **Gd** 157.25 —18,25,9,2	65 Terbium **Tb** 158.924 —18,27,8,2	66 Dysprosium **Dy** 162.50 —18,28,8,2	67 Holmium **Ho** 164.930 —18,29,8,2	68 Erbium **Er** 167.26 —18,30,8,2,	69 Thulium **Tm** 168.934 —18,31,8,2	70 Ytterbium **Yb** 173.04 —18,32,8,2	71 Lutetium **Lu** 174.97 —18,32,9,2
95 Americium **Am** (243) —18,32,25,8,2	96 Curium **Cm** (245) —18,32,25,9,2	97 Berkelium **Bk** (249) —18,32,26,9,2	98 Californium **Cf** (250) —18,32,28,8,2	99 Einsteinium **Es** (254) —18,32,29,8,2	100 Fermium **Fm** (252) —18,32,30,8,2	101 Mendelevium **Md** (256) —18,32,31,8,2	102 Nobelium **No** (254) —18,32,32,8,2	103 Lawrencium **Lw** (257) —18,32,32,9,2

The halogens, like the alkali metals, are extremely reactive. None is found as an element. They are always in compounds in nature. The halogens react with hydrogen in a one-to-one ratio.

The hydrogen halogen compounds are all gases at room temperature. They all form acid solutions in water. **These acid solutions will react with the solutions formed by the alkali metals and water to form alkali halides, or salt.** An example of this is table salt, NaCl. In fact, the word *halogen* comes from the Greek words meaning "salt formers."

Although the halogens, particularly fluorine, are difficult to contain, halogen compounds are used in household products. Bleach, antiseptics, and insecticides are examples of halogen compounds. Industries use halogens in many different types of chemical reactions.

The young woman applying antiseptic to her finger, the young man using bleach, and the pilot spraying crops are all using halogen compounds.

From industrial use, many practical uses for the halogens have emerged. For example, *Teflon** is the brand name for a plastic that contains fluorine. It will resist most acids and was developed to resist fluorine compounds in atomic energy work. Of course, you are familiar with nonstick coating on fry pans, waffle irons, and sauce pans.

PROPERTIES OF THE HALOGENS

They are highly reactive.

They are gases at room temperature.

They form acid solutions in water.

10. Where are the halogens located in the periodic table?
11. What form do all the halogens take at room temperature?
12. Give three examples of halogen compounds.

19E THE NOBLE GASES

The last column on the right in the periodic table contains the NOBLE GASES. These elements are helium, neon, argon, krypton, xenon, and radon. The noble gases are so unreactive that they are

**Teflon®* is the DuPont Company's trademark.

sometimes referred to as the INERT gases. They don't even form molecules of two atoms. **Noble gases form molecules of only one atom.**

There are only a very few compounds of noble gases known. None of them occurs in nature. They were first formed in 1962, when techniques for handling the most reactive element, fluorine, were developed. It takes exposure to extremely reactive fluorine compounds to make xenon compounds. So far, only xenon and radon have been made into compounds. These compounds react easily with other compounds and release the noble gas atoms as elements again.

PROPERTIES OF THE NOBLE GASES

They are very unreactive.

They are gases under normal conditions.

All the noble gases, except helium, are found in small amounts in the earth's atmosphere. Helium is obtained from natural gas. It is so light and fast a particle that earth's gravity can't hold it. The helium in the earth's atmosphere is constantly being lost to space.

It was by analyzing the composition of the air that scientists discovered the first noble gas, argon, in 1894. **Argon is the most common noble gas in the atmosphere and makes up about one percent of the air.**

Although the noble gases are so scarce and unreactive, they had all been discovered by 1900. Remember that this was long after Mendeleev had published the original periodic table.

13. Where are the noble gases located in the periodic table?
14. What is one common property of the noble gases?
15. What is the most common noble gas in the atmosphere?

19F SUMMARY OF THE PERIODIC TABLE

Imagine that you had to make a family tree. All the members of one family would be arranged from top to bottom, with the ancestors at the top and the present-day children at the bottom. The time period that each person lived would be printed along a line from left to right.

The periodic table is arranged like a family tree. The periodic table is used by scientists to organize all the chemical elements into related families.

THE PERIODIC TABLE OF THE ELEMENTS

The table is organized into rows and columns.

The elements are arranged according to their properties..

Elements of the same family are arranged in columns.

Elements are listed by their atomic number in rows.

Mendeleev constructed the first periodic table, and other scientists have added to it and are still adding to it.

16. What is the periodic table?

ACTIVITY: Properties of a Chemical Family

MATERIALS: Test tube, alkali metal solutions, hydroxide solutions, indicator

Solution	Feel Test	Indicator Color Test

The periodic table lists the elements by their properties. You will test several solutions for two of their properties: their feel and their color. You will test their color with an indicator.

Rinse and wipe all chemical spills, and wash your hands after handling any chemicals. Rinse your glassware promptly.

- a. In your notebook, draw a table like the one shown.
- b. List all the solutions you will be testing in your table.
- c. Take one third of a test tube of one solution.
- d. Rub a few drops of the solution between your thumb and index finger. Record whether the solution feels sticky, slippery, or soapy. Wash your hands.
- e. Add one or two drops of indicator to the test tube. (If you are using test paper strips, dip the paper into the liquid in the test tube.) Record the color that appears.
- f. Rinse your test tube and repeat steps c to e with another solution until all solutions have been tested.

17. How do the properties of the different liquids compare?
18. Why would chemists group these chemicals together?

19G THE USES OF ELEMENTS

There are more than 100 elements. Suppose you could reduce everything on the earth to its simplest elements. You would have more than 100 separate piles, each of a different element.

You would recognize some of these piles, such as oxygen, copper, and silver. Some piles might be strange to you, such as ytterbium and americium.

The elements occur in different states. Some of the piles would be solid, others liquids, and others gaseous. **The elements occur in different amounts.** Some elements are very common, while others are very scarce.

Some elements, along with their compounds, are very useful. **Just as you are made of many different chemical elements, so is everything on the earth.**

Uses of Common Elements

Element	Symbol	Uses
Aluminum	Al	building, foils, outdoor furniture
Barium	Ba	paint, rat poison
Boron	B	antiseptic, water softening, cleaning
Calcium	Ca	limestone, cement, plaster
Carbon	C	petroleum, alcohol, ink, pencils
Chlorine	Cl	swimming pools, bleach, germicide
Chromium	Cr	plating, tanning leather, stainless steel
Cobalt	Co	coloring glass, high temperature alloys
Copper	Cu	brass, bronze, coins
Fluorine	F	etching glass, air conditioning
Iodine	I	table salt, antiseptic
Iron	Fe	steel, wrought iron
Lead	Pb	solder, batteries, X-ray shields
Lithium	Li	flares, paint
Magnesium	Mg	flash bulbs, flares, airplane construction
Mercury	Hg	light switches, thermometers
Nickel	Ni	coins, safes, plating
Sodium	Na	table salt, soap
Sulfur	S	making paper, gunpowder, sulfa drugs
Zinc	Zn	paints, galvanizing

19. What do you call the simplest unit of matter?
20. How many different kinds of elements are there?
21. Name an element found in bleach.
22. What are some uses of sodium?
23. Why do you think magnesium is used in airplane production?
24. Why are elements important?

SUMMARY

VOCABULARY

periodic table
alkali metal
luster
conductor
melting point
reactive
corrosive
halogen
noble gas
inert

KEY FACTS AND CONCEPTS

Different elements have atoms of different masses.

When the elements were first listed by their atomic masses, similar properties appeared at regular intervals.

Dmitri Mendeleev organized the elements in a table known as the periodic table.

The group of elements in any given column of the table is called a family.

Elements that have similar properties form the columns of the periodic table.

The first column on the left in the table contains the alkali metals.

The alkali metals are highly reactive.

The second column from the right in the table contains the halogens.

The halogens are highly reactive.

Highly reactive elements are not found as elements in nature. They are always found as compounds.

The last column on the right in the table contains the noble gases.

The noble gases are so unreactive that they are referred to as the inert gases.

The periodic table has changed considerably since Mendeleev's time.

CONCLUSION

The periodic table organizes all the chemical elements. It organizes the elements into families. It also shows the patterns of properties that run through the elements. The modern periodic table has come a long way from Mendeleev's original. Scientists all over the world use the table as a tool in working with the elements.

25. What is the KEY IDEA of this chapter?

CHAPTER

20 Analyzing the Atom

An Atom Has Charged Particles

20A INTRODUCTION

The periodic table aided research on matter in two important ways. The table organized what was known about the elements at that time. To make compounds, chemists could then quickly find the elements with the desired properties. The table further aided research by raising an important question: Why did the properties of elements repeat periodically? Since each element is made up of a single kind of atom, scientists went to the atom to find the answer.

So scientists began to look at the structure of the atom. At one time, the atom was thought to be the smallest piece of matter. But in 1897, the scientist J. J. Thomson discovered that even the atom has parts.

By investigating electricity, Thomson discovered that there are charged particles in atoms. Charges account for electrical forces. To understand the parts of the atom, it is necessary to first understand electrical charges.

J.J. Thomson

1. In what ways did the periodic table aid research on matter?
2. Who discovered that the atom has parts?
3. To understand the atom, what is it necessary to first understand?

20B ELECTRICAL CHARGES

Rubbing some objects together causes them to attract other objects. For example, rubbing a plastic comb with fabric causes the comb to attract hair. This is because the comb becomes charged.

This kind of attraction was first recorded by the Greeks about 2,500 years ago. When the ancient Greeks rubbed a piece of amber with wool or fur, they found that the amber attracted feathers and dust. Amber is a clear yellow substance often used in the making of jewelry. In fact, the word *electricity* comes from the Greek word for amber.

TWO KINDS OF CHARGE
Positive
Negative

Centuries later, when scientists began investigating electricity, they found that there are two kinds of charge. The two kinds of charge are called POSITIVE and NEGATIVE. Two positive or two negative charges are called like charges. A positive and a negative charge are a pair of unlike charges.

The Law of Electrical Charges states that like charges repel and unlike charges attract each other. When objects pull together they are said to be ATTRACTED. When objects push apart they are said to be REPELLED. Materials with different charges attract each other. Materials with the same charge repel each other.

LAW OF ELECTRICAL CHARGES
Like charges repel and unlike charges attract each other.

To illustrate this, note what scientists discovered when they first experimented with glass and amber. They found that a charged piece of amber attracted a charged piece of glass. That is, the two pieces pulled together. A charged piece of amber repelled another charged piece of amber. That is, they pushed apart. Two charged pieces of glass also repelled each other. There is a reason why this happened. The charge on the glass was positive and the charge on the amber was negative.

4. Why will a rubbed comb attract hair?
5. What are the two kinds of charge?
6. What does the Law of Electrical Charges state?

20C THE ELECTRON

In the late 19th century, scientists experimented with passing electricity through gases in a tube. A stream of particles passed through the tube during the experiment. The particles were attracted by positive charges and repelled by negative charges. The scientists worked out the particle's charge by measuring the force needed to attract or repel the particle. **They found that the particle was negatively charged.** The particle was named the ELECTRON.

The electron was the first part of the atom to be discovered. Electrons are found in all atoms. No matter which gas was used in the tube, an electron appeared. **It could be identified by its small mass and its negative charge.** An electron's properties do not change, whether it is found in an element or in a compound. All of the matter that you see contains electrons.

In a neon sign, electricity passes through neon gas. This causes the electrons in the neon to give off the energy they have gained as light.

The electron, a particle with a negative charge and a very small mass, is found in all the matter that you see around you.

7. What is an electron?
8. How could the electron be identified?
9. What contains electrons?

ACTIVITY: Static Electricity

MATERIALS: 2 pyrex test tubes, 2 plastic rods, silk, wool, masking tape, matches

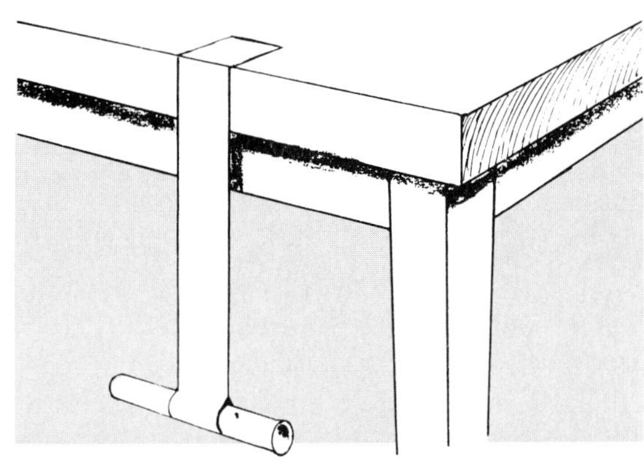

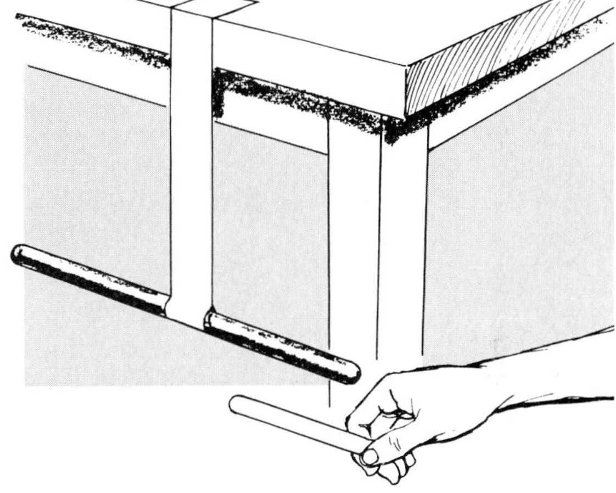

a. Hang one test tube from the edge of your table or desk with a piece of tape.

b. Rub one end of the test tube with the piece of silk.

c. Rub a second test tube with the piece of silk.

d. Bring the second test tube close to the first tube. Observe what happens. Answer question 10.

e. Hang a plastic rod with tape. Rub one end of the rod with wool. Rub the second plastic rod with wool and bring it close to the first. Observe what happens. Answer question 11.

f. Bring the rubbed test tube near the rubbed hanging rod. Observe what happens. Answer question 12.

g. Pass a lighted match around the hanging rod and the rubbed test tube. Bring the rod and the tube close together *without* rubbing them again. Observe what happens. Answer question 13.

10. What happens when the two tubes are close together?
11. What happens when the two rods are close together?
12. What reaction do you see when the rubbed rod is near the rubbed test tube?
13. What reaction do you see when the heated rod is near the heated test tube?
14. What did the match's flame do to the electrical charges on the rod and tube?
15. How does this show that electrical charges are coming from the flame?

20D RADIOACTIVITY

Certain atoms emit powerful waves or particles called radiation. This emitting, or radiating, property that certain atoms have is called RADIOACTIVITY. Radioactivity was discovered when the scientist Antoine Becquerel found that rock samples containing uranium would expose photographic negatives. Becquerel told his friends Marie and Pierre Curie about his discovery. They decided to investigate further.

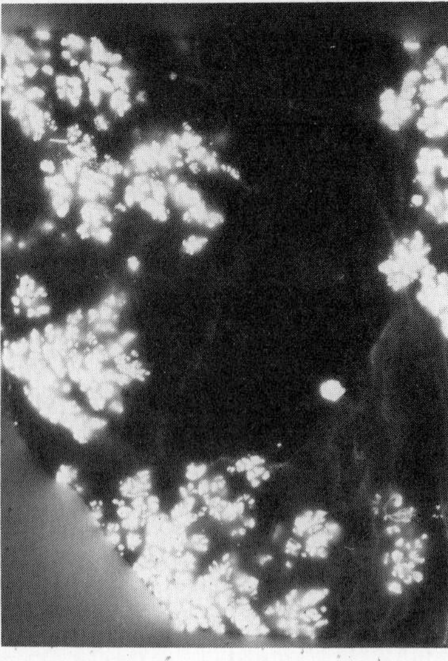

The photograph on the left shows a radioactive mineral called uraninite. The photograph on the right shows the marks left on photographic paper that has been exposed to uraninite. The fact that certain minerals have this effect on photographic paper led to the discovery of radioactivity.

The Curies discovered several radioactive elements. The atoms of these elements were emitting particles. Radium and polonium are two radioactive elements discovered by the Curies.

An experiment was set up to learn more about the beam of radiation being emitted by certain atoms. A beam of radiation was passed through a magnet, splitting the beam into three parts. These parts were named ALPHA, BETA, and GAMMA rays. When these rays hit atoms, the atoms became charged. These charged atoms are called IONS. Therefore, alpha, beta, and gamma rays are known as IONIZING RADIATION.

Alpha rays
Beta rays
Gamma rays

Alpha rays consist of charged helium atoms, or helium ions. The ions are positively charged and are moving at a speed of thousands of kilometers a second. They are slowed down when they hit other atoms.

Beta rays are made up of electrons. That is, they are made up of particles with a negative charge. When they are first emitted, the electrons move at thousands of kilometers a second.

Gamma rays are waves. They have properties similar to light waves or X-rays, but they are much shorter and more powerful. Gamma rays penetrate matter more easily than either alpha or beta rays. Gamma rays can damage or destroy living tissue in people.

After an atom has emitted radiation, it forms a different element. For example, radium turns into radon, a noble gas. Radon is also radioactive and turns into polonium. Polonium turns into lead. In radioactive substances, these changes are called RADIOACTIVE DECAY. A radioactive element will continue to decay until a nonradioactive element has been formed.

16. What is the radiating property of certain atoms called?

17. Who discovered that uranium is radioactive? How was this discovered?

18. Name the three parts of the radiation beam that form ions. What does each part consist of?

19. What happens during radioactive decay?

20E HALF-LIFE

The rate at which radioactive material decays is constant. The HALF-LIFE of a radioactive element is the amount of time it takes for one half of the atoms of a radioactive material to decay. **No matter how much of a radioactive substance is present, half of it will decay in a specific amount of time.** For example, it you began with a kilogram of radioactive material, half of the kilogram would decay after one half-life. Half of the remaining half would decay in another half-life.

This diagram illustrates the decay of a radioactive material that has a half-life of one million years. Note that after one million years, half of the radioactive material has decayed.

DECAY OF RADIOACTIVE MATERIAL
(with a half-life of 1 million years)

	Radioactive material	Decay element
Original radioactive material		
After 1 million years	$\frac{1}{2}$	$\frac{1}{2}$
After 2 million years	$\frac{1}{4}$	$\frac{3}{4}$
After 3 million years	$\frac{1}{8}$	$\frac{7}{8}$
After 4 million years	$\frac{1}{16}$	$\frac{15}{16}$

Radioactive material Decay element

The half-lives of radioactive elements are not all the same. Some elements take longer to decay than others. **Each radioactive substance has its own half-life.** Some half-lives are billions of years. Other half-lives are millionths of a second.

Some elements in the periodic table are hard to find in nature because of their short half-lives. That is, they decay too quickly to be studied. That is why the properties of astatine and francium, for example, are not well known.

20. What does half-life refer to?

21. What is the time of some half-lives?

SUMMARY

VOCABULARY

positive
negative
attract
repel
electron
radioactivity
alpha ray
beta ray
gamma ray
ion
ionizing radiation
radioactive decay
half-life

KEY FACTS AND CONCEPTS

There are charged particles in atoms.

There are two kinds of charge: positive and negative.

Two positive or two negative charges are called like charges.

A positive and a negative charge are a pair of unlike charges.

The Law of Electrical Charges states that like charges repel and unlike charges attract each other.

When objects pull together they are said to be attracted.

When objects push apart they are said to be repelled.

The electron is the negatively charged particle in the atom.

An electron is found in all atoms.

Certain atoms emit waves or particles called radiation. This property of certain atoms is called radioactivity.

There are three kinds of radiation. Alpha rays are positive helium ions. Beta rays are electrons. Gamma rays are powerful waves.

After an atom has emitted radiation, it forms a different element. This change is called radioactive decay.

The half-life of a radioactive element is the amount of time it takes for one half of the atoms of a radioactive material to decay.

CONCLUSION

Atoms contain parts. The first part of the atom to be discovered was the electron. Electrons have a negative charge. Other parts have positive charges. Knowing how charges attract and repel helped scientists identify the parts of the atom and how they behave.

22. What is the KEY IDEA of this chapter?

CHAPTER

21 Analyzing Atomic Structure

Protrons, Neutrons, and Electrons

21A INTRODUCTION

When scientists learned that there were smaller parts inside atoms, they set to work to find out more details. They were faced with a problem. How can you see inside something that is too small to see?

Most research on the structure of the atom is done by bombardment. That is, the atom is bombarded in a chamber by high-speed particles. Then, the pieces that break off the atom are analyzed. At first, radioactivity was used to bombard the atom. Now, huge machines called PARTICLE ACCELERATORS are used.

This photograph shows an atomic research facility in the state of Washington.

A particle accelerator is a device that speeds up the movement of atomic particles. These high-speed particles then collide and break apart. For this reason, accelerators are sometimes called atom smashers. These machines are so large and expensive that several European countries have cooperated to build them. You will learn more about accelerators later in this chapter.

1. How is most research on the structure of the atom done?
2. What is a particle accelerator?

21B SUBATOMIC PARTICLES

There are at least three kinds of particles that make up most atoms. You already learned about electrons in Chapter 20. In this chapter, you will learn about PROTONS and NEUTRONS. These three parts of the atom—protons, neutrons, and electrons—are called SUBATOMIC PARTICLES.

Ernest Rutherford

SUBATOMIC PARTICLES

Protons
Neutrons
Electrons

A scientist named Ernest Rutherford performed an experiment that helped to explain the make-up of the atom. From his experiment, Rutherford concluded that the atom is mostly empty space. **But located in the atom is a tiny, heavy, positively charged part.** He called this part the NUCLEUS. Rutherford's idea of the atom was that negatively charged electrons moved in the empty space that surrounds the nucleus.

Since Rutherford's time, further experiments have shown that the nucleus has parts, too. **Two kinds of particles that make up the nucleus are protons and neutrons.**

Protons are positively charged. Every atom has at least one proton in its nucleus. The mass of a proton is large compared with the mass of an electron. It would take more than 1,800 electrons to equal the mass of 1 proton.

The positive charge of a proton balances the negative charge of an electron. The number of protons in the nucleus normally equals the number of electrons outside the nucleus. An atom whose charges are usually balanced is said to be NEUTRAL.

The nuclei of most atoms also contain neutrons. A neutron has about the same mass as a proton. **A neutron has no charge; it is neutral.** That is how the neutron got its name.

3. What are three subatomic particles?
4. What is the charge of the nucleus?
5. What was Rutherford's idea of the atom?
6. How are the charges of protons and electrons in an atom related?
7. How did the neutron get its name?

21C RUTHERFORD'S EXPERIMENT

In the last section, you read that Ernest Rutherford performed an experiment to understand how the atom is made up. **He used radioactivity in his experiment to bombard other atoms.** As you recall from Chapter 20, radioactivity is a property of certain atoms. Radioactive atoms emit invisible particles, or radiation.

In Rutherford's experiment, a radioactive gas was placed in a lead container. Radiation escaped through a narrow passage in the container. This kept the radiation, or stream of particles, from spreading out. The particles were directed at a sheet of gold foil. A particle detector was gradually moved around the gold foil. **The detector was used to count how many particles went in each direction after hitting the foil.**

Rutherford found that almost all the particles passed straight through the gold foil. Some had changed direction slightly. But a few particles bounced back after hitting the foil.

Rutherford realized that the particles that had bounced back must have collided with something. **This "something" he called the nucleus.**

Most of the mass of the atom is concentrated in the tiny nucleus. The nucleus takes up very little space within the atom.

8. What did Rutherford use in his experiments to bombard atoms?
9. Why was a particle detector used in Rutherford's experiment?
10. Why did some particles bounce back from the gold foil?

21D PARTICLE ACCELERATORS

Soon after Rutherford's experiment, scientists began looking for particles that moved faster than radioactive particles normally move. Faster particles would penetrate deeper into the atom. Scientists knew that they could learn much more about matter if they had faster atomic bullets. Thus, scientists began designing different machines to speed up, or accelerate, particles.

The first particle accelerator was built in 1932. There are different kinds of accelerators. **To accelerate particles, a particle accelerator makes use of the fact that the particles are charged.** For example, if a positively charged particle is placed near a negatively charged object, the particle will be attracted to the object. The higher the negative charge, the faster the particle moves.

Magnetism is used to steer the charged particles. When a charged particle moves near a magnet, it turns. The stronger the magnet, the sharper the turn. Many particle accelerators use magnets to turn the particles in complete circles. Then, by switching opposite charges on and off, the particles can be made to go faster and faster.

This is one type of particle accelerator.

Particles have been accelerated until they have gone more than ninety-nine percent of the speed of light. The speed of light is 300,000 kilometers per second. It is theoretically impossible for matter to reach the speed of light.

11. Why did scientists look for particles that would be faster than radioactive particles?
12. How are particles made to move in particle accelerators?
13. How are particles steered in particle accelerators?

ACTIVITY: Bombarding a Nucleus

MATERIALS: 15 white marbles, 5 black marbles, 1 red marble, string, plastic ruler

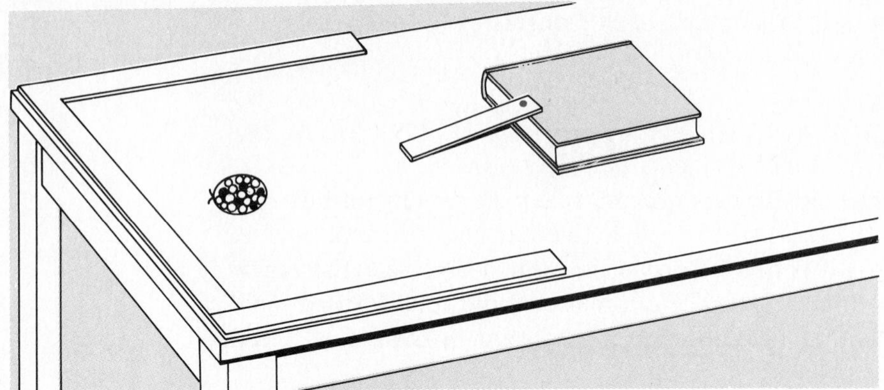

Before you begin, draw a table. It should have three columns. Head the columns *Trial, White,* and *Black*. In the Trial column, number spaces for 15 trials. You can use marbles of any 3 colors as long as you have the same number of marbles.

a. Tie the string in a loop. Make the loop barely large enough to surround 20 marbles bunched together on a table.
b. Place the 20 white and black marbles in the loop of string on your table top. Be sure that the 5 black marbles are scattered among the 15 white. Do not bunch one color together.
c. Lay the ruler on the table. Raise one end by placing it on one or two books. Aim the low end of the ruler at the marbles in the string. Do not move the ruler once you start taking data.
d. Use the red marble as your bombarding particle. Let it roll down the ruler and hit the other marbles.
• e. Count the number of black and white marbles that come out of the string. Enter the numbers in the table. You will have some zero entries, but if no marbles come out, repeat that trial. Replace the marbles after each trial.
f. After 15 trials, put away the equipment. Add up the number of marbles under each heading and divide by 15 for the averages. Write your averages on the board. Find the class averages.
g. The ratio of 15 (white marbles) to 5 (black marbles) can also be expressed as 3 to 1. Compare the ratio of 3 to 1 with the class averages.

---

14. To the nearest whole numbers, what are the class averages?
15. How do the class averages compare with the ratio of 3 to 1?
16. The marbles in the string represent particles in the nucleus of an atom. Use the class data to answer this question. How confident should a scientist be that the particles knocked out of the nucleus of an atom are the particles that were inside?

21E ATOMIC STRUCTURE

As you recall from Section 21B, there are protons and neutrons in the nucleus of an atom. The charge of the nucleus is the same as the charge of the protons inside it. **Therefore, the nucleus has a positive charge because protons are positively charged.** The neutral neutrons do not affect the charge of the nucleus.

Electrons are outside the positively charged nucleus. The negative electrons are attracted by the positive protons in the nucleus. **The number of negative electrons outside the nucleus normally equals the**

number of positive protons inside the nucleus. Thus, atoms are said to be neutral if their charges are balanced.

The electrons surround the nucleus in layers, or LEVELS. Each level can contain a certain number of electrons. **When the level closest to the nucleus is filled, an outer level starts to fill.** For example, an atom of oxygen has a total of eight electrons. Two of them are in the level closest to the nucleus. This level is filled with two electrons. The other six electrons are in a second level.

There is a force, called NUCLEAR FORCE, that holds the nucleus together. As you now know, all the protons in the nucleus are positive. Because like charges repel, the protons repel each other. The nuclear force overcomes this repelling force. **When the nuclear force is not strong enough to overcome the repelling force, the atom is said to be radioactive.** All atoms with more than eighty-three protons are radioactive.

Most of the atom is empty space. The mass is concentrated in the tiny nucleus. The electrons outside the nucleus have very little mass. The electron layers take up most of the atomic volume. And there isn't much matter in most of that volume! To give you an idea of just how small the nucleus is, imagine that an atom is the size of a football stadium. The nucleus would be the size of a small bird standing on the fifty-yard line.

If an atom were the size of a football stadium, the nucleus would be the size of a small bird standing on the fifty-yard line.

17. Why does the nucleus have a positive charge?
18. Where are the electrons located in the atom?
19. What happens when the electron layer closest to the nucleus is filled?
20. What force holds the nucleus together?
21. What is most of the atom composed of?

21F ATOMIC NUMBER AND ATOMIC MASS

Each kind of atom has a certain number of protons in its nucleus. The number of protons in the nucleus of an atom is called the ATOMIC NUMBER. This is the property that identifies an atom. **A certain kind of atom has a certain atomic number. An element, then, is a substance made up entirely of atoms that have the same atomic number.**

For example, an atom of oxygen always has eight protons in its nucleus. Therefore, oxygen has an atomic number of eight. There is another way to look at it. **Every atom with eight protons in its nucleus is an oxygen atom.** An element can be referred to by its atomic number alone. Element number 8 is oxygen. **Each element has its own atomic number.**

The total number of protons and neutrons in the nucleus is called the ATOMIC MASS NUMBER. To illustrate, fluorine has nine protons and ten neutrons in its nucleus. Fluorine has an atomic *number* of nine. The atomic *mass* of fluorine is nineteen.

The number of protons in an atom of an element is always the same. However, the number of neutrons may vary. **Thus, not all the atoms of some elements have the same mass number.** Atoms of the same element that have the same atomic number but different mass numbers are called ISOTOPES.

For example, there are three carbon isotopes. All three have atomic number six. That means that they all have six protons. Most carbon atoms also have six neutrons. So most carbon isotopes have a mass number of twelve. A small number of carbon atoms have seven neutrons. So these carbon isotopes have a mass number of thirteen. A very small number of carbon atoms have eight neutrons. So these carbon isotopes have a mass number of fourteen.

THREE CARBON ISOTOPES

Name	No. of Protons	No. of Neutrons	Atomic No.	Atomic Mass
carbon-12	6	6	6	12
carbon-13	6	7	6	13
carbon-14	6	8	6	14

22. What is atomic number?
23. What is atomic mass number?
24. What are isotopes?
25. How many isotopes does carbon have?

The tracks that a subatomic particle leaves in a bubble chamber are shown in this photograph. Scientists can study and analyze these tracks.

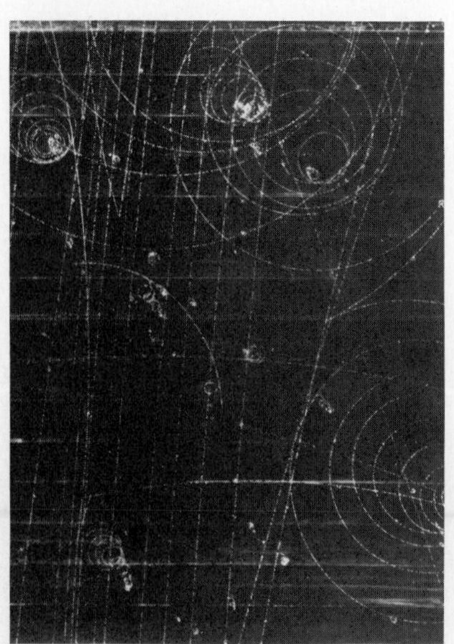

21G NEW IDEAS IN ATOMIC RESEARCH

No one has ever seen a subatomic particle. But today, these particles are analyzed by studying the tracks they leave in a device called a bubble chamber. A bubble chamber is a liquid-filled chamber. When a particle shoots through the chamber, it leaves a trail of bubbles in the liquid. Photographs are taken of the particle's course from different angles. Scientists use these photographs to measure the charge and mass of the particle.

New particles are being studied to find out more about the structure of protons, neutrons, and electrons. The new particles may play a part in holding the nucleus together. Data are being collected, but there is still much work to be done. The mystery of what matter is made of is far from being solved.

26. How are subatomic particles analyzed since no one can see them?

27. Why are new particles studied?

SUMMARY

VOCABULARY

particle accelerator
proton
neutron
subatomic particle
nucleus
neutral
level
nuclear force
atomic number
atomic mass number
isotope

KEY FACTS AND CONCEPTS

Atoms can be bombarded by fast particles. The pieces that break off of the atom are analyzed to discover what makes up the atom.

There are at least three particles that make up the atom—protons, neutrons, and electrons.

The nucleus is a tiny, heavy, positively charged part of the atom.

The two kinds of particles that make up the nucleus are protons and neutrons.

Protons are positively charged.

Neutrons are neutral; they have no charge.

Ernest Rutherford discovered the nucleus with his now-famous gold foil experiment.

Particle accelerators use electrical charges to speed up particles. The particles are steered by magnets.

The nucleus is positively charged because the protons inside it are positively charged.

Electrons are located outside the nucleus in layers.

The negative electrons outside the nucleus balance the positive protons inside the nucleus.

Nuclear force is the force that holds the nucleus together.

Most of the atom is empty space.

The number of protons in the nucleus is called the atomic number.

An element is a substance made up entirely of atoms that have the same atomic number.

The number of protons and neutrons in the nucleus is called the mass number.

Atoms of the same element that have the same atomic number but different mass numbers are called isotopes.

No one has ever seen a subatomic particle.

CONCLUSION

The atom is made up of subatomic particles. Three of these particles are protons, neutrons, and electrons. There is still more to be learned about subatomic particles. Scientists are finding that there are particles within particles.

28. What is the KEY IDEA of this chapter?

CHAPTER

22 Electrons and Chemical Properties Bonds That Hold Atoms Together

The scientist in this photograph is holding a molecular model that contains many different kinds of atoms.

22A INTRODUCTION

Scientists have used their knowledge of the atom to answer many questions. For example, how could the arrangement of electrons in layers in the atom explain chemical properties? Why do elements from the seventh column of the periodic table react so strongly with elements from the first column? Why are the noble gases so unreactive?

Studying the structure of the atom provides the answers to all of these questions. As you learned in Chapter 21, electrons in the atom are located in energy levels. The electrons in the level farthest from the nucleus form CHEMICAL BONDS. **Chemical bonds are the links that hold atoms together in molecules.** Atoms form these bonds and fill their outer levels with electrons. Atoms that already have filled outer energy levels have little tendency to form bonds and, therefore, molecules. These atoms are said to be unreactive.

1. What are chemical bonds?
2. Why are some atoms unreactive?

22B ELECTRON LEVELS

Each energy level in an atom has a maximum number of electrons it can hold. The level closest to the nucleus cannot hold more than two electrons. **When a level has as many electrons as it can hold, the level is said to be filled.** It takes eight electrons to fill the second energy level. The third level is filled by eighteen electrons. The fourth and fifth levels can each hold thirty-two electrons.

In Chapter 19, you studied the periodic table, which appears on pages 110-111. The table tells you how many energy levels are in each atom of an element. The table also lists the number of electrons in each energy level of that atom. This information is located in the lower left-hand corner of each square. These numbers were identified in the Key on page 110 as "Electron arrangement."

For example, look at sulfur, element number 16, in the table. You will see the numbers *2, 8, 6*. **The three numbers show that each atom of sulfur has three energy levels that contain electrons.** The first energy level has two electrons, the second level has eight, and the third level has six electrons. **The last number always represents the number of electrons in the outermost level of the atom.**

Look at the second row of the periodic table, illustrated below. As you go from left to right in this row, the number of outermost electrons goes from one to eight. When the outermost energy level has eight electrons, as in neon, Ne, that level is filled and the row ends. All the rows in the periodic table follow a similar pattern.

3 Lithium	4 Beryllium	5 Boron	6 Carbon	7 Nitrogen	8 Oxygen	9 Fluorine	10 Neon
Li	**Be**	**B**	**C**	**N**	**O**	**F**	**Ne**
6.939	9.01218	10.81	12.011	14.0067	15.9994	18.9984	20.183
2,1	2,2	2,3	2,4	2,5	2,6	2,7	2,8

This is the second row of the periodic table.

3. When is an energy level filled?
4. How many electrons can the different levels hold?
5. How does the periodic table show where the electrons are?
6. Find the element nitrogen, N, in the row of the table, illustrated above. How many electrons are in the second level of the nitrogen atom?

22C ELECTRON DONORS AND ACCEPTORS

When an atom has eight electrons in its outermost level, it has little tendency to react chemically with other atoms. The noble gases, except helium, all have eight electrons in their outermost levels. That is, their outer levels are filled. This explains why the noble gases are so unreactive. Only xenon, krypton, and radon form any known compounds. These compounds are very easily decomposed. The reacting atoms of other elements will gain, lose, or share electrons to form an eight-electron outer energy level.

> By undergoing chemical reactions, an atom achieves a filled outer energy level.

The electrons that an atom can gain or lose in chemical reactions are called VALENCE ELECTRONS. **These are the electrons in the outermost energy level of an atom. So *valence* refers to a number that indicates the ability of an element to combine with other elements.** A knowledge of valence electrons helps chemists to understand why an element will or will not react with other elements.

Elements with only one or two valence electrons tend to lose electrons in chemical reactions. These elements are ELECTRON DONORS. When an atom has lost negative electrons, it becomes more positive. The atom is then a positive ion.

All alkali metal atoms have only one valence electron. They all form positive ions because they lose electrons in reactions. The sodium in a salt crystal is in the form of positive ions. Each sodium ion has lost an electron.

Atoms of calcium, Ca, have two valence electrons. They form positive ions with twice as much charge as sodium ions. All the other elements in the second column of the periodic table also have two

Balloons are filled with the noble gas helium.

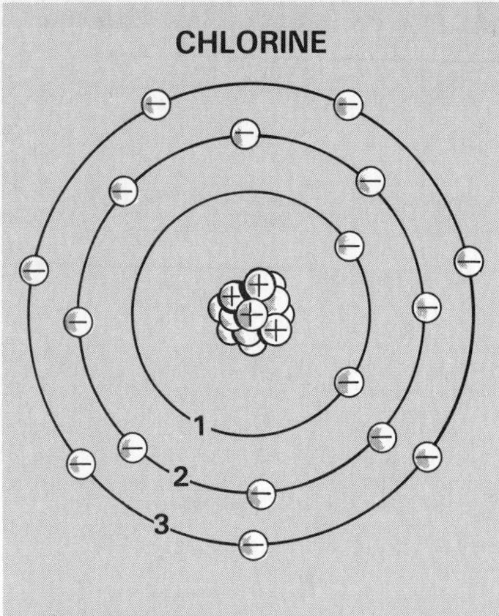

This diagram shows how the electrons are arranged in an atom of chlorine. Note that chlorine has seven electrons in its outer level.

valence electrons. They all form positive ions with the same charge as calcium. They are all electron donors.

All of the atoms of the elements in a given numbered column of the periodic table are similar. They have the same valence number. This makes them react in similar ways with atoms of other elements.

Elements with six or seven electrons in their outer levels tend to gain electrons during reactions. They are ELECTRON ACCEPTORS. These atoms tend to gain negative electrons and become negative ions.

Chlorine, Cl, has seven valence electrons. When chlorine and sodium, Na, react, each chlorine atom takes an electron from a sodium atom. The sodium atoms become positive ions. The chlorine atoms become negative ions. The chlorine in a salt crystal is in the form of negative ions. The sodium donor has combined with the chlorine acceptor.

An atom of oxygen has six valence electrons. An atom of oxygen is an electron acceptor in chemical reactions. The atom usually accepts two electrons to fill its outer level with eight electrons.

7. Why don't the noble gases react easily to form compounds?
8. Which electrons in the atom are valence electrons?
9. What is an electron donor?
10. What is an electron acceptor?
11. Which charge is found on ions of electron donors?
12. Which charge is found on ions of electron acceptors?

22D CHEMICAL BONDS

Ions of opposite charges form compounds. These compounds have IONIC BONDS. The electrical attractions of opposite charges hold the ions together.

Electrons are transferred to form compounds held together by ionic bonds. The donor atom loses one or more electrons from its outer level. The acceptor atom gains one or more electrons in its outer level.

The best example of a compound held together by an ionic bond is ordinary table salt. In salt, the positive sodium ions and the negative chlorine ions are locked together.

Ordinary table salt is a compound held together by ionic bonds. This photograph shows highly magnified salt crystals.

TWO KINDS OF CHEMICAL BONDS
Ionic bond
Covalent bond

The elements in the first column of the periodic table combine with the elements of the seventh column to form ionic bonds. The alkali metals become positive ions. The halogens become negative ions. They combine to form salt-like compounds. These compounds are held together by ionic bonds.

Another important chemical bond is the COVALENT BOND. **In a covalent bond, atoms share electrons to fill their outer levels.** When atoms have filled their outer levels with shared electrons, the molecules they form are chemically stable. **Water is an example of a compound held together by covalent bonds.**

The element that can form the greatest number of covalently bonded compounds is carbon. Carbon has four valence electrons. Four more electrons are needed to fill the level with eight. If four hydrogen atoms share their electrons with carbon, an eight-electron level is formed. In this case, covalent bonds are holding together a compound called methane, CH_4. You will learn more about carbon later in this chapter.

13. What do atoms exchange to form ionic bonds?
14. What do atoms share to form covalent bonds?

The methane in natural gas has molecules held together by covalent bonds.

22E VALENCE AND COMPOUNDS

Atoms react in such a way as to fill their outer energy levels. They may do this by losing, gaining, or sharing electrons. Knowing the number of valence electrons of elements helps you know how the elements will combine to form compounds.

All the elements in any given column of the periodic table are alike in one way. They all have the same number of valence electrons. This number is equal to the column number, which is the Roman numeral at the top of the column. The column labeled IIIA, for example, contains elements whose valence is 3.

The alkali metals in the first column of the periodic table, IA, can lose one electron. The alkali metals have a valence of 1. The halogens, in column VIIA, also have a valence of 1. They can all gain one electron. The outermost energy level of each noble gas element is filled. This is why these gases rarely react with other elements.

All the atoms of the elements in a given column of the periodic table have the same number of valence electrons.

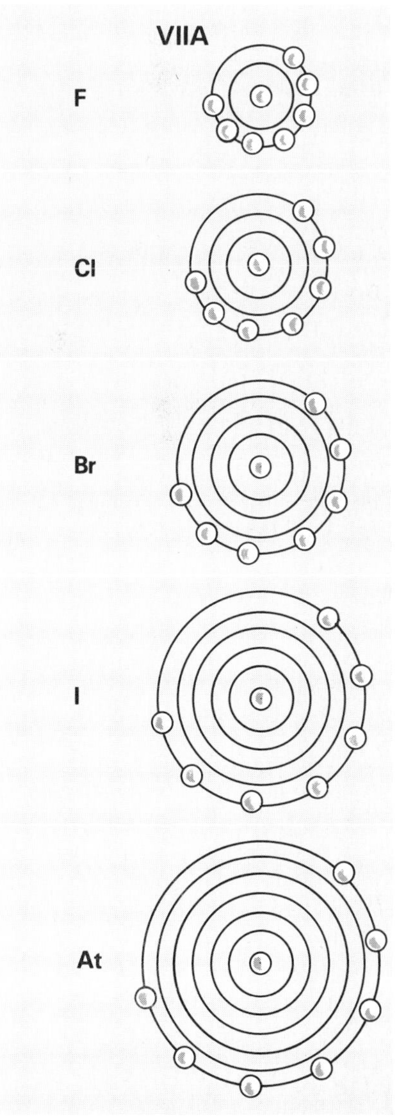

> It is the valence electrons that are shared, donated, or accepted by atoms to form bonds.

Many elements can combine in more than one way. These elements have more than one valence. As you now know, electrons are gained, lost, or shared during chemical reactions. The number of gained, lost, or shared electrons in elements that have more than one valence is determined by the conditions present during the chemical reaction. Reaction conditions include such factors as temperature, pressure, and the presence of other reactive elements.

An element that has more than one valence is copper. Copper can combine with oxygen in two ways. Copper can combine with oxygen to form Cu_2O. In this molecule, copper has a valence of 1. Copper can also combine with oxygen to form CuO. In this molecule, copper has a valence of 2.

15. Which electrons in the atom are the valence electrons?
16. How can an element have more than one valence?
17. What possible things may happen to valence electrons during chemical reactions?

ACTIVITY: Finding Valences

MATERIALS: None

Below are the molecular formulas for several compounds. Use them to answer the questions at the right.

NaCl	Na_2O	CaO	H_2O
KCl	K_2O	$CaCl_2$	HCl
LiCl	Li_2O	Al_2O_3	CH_4

18. What is the valence of chlorine?
19. What is the valence of oxygen?
20. What is the valence of carbon?
21. What is the valence of aluminum?
22. What is the valence of calcium?

22F CARBON CHEMISTRY

CARBON COMPOUNDS PROVIDE YOU WITH:

Food
Fuel
Plastic
Drugs
Textiles

Almost all compounds that contain carbon are called ORGANIC COMPOUNDS. **All the living organisms on earth contain carbon compounds.** People who study the chemistry of living things are called BIOCHEMISTS.

Proteins, fats, and carbohydrates are carbon compounds. Vitamins, enzymes, and hormones are carbon compounds. The study of carbon compounds is called ORGANIC CHEMISTRY. **Organic chemistry also refers to the study of nonliving carbon compounds.** Organic chemistry affects you in many ways. Carbon compounds provide you with foods, fuels, plastics, drugs, and textiles every day.

Carbon can form a remarkably large number of compounds. **No other element forms as many compounds as carbon.** Carbon atoms can do this because they can bond with other carbon atoms to form long, complicated chains and loops. No other atom can form as many chains and loops as the carbon atom can.

There are so many ways the carbon atoms can bond with each other and with other elements that STRUCTURAL FORMULAS are needed to represent the compounds. **Structural formulas show the arrangement of atoms.** Two carbon compounds with the same molecular formula are butane and isobutane. Their formula is C_4H_{10}. But they are different compounds with different properties. **You have to see the structural formulas of butane and isobutane to tell them apart on paper.** Their different properties enable you to tell them apart in the laboratory.

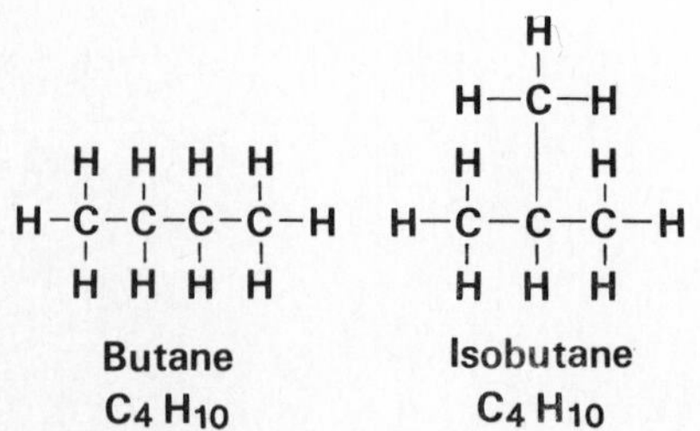
Butane C_4H_{10}

Isobutane C_4H_{10}

In structural formulas as in molecular formulas, the letter symbol represents the atom. **Each line between atoms represents a pair of electrons in a covalent bond.** This is a single bond. As you recall from Section 22E, the carbon atom has a valence of 4. Therefore, carbon must make four bonds to have a filled outer energy level of eight electrons. In a structural formula, four lines must appear around each carbon atom—one for each bond.

Carbon can also form double and triple bonds. These bonds are more reactive than the single bond. Chemists use molecules with double and triple bonds to make new compounds. They know it is easier to add extra atoms to a molecule with a double or triple bond.

23. What element is found in all living organisms?
24. What is organic chemistry?

25. What do structural formulas tell you?

26. How can two compounds have the same molecular formula?

27. How do chemists use the double and triple bonds between carbon atoms?

SUMMARY

VOCABULARY

chemical bonds
valence electron
electron donor
electron acceptor
ionic bond
covalent bond
organic compounds
biochemist
organic chemistry
structural formula

KEY FACTS AND CONCEPTS

The chemical properties of atoms are determined by the electrons in the outer level.

The electrons in the outer levels of atoms form chemical bonds that hold molecules together.

An atom will gain, lose, or share electrons during a chemical reaction. The molecule that results has atoms with filled outer levels.

The electrons involved in chemical reactions are the valence electrons.

Electron acceptors are atoms with six or seven electrons in their outer levels. These elements are located in the sixth and seventh columns of the periodic table.

Electron donors are atoms with one or two electrons in their outermost levels. The elements in the first and second columns of the periodic table are electron donors.

Ionized atoms of opposite charges are held together by ionic bonds.

Atoms with shared electrons are held together in molecules by covalent bonds.

The elements in any one numbered column of the periodic table have the same number of valence electrons.

Carbon atoms bond to each other to form long chains and many complex combinations.

Scientists describe carbon compounds by using structural formulas.

In structural formulas, lines represent shared electron pairs.

Biochemists study the chemistry of living things. Organic chemistry is the study of carbon compounds.

CONCLUSION

The study of matter has come a long way since the 19th century. The study may have started with a simple description of properties. Now, scientists have particle accelerators and bubble chambers to look inside matter. They have found particles within particles. The study of matter continues.

28. What is the KEY IDEA of this chapter?

UNIT THREE

Work and Energy

SCIENCE COMPETENCIES

Unit 3 will help you to master one LIFE SKILL:

USING MATERIALS AND ENERGY—How to Use Matter and Energy Wisely

CHAPTER

23 Forms of Energy

Stored Energy and Useful Energy

23A INTRODUCTION

You do work every day. You move. You pick things up. You push and pull things. In other words, you use ENERGY. *Energy* is a word that you hear all the time. Energy is in the news because the United States seems to be running out of it. Old sources of energy are becoming more expensive. With all the attention energy receives, you have probably asked yourself, "What is energy?"

Energy is the ability to do work. Food is eaten for the energy to do work. Electric hedge shears are plugged into electric outlets for the energy to do work. Oil is pumped up from the ground for the energy to do work. Water is stored behind dams for the energy to do work. Windmills catch energy from the wind to do work. Geothermal energy plants harness heat energy from the earth's interior to do work.

Each of these photographs represents an example of energy ready to do work. The photos are of an oil rig, solar collectors, a windmill, and a geothermal energy plant.

1. What is energy?

How is gravity involved in what the girl in this photograph is doing?

23B KINDS OF FORCE

Work and movement start with FORCE. **Force is a push or a pull.** Force is needed to make things move. You pull on your sweater, push the refrigerator door shut, push down the lever on the toaster, pull the car door open. Pushes and pulls make up much of your daily activity. **There are four main kinds of force in nature.**

> All of the pushes and pulls it takes to get things done are examples of force.

Gravitational Force. GRAVITY, which is a property of all matter, is one of the four forces in nature. **Gravity is the force of attraction, or the pull, between all pieces of matter.** Gravity is the weakest of the four forces. Because gravity pulls objects together without direct contact, it is called an action-at-a-distance force. Gravitational forces are partly responsible for the round shape of the earth. Gravity also keeps the atmosphere in place around the earth.

Gravitational force on an object is called weight. To determine your weight, you step on a scale. The earth's gravity pulls down on you with a certain force. The amount of force exerted on you depends on your mass. At the same time as the earth is pulling down on you, you are pulling the earth up with a certain force. It is amazing to think that you and the earth are pulling on each other!

Strong Nuclear Force. The strongest force is the STRONG NUCLEAR FORCE. **This is the force that holds the nucleus of an atom together.** It is strong enough to overcome the repelling forces of the positive protons packed together inside the nucleus. **However, the strong nuclear force does not extend beyond the nucleus of the atom.**

Weak Nuclear Force. Another nuclear force is called the WEAK NUCLEAR FORCE. **The weak nuclear force is present among the particles in the nucleus of an atom.** This force is involved in such nuclear events as the beta decay type of radioactivity.

Electromagnetic Force. The fourth kind of force is called the ELECTROMAGNETIC FORCE. **This type of force is made up of the forces of attraction and repulsion caused by electrical charges and magnetism.** Electromagnetic force holds molecules together and binds molecules to each other. Electromagnetic forces are at work in more than just electric motors. **The forces that make your muscles work are also electromagnetic forces.** Muscles are moved by the attractions among the electrical charges in muscle molecules.

FOUR KINDS OF FORCE

- Gravity
- Strong nuclear force
- Weak nuclear force
- Electromagnetic force

2. What is force?
3. What are the four kinds of force in nature?
4. Name three things that involve electromagnetic force.

23C MEASURING WORK

WORK is done when a force changes the motion and position of an object. Pushing a stalled car is work only if the car moves. **To a scientist, work is done only when a force moves something.** Pushing against a car with locked brakes may tire you out. But if the car doesn't move, no work was done. **For work to be performed in the scientific sense, an object has to move some distance in the direction of the force.**

To find the amount of work done in a given situation, force is multiplied by the distance through which the force was applied. **Distance is measured in meters.** Force is measured in a unit called the NEWTON. The newton is a metric unit, abbreviated by the capital letter "N." **To calculate the amount of work done, newtons are multiplied by meters.**

The work unit could be called the newton-meter, but it has its own name. Remember, energy is the ability to do work. The amount of work done by one newton acting over a distance of one meter is expressed in a unit called the JOULE. The joule is abbreviated by the capital letter "J." Both the newton and the joule are named after scientists—Isaac Newton and James Prescott Joule.

Isaac Newton

James Prescott Joule

Work	=	Force × distance
Work	=	newtons × meters
Work	=	N × m
Joule	=	N × m

5. When is work done?
6. How do you calculate the amount of work done?
7. What is the unit that expresses the amount of work done?

23D POWER

You probably already know what the word *rate* means. If you take a short amount of time to walk to school, your rate of walking is high. If you walk to school slowly, your rate of walking is low. The concept of rate can also be applied to problems involving work. The rate at which work is done is called POWER. **If work is done in a short amount of time, the power is higher than if the work is done more slowly.**

For example, suppose two loads of the same mass were lifted through the same distance. The first load is lifted more slowly than the second. **The rate at which energy is used to lift the first load is smaller. But the amount of work done, the energy, stays the same.** The only thing that changes is the time needed to do the work.

There are many other instances in which rate differs but amount of work done is the same. A mini-bike and a motorcycle do just as much work carrying you up a hill. The only difference is that the mini-bike can't work as fast as the motorcycle. This is because the motorcycle has more power than the mini-bike. The motorcycle does the same amount of work faster.

If you wanted to make an elevator rise faster, you would use a motor with more power. A motor that raises an elevator one floor every five seconds would have a power rating twice that of a motor that takes ten seconds to do the same work. The first motor would not be doing more work. It would just be doing the work faster.

Power is measured in joules per second. The unit of power is called the WATT. One thousand watts is a kilowatt. This is the same unit you see on the family electric bill. **Notice that electric measurements are metric.**

8. Explain the difference between work and power.
9. Which does more work, a train traveling at 125 miles per hour or a bicycle traveling at 3 miles per hour? Which vehicle has more power?
10. What are the names of the units of force, work, and power?

23E KINETIC AND POTENTIAL ENERGY

Energy in action is KINETIC ENERGY. **Kinetic energy is the energy of motion.** A moving car has kinetic energy. The faster the car moves, the more kinetic energy it has. Like other forms of energy, kinetic energy can be measured. When the car's speed is doubled, its kinetic energy is four times as great. This is why a car takes four times as much distance to stop when it goes twice as fast.

To lift 10 kg of mass a distance of 1.4 m, 137.2 J of energy must be used.

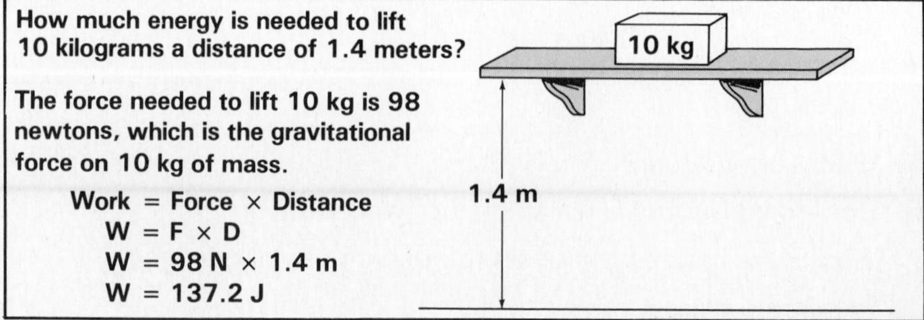

An automobile gains kinetic energy as it speeds up. The brakes turn kinetic energy to heat to slow the automobile down.

POTENTIAL ENERGY is stored energy. This is the energy stored in the gasoline tank of a car. It is the energy of water stored behind a dam. It is the energy in gas, oil, coal, dynamite, and the nucleus of an atom. A box on a shelf also has potential energy.

Potential energy is the energy of water stored behind a dam.

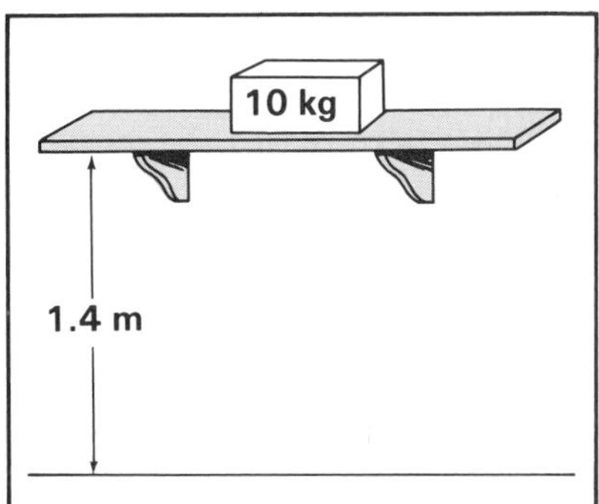

The box on the shelf has 137.2 J of potential energy.

The kinetic energy of the box turns into heat when it hits the floor.

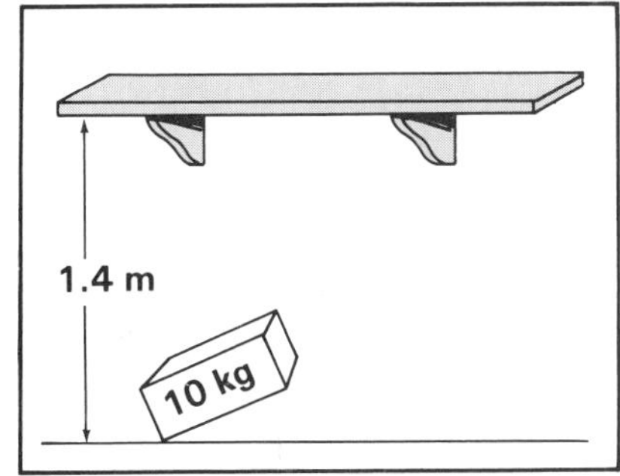

Suppose it takes 137.2 joules of energy to lift a 10-kilogram box a distance of 1.4 meters onto a shelf. The box can do 137.2 joules of work by itself if it falls off the shelf. Sitting on the shelf, the box has 137.2 joules of potential energy. When the box falls off the shelf and hits the floor, it has 137.2 joules of kinetic energy and no potential energy. Energy is always present in some form.

Energy obeys the LAW OF CONSERVATION OF ENERGY. **This means that energy is neither created nor destroyed.** It is very similar to the law of conservation of matter, which you learned in Unit 2.

What happens to kinetic energy when a box falls off a shelf and hits the floor? The box and the floor become warmer where the box hits the floor. **Energy of motion, kinetic energy, usually turns into heat.** The kinetic energy of an automobile turns into heat when the brakes are applied. In fact, brakes can get hot enough to start a fire during a fast stop from a high speed.

Energy can take many forms. Chemical energy is the energy released when atoms exchange electrons during a reaction. Chemical energy is turned into heat and light during burning.

Chemical energy is turned into electrical energy by a battery. When the lead and sulfuric acid combine in an automobile battery, energy from the reaction pushes the electrons through the wires. The electrons can do work by using the push or pull of magnetism. Electrical energy can also turn into heat.

The heat from electrical energy is often turned into light. **Light is another form of energy.** When the wire in a light bulb is very hot, electrons in the wire absorb some of the energy. This makes the electrons change energy levels. The electrons give off the energy when they go back to their original level. Part of that energy comes out as visible light. When the light is absorbed by various substances, the energy becomes heat again.

Electrical energy is turned into heat in a toaster.

Light, heat, electricity, and chemicals are all forms or sources of energy. Energy in motion is kinetic energy. Energy stored in some way is potential energy. Everything and everyone runs on energy. **Most action takes place when energy changes form. Energy can keep changing form, but it is never destroyed.**

Most useful work is done when energy is changing form.

11. What is kinetic energy?
12. What is potential energy?
13. What do heat, light, electricity, and chemical reactions have in common?
14. What does the Law of Conservation of Energy mean?

ACTIVITY: Heat Energy

MATERIALS: Rubber band, paper clip

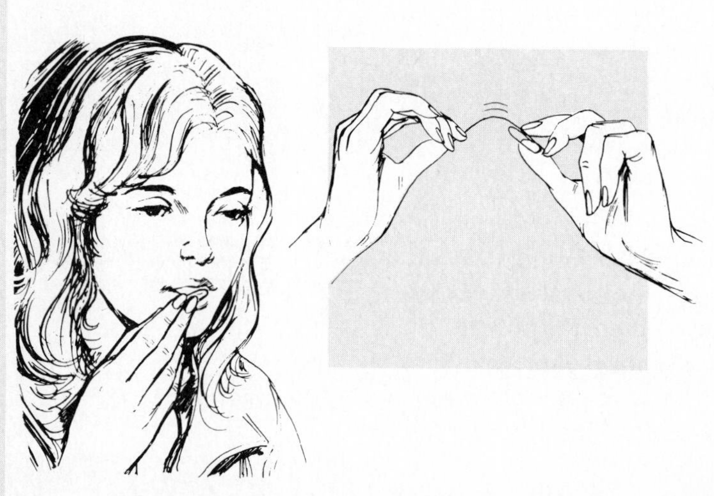

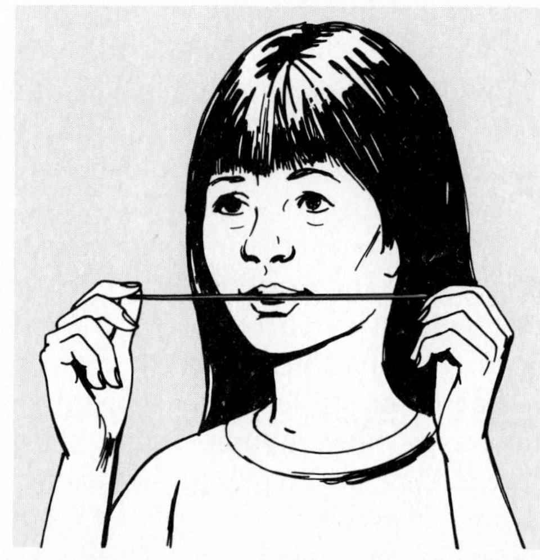

a. Touch the end of a paper clip briefly to your lips.

b. Quickly straighten the paper clip and touch it to your lips again. Answer question 15.

c. Hold a rubber band with your thumbs and index fingers. Touch the rubber band briefly to your lips.

d. Quickly stretch the rubber band and touch it to your lips again. Answer question 16.

15. How does the temperature of the paper clip change when it is bent?
16. How does the temperature of the rubber band change when it is stretched?
17. You used energy to bend the paper clip. What happened to that energy?
18. You used energy to stretch the rubber band. What happened to that energy?
19. What seems to eventually happen to energy?

SUMMARY

VOCABULARY

energy
force
gravity
strong nuclear force
weak nuclear force
electromagnetic force
work
newton
joule
power
watt
kinetic energy
potential energy
Law of Conservation of Energy

KEY FACTS AND CONCEPTS

Energy is the ability to do work.
Force is a push or a pull.
The unit of force is the newton.
Four main forces act in nature: gravity, strong nuclear force, weak nuclear force, and electromagnetic force.
Work is done when force acts over a distance.
The unit of work energy is the joule.
Power is the rate at which work is done or energy is used.
A watt of power is equal to one joule of energy per second.
Kinetic energy is the energy of motion.
Potential energy is stored energy.
Energy can neither be created nor destroyed.
Light, heat, and electricity are all forms or sources of energy.
Energy eventually takes the form of heat.

CONCLUSION

Work is done when a force acts over a distance. Energy is used to do that work. Whether the activity is climbing stairs or going to the moon, nothing will happen unless energy is available to do the work.

20. What is the KEY IDEA of this chapter?

CHAPTER

24 Motion

How Objects Move

24A INTRODUCTION

As you learned in Chapter 23, force is a push or a pull. When force acts over a distance, work is done. The phrase "acting over a distance" means that something is moving, or is in motion. This chapter is about motion.

1. What does the phrase "acting over a distance" mean?

24B DISTANCE, SPEED, AND TIME

The word *motion* means movement from one place to another. When you move from one place to another, you cover a distance. This distance is measurable. **You record the motion of an object by measuring the distance it moved.** Units such as meters and kilometers are used to measure distance.

It takes a certain amount of time for an object to cover a distance. Of course, the units for time are seconds, minutes, and hours. SPEED is the rate at which something covers a given distance. Whenever the word *rate* is used, time must be part of the measurement. Speed is measured in meters per second, abbreviated m/sec. It is calculated by dividing the distance traveled by the time taken to travel that distance. That is:

$$\text{speed} = \frac{\text{distance}}{\text{time}} = \frac{\text{meters}}{\text{seconds}}$$

Suppose that a toy train travels along a straight track that is 16 meters long in 8 seconds. What is the train's speed?

$$\text{speed} = \frac{16\text{ m}}{8\text{ sec}} = \frac{2\text{ m}}{\text{sec}} \quad \text{or } 2\text{ m/sec}$$

If the problem gave you the speed of the train, 2 m/sec, and the distance it traveled, 16 m, you could determine the time. You would have to rearrange the formula to read:

$$\text{time} = \frac{\text{distance}}{\text{speed}}$$

So, if you substituted your values in this equation, you would have:

$$\text{time} = \frac{16\text{ m}}{2\text{ m/sec}} = 8\text{ sec}$$

If the speed and time were given, the distance covered could be determined by using the formula this way:

$$\text{distance} = \text{speed} \times \text{time}$$

So, substituting your values, you would have:

$$\text{distance} = 2\text{ m/sec} \times 8\text{ sec} = 16\text{ m}$$

$$\text{speed} = \frac{\text{distance}}{\text{time}}$$

$$\text{time} = \frac{\text{distance}}{\text{speed}}$$

$$\text{distance} = \text{time} \times \text{speed}$$

To do these calculations on a real vehicle, you have to think in terms of the average speed of the vehicle. After all, a car travelling a long distance will not always be moving at the same speed. However, the formulas remain the same.

$$\text{average speed} = \frac{\text{distance}}{\text{time}}$$

$$\text{time} = \frac{\text{distance}}{\text{average speed}}$$

$$\text{distance} = \text{average speed} \times \text{time}$$

When planning a car trip, it is important to know how far you can drive in a day. You can calculate your distance, using average speed and the amount of time you want to spend driving. For example, how far will you travel if you drive 6 hours at an average speed of 80 km/hr?

$$\text{distance} = 80\text{ km/hr} \times 6\text{ hr} = 480\text{ km}$$

2. What is speed?
3. What is the formula for calculating distance? Speed? Time?
4. Why do you have to speak in terms of average speed when calculating with a real vehicle?

To fly an aircraft, a pilot must understand velocity.

24C VELOCITY AND ACCELERATION

In the preceding section, you learned that speed describes only the amount of the rate of motion. To describe the direction of the motion, the term VELOCITY is used. **Velocity is a measure of both speed and direction.** For example, a jet has a speed of 600 km/hr. This jet has a velocity of 600 km/hr due south. **Velocity gives more information than speed.**

The rate of change of velocity is called ACCELERATION. Because velocity is involved, you know that acceleration is more than just a change of speed. **Acceleration is also a change in direction. In fact, acceleration is any change in velocity.** Therefore, it is acceleration when a car turns a corner, even if its speed is unchanged.

When an object slows down, its velocity changes. Stopping is also acceleration. Stopping is a change of speed. This change is called negative acceleration, or DECELERATION. Increasing or reducing speed in a given direction are changes in velocity. **Velocity must change in order for there to be an acceleration or deceleration.**

Acceleration is measured in meters per second per second. Notice the extra "per second". **This means that an object changes speed by so many meters per second for each second it accelerates.** For example, when an object falls near the surface of the earth, it accelerates downward at 9.8 m/sec/sec. This means that the object is changing speed by 9.8 meters per second for each second it falls.

5. What is velocity?
6. What is acceleration?
7. What is deceleration?
8. How is acceleration measured?

Gravity provides the centripetal force that holds the moon in its path around the earth.

24D CENTRIPETAL FORCE

Acceleration requires a force. A mass kept in circular motion is constantly changing direction. A force must be applied to it continuously. The force holding an object in a circular path is called a CENTRIPETAL FORCE. **The centripetal force on an object produces acceleration.**

The force of gravity between the earth and the moon is the centripetal force that holds the moon in orbit. **Centripetal force is an inward pulling force that prevents an object from flying off in a straight line.**

There are many examples of centripetal force in your everyday experiences. During the spin cycle in a washing machine, the laundry is turned by the force of the walls of the basket. The walls exert a centripetal force on the laundry.

Centripetal force must act on a car to make it travel around a curve. Without centripetal force, a speeding car tends to move forward in a straight line. The force comes from the attraction between the car's tires and the road. If the road is icy, this attracting force is reduced. An accident may occur because there is not enough centripetal force to keep the car moving in its curved path.

9. What is centripetal force?
10. Give some examples of centripetal force.

24E NEWTON'S LAWS OF MOTION

You have already seen Isaac Newton's name in other chapters of this book. He was a scientist who worked out many scientific principles. In the 17th century, Newton studied the relationship between forces and motion. He began a branch of science called MECHANICS. **Mechanics is the study of motion and the causes of changes in motion.** Newton found three basic laws of motion. These laws are still used to describe and explain motion today.

Cars entering a highway must accelerate to match the speed of moving traffic. Force from the engine causes the car to accelerate.

NEWTON'S LAWS RELATE:
Force
Mass
Acceleration

Newton's First Law. In this chapter, you have learned what acceleration is. But what causes mass to accelerate? The answer is, force makes mass accelerate. Acceleration requires force because of INERTIA. The law of inertia is Newton's first law. **The law states that a mass at rest tends to remain at rest. A mass moving at a constant velocity tends to keep moving at that velocity, unless acted upon by an outside force.**

Force must overcome the inertia of an object to make it move. All objects resist having their motion changed because inertia is a property of all matter. Newton's first law states that no force is needed to keep something moving in a straight line at a constant speed. But a force is needed to stop that motion or change it in some way. **Thus, Newton's law of inertia involves the problem of changing velocity, or of acceleration.**

Newton's Second Law. Newton's second law involves the concepts of force, mass, and acceleration. There is a relationship among the three. **The second law of motion states that the acceleration of an object depends upon its mass and on the applied force.** This means that for a given mass, the larger the force, the greater the acceleration, or the more rapidly the velocity of the object is changed. The greater the mass, the lower the acceleration. If equal forces are applied to a light object and a heavy object, the light object will be accelerated more than the heavy object. That is because the heavy object has more inertia.

Newton's Third Law. Newton's third law of motion states that for every action there is an equal and opposite reaction. That is, a force exerted in one direction is balanced by an equal force in the opposite direction. For example, rockets launched into space work on this principle. Hot gases are pushed downward, and the rocket is pushed upward. The action is the gases escaping from the rear of the rocket. The equal and opposite reaction is the rocket moving upward.

NEWTON'S LAWS SHOW THAT:

The motion of an object is changed only by force.

The greater the force, the greater the acceleration.

The greater the mass, the less the acceleration.

For every action there is an equal and opposite reaction.

11. Who originated the branch of science called mechanics?
12. What is mechanics?
13. What is Newton's first law of motion?
14. Why does acceleration require force?
15. Why do all objects resist having their motion changed?
16. Explain Newton's second law of motion.
17. If equal forces are applied to a light object and a heavy object, which will accelerate more? Why?
18. State Newton's third law of motion.
19. How do rockets use Newton's third law?

24F FRICTION

You are probably used to thinking that moving objects eventually slow down by themselves. But this slowing down is the result of forces such as FRICTION. **Friction is the force that opposes, or slows down, motion between the surfaces of objects.** Without forces such as friction, an object set moving would move forever.

Cars are lubricated to reduce friction. Excessive friction in a car's engine wastes energy and results in greater wear and tear.

The force of friction is caused by the attractions of the molecules of the two surfaces. There are several kinds of friction. **Two kinds of friction are rolling friction and sliding friction.** Oils and greases reduce friction by separating the molecules of the surfaces from each other.

Friction is a force opposing motion. There is a constant struggle to reduce friction in engines and machinery. There are scientists and engineers all over the world studying surfaces and different materials that can reduce friction and wear. Much of the energy used in engines and machinery is wasted. The energy is turned into wasted heat by friction.

Friction is also useful. Friction has such useful functions as holding nails in wood, making the fibers in your clothes cling together, and making rubber tires grip the pavement during a fast turn. Lower friction because of wet pavement causes accidents. Cars cannot stop as soon as drivers expect them to. There is less force available to make the mass of the car change its speed. Friction can be either harmful or helpful.

20. What is friction?
21. Name some unwanted effects of friction.
22. What are some helpful effects of friction?

ACTIVITY: Rolling and Sliding Friction

MATERIALS: Skateboard, string, rubber band, tape, meter stick

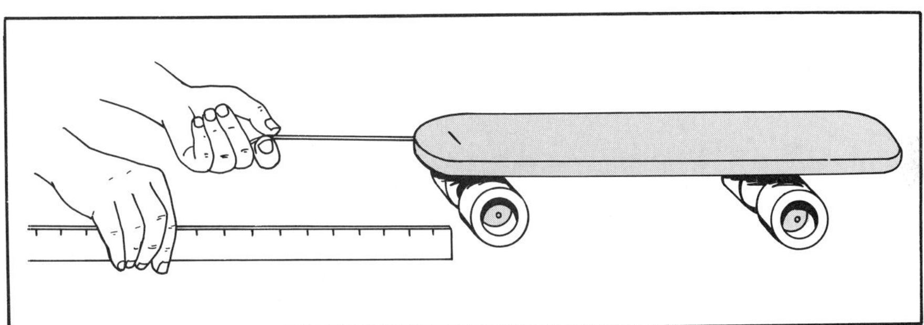

a. Attach the rubber band to the end of the skateboard. If there is no place to attach the rubber band, tape string to the end of the skateboard and tie the string to the rubber band.
b. Pull the rubber band hard enough to keep the skate board moving at a constant speed. Have your lab partner use the meter stick to measure the length of the rubber band as you pull the skate board. Answer question 23.
c. Use string, paper, or tape to lock the wheels of the skateboard. Pull the rubber band to keep the skateboard moving at a constant speed. Try to keep the speed as close to the same speed you used in step b. Have your lab partner measure the length of the rubber band while the board is in motion. Answer question 24.

23. What is the length of the rubber band?
24. What is the length of the rubber band now?
25. If the force pulling the skateboard is directly related to the length of the rubber band, when is the skateboard harder to pull?
26. Which has greater force, rolling friction or sliding friction?

SUMMARY

VOCABULARY

speed
velocity
acceleration
deceleration
centripetal force
mechanics
inertia
friction

KEY FACTS AND CONCEPTS

Speed is the rate at which something covers a given distance.

Speed, distance, and time are related. The formula for determining speed when distance and time are known is speed $= \frac{\text{distance}}{\text{time}}$.

To determine time when distance and speed are known, the formula is time $= \frac{\text{distance}}{\text{speed}}$.

To calculate distance when speed and time are known, the formula is distance = speed × time.

Velocity is a measure of both speed and direction.

The rate of change of velocity is called acceleration.

Velocity must change in order for there to be an acceleration or deceleration.

Centripetal force is an inward pulling force that holds an object in a circular path.

Centripetal force produces acceleration.

Mechanics is the study of motion and the causes of changes in motion.

Newton formulated three laws of motion.

Newton's first law is the law of inertia.

Inertia is a property of all matter that causes objects to resist having their motion changed.

Newton's second law states that the acceleration of an object depends upon its mass and on the force applied to it.

Newton's third law states that for every action there is an equal and opposite reaction.

Friction is the force between surfaces of objects.

Friction is a force opposing motion.

Without forces such as friction, an object set in motion would keep moving forever.

CONCLUSION

Motion results when a force acts upon an object. The property of inertia resists changing motion. The greater the mass, the greater its inertia. Once an object is set in motion, it takes a force to stop it. One of these forces is friction. In outer space where there is no friction, an object set in motion might keep moving forever.

27. What is the KEY IDEA of this chapter?

CHAPTER

25 Simple Machines

Making Work Easier and Faster

25A INTRODUCTION

As you now know, work is force acting over a distance. There is a limit to the amount of force the human body can exert. People use SIMPLE MACHINES to increase the force provided by muscle power.

Simple machines are mechanical devices that change force. They can change the amount of force or the direction in which a force acts. **However, machines do not increase the amount of work done.** Simple machines just make work easier or faster.

There are six kinds of simple machines. They are the LEVER, WHEEL AND AXLE, PULLEY, INCLINED PLANE, WEDGE, and SCREW. Many of the devices you use daily are simple machines or combinations of simple machines. Pliers, screwdrivers, automobile jacks, nutcrackers, lemon squeezers, egg beaters, and stairs are all simple machines.

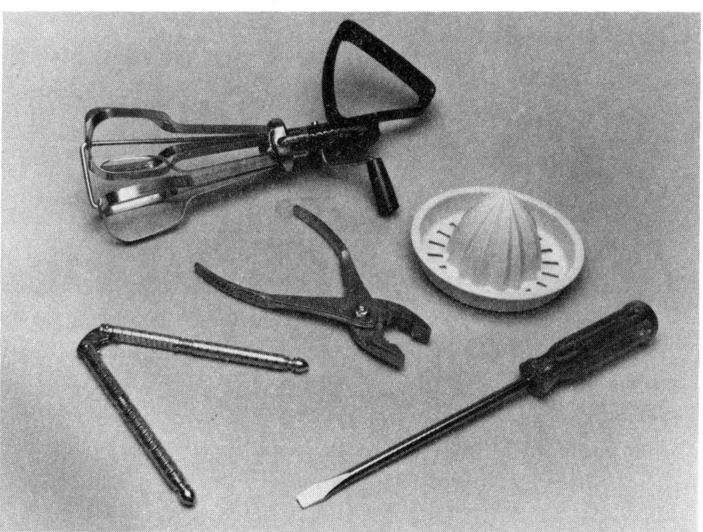

THE SIX SIMPLE MACHINES	
Lever	Inclined plane
Pulley	Wedge
Wheel and axle	Screw

1. Why do people use simple machines?
2. What are the six kinds of simple machines?

25B THE LEVER

First-Class Levers. People in ancient times used tree branches balanced on rocks to pry up heavy objects. These branches were acting as levers. **A lever is a simple machine that is supported at one place while a force is applied at another place.** The place at which the lever is supported is called the FULCRUM, or pivot. The force of the load being moved is the RESISTANCE. The force applied to the lever is the EFFORT. The distance through which the effort is applied is the EFFORT DISTANCE.

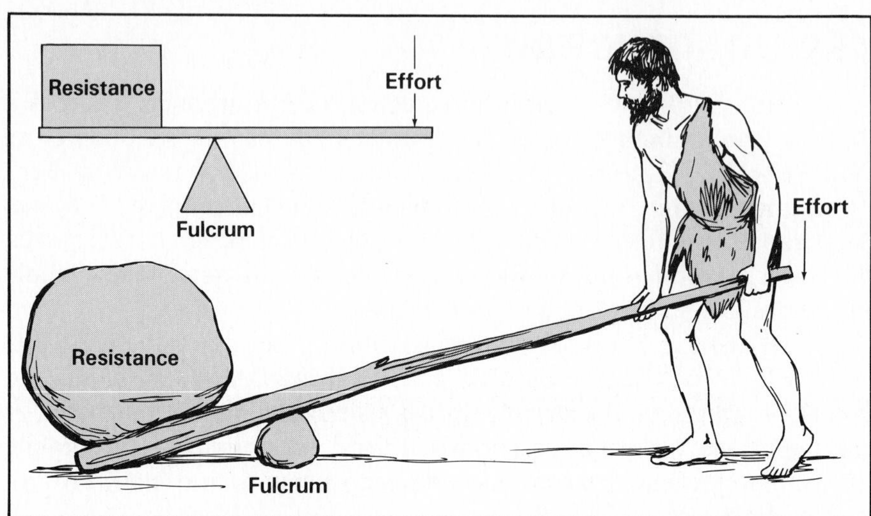

A tree branch used to pry up heavy objects is a first-class lever. People have used levers to move heavy loads for thousands of years.

Levers are divided into three classes, based on the positions of the fulcrum, effort force, and the resistance. In a first-class lever, the fulcrum is between the effort and the resistance. The tree branches used in ancient times to pry up heavy objects were first-class levers.

FIRST-CLASS LEVER:	Effort	Fulcrum	Resistance
SECOND-CLASS LEVER:	Effort	Resistance	Fulcrum
THIRD-CLASS LEVER:	Resistance	Effort	Fulcrum

First-class levers help move heavy objects by multiplying a small effort force. The small effort force is multiplied to overcome a large resistance force. The amount by which a lever, or any simple machine, multiplies force is called its MECHANICAL ADVANTAGE, or MA. This ability of machines to multiply the effort force gives you the advantage of being able to do jobs that might otherwise be impossible.

The lever, like all simple machines, makes work easier. **A small force acting over a long distance is converted to a large force acting over a short distance.** Remember, work is equal to force times distance. The work put into the machine is the small force times the long distance. The useful work coming out of the machine is the large force times the short distance. Allowing for friction, the work output will equal the work input. The Conservation of Energy Law applies even to simple machines!

ACTIVITY: The Lever

MATERIALS: Meter stick, string, 100 g mass, paper clip, 200 g mass, tape

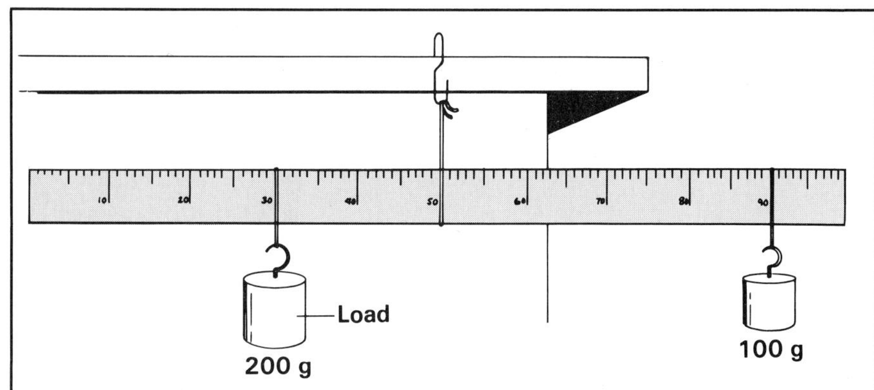

a. Bend the paper clip into a hook. Use a loop of string to support the meter stick at its balance point, about the 50 cm mark. The hook should rest on the table edge. If it slips, use tape to hold it.
b. Use a loop of string to hang the 200 g mass 20 cm from the balance point.
c. Hang the 100 g mass where it will make the meter stick balance again.
d. Measure the distance from the 100 g mass to the balance point. Answer question 3.

____

3. How far from the balance is the 100 g mass?
4. To find the mechanical advantage, or MA, divide the distance found in question 3 by the 20 cm used for the 200 g mass. What is your answer?
5. Divide 200 g by 100 g. What is your answer?
6. How closely does the MA compare to the ratio of the two masses?

Second-Class Levers. In a second-class lever, the resistance is between the fulcrum and the effort. Such levers multiply the force that is applied to them. The fulcrum is at one end in this kind of lever. Wheelbarrows and some kinds of nutcrackers are examples of second-class levers.

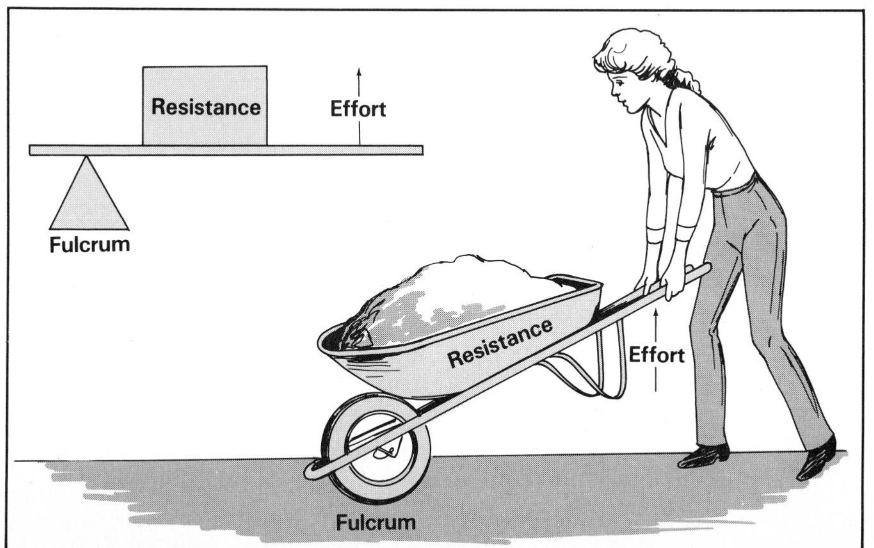

The wheelbarrow is a second-class lever.

Third-Class Levers. In a third-class lever, the effort is between the resistance and the fulcrum. When people use rakes and brooms or when they throw a ball, they are using third-class levers to move a load. **Third-class levers do not increase force.** Instead, these levers increase the distance a load travels or the speed it travels.

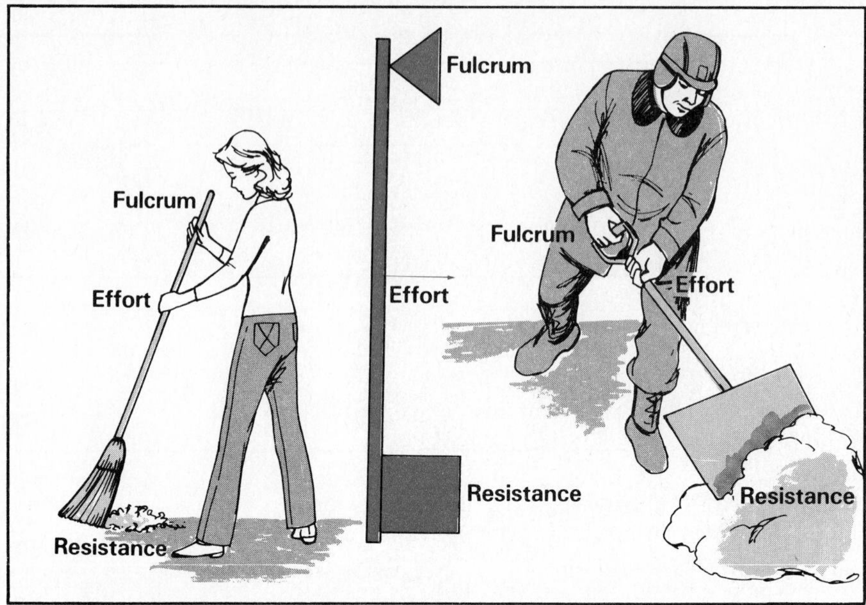

A broom and a shovel are examples of third-class levers.

7. How does a lever work?

8. What is meant by the terms "resistance force," "effort force," and "effort distance?"

9. What is mechanical advantage?

10. How do all simple machines make work easier?

11. Give an example of each of the three types of levers.

25C THE WHEEL AND AXLE

The wheel was an important invention that helped people to translate force into motion. It is hard to imagine what life would be like without wheels. With the invention of the wheel, the age of machines took a giant step forward.

The wheel and axle is a combination of two different-sized wheels that rotate together. The smaller wheel is often shaped like a roller or a shaft. This smaller wheel is the axle. The large wheel takes the effort force; the smaller wheel, or axle, handles the resistance force. An automobile steering wheel, the crank on an old-fashioned well, and a wrench are examples of the wheel and axle.

The effort force applied to a large circle (the handle) multiplies the force exerted on a smaller circle (the axle). This makes lifting the bucket easier.

You may wonder how a wrench could be considered a wheel and axle. When you tighten a nut with a wrench, you turn the wrench in a large circle. This is the effort force. The nut turns in a small circle. In this way, the effort force is multiplied. The wheel and axle can be used to gain force or distance.

The wheel and axle follows the rule for all simple machines. A smaller force acts over a longer distance to produce a larger force acting over a shorter distance. **Work is thus made easier but does not increase.** No more work is done with the wheel and axle than without.

This is because a small force times a long distance equals a large force times a short distance. Once again, the Law of Conservation of Energy applies.

Sometimes, teeth or cogs may be found around the edge of the wheel. Then the wheel is a GEAR. **Gears are wheels that can connect with one another.** Force from one gear is transmitted to a second gear through the teeth. An example of a gear is the large wheel on an old-fashioned egg beater. It turns the small gears attached to the beater blades. If you looked inside a pocket watch, you would see many gears.

Gears on a bicycle pedal turn the wheels of a bicycle. The gears in a pocket watch transmit force from the spring to the hands.

12. What does a wheel and axle consist of?
13. What rule do all simple machines follow?
14. Why is no more work done with a wheel and axle than without?
15. Why use a wheel and axle?
16. What are gears?

25D THE PULLEY

Pulleys are useful simple machines. **They are used to multiply force, change direction, or both.** It is often easier to pull down on something than to pull up. A pulley gives you the advantage of pulling down instead of pulling up.

The simplest pulley consists of one grooved wheel and a rope passed over the wheel. A single pulley is used to change the direction of an applied force. That simply means that when you pull down on one end of a simple pulley, the load at the other end will go up. **Your pull is the effort force and the weight is the resistance force.**

This is a simple pulley.

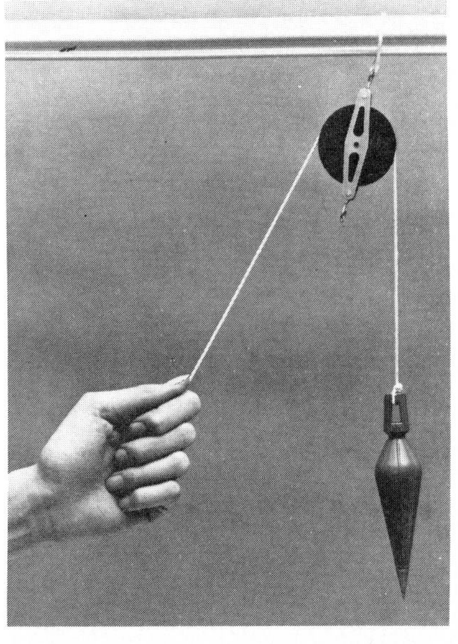

Fixed Pulley. When a pulley is attached to a wall or ceiling, the pulley is a fixed pulley. Window blinds and the rope on a flag pole are examples of common fixed pulleys. Fixed pulleys do not multiply the effort force put into them.

Movable Pulley. In order to lift heavier weights with less effort, the pulley itself may be hung on a rope. This is done so that the pulley moves upward when the rope is pulled. This type of pulley is a movable pulley. **The mechanical advantage of a movable pulley is 2. This means that the pull applied to the free end of the rope need be only half the weight of the load.**

Pulley System. With the movable pulley, additional pulleys may be added to create a pulley system. More ropes may be used in this

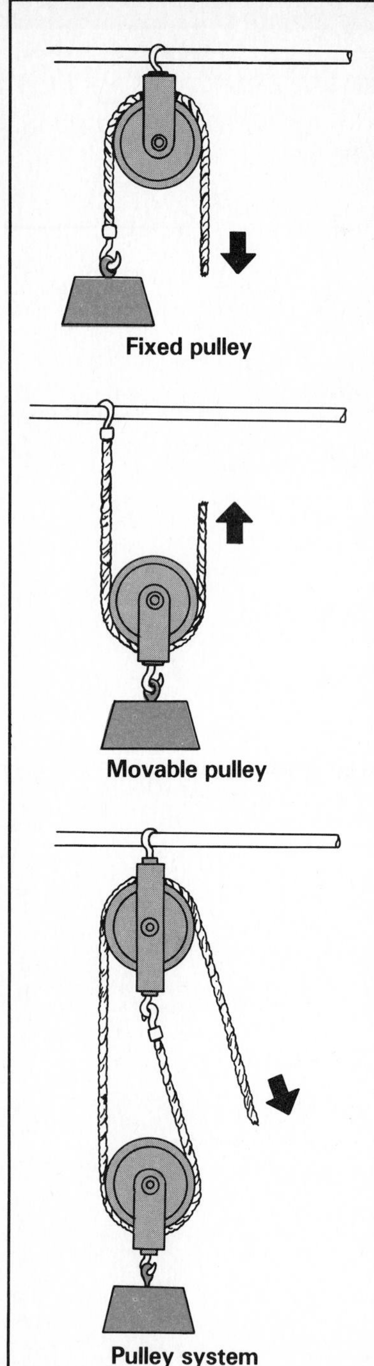

arrangement to increase mechanical advantage. **The mechanical advantage is equal to the number of supporting ropes.** That is, when there is one rope supporting the load, the MA is 1. When there are two ropes supporting the load, the MA is 2, and so on.

KINDS OF PULLEYS

- Fixed
- Movable
- Pulley system

17. What are pulleys used for?
18. What is the difference between a fixed pulley and a movable pulley?
19. What is a simple way to determine the MA of a pulley system?
20. If the MA of a pulley system is 6, how many ropes are supporting the load?

25E THE INCLINED PLANE

The inclined plane uses a smaller force over a longer distance to make work easier. It takes less effort on your part to raise a weight by pushing it up at an angle than by lifting it straight up. A smaller force acting over a longer distance does the work of moving a larger force over a shorter distance.

Any sloping surface used to make work easier is an inclined plane. The mechanical advantage of an inclined plane is found by dividing the length of the plane by its height. **The more gradual the slope, the greater the mechanical advantage.**

Inclined planes have been used for thousands of years all over the world. A flight of stairs is an inclined plane. In the days before power machinery, workers would pile up earth to make a sloping surface. They then used this to drag or roll heavy stones up and down as they constructed tall buildings. No doubt the ancient Egyptians used the principle of the inclined plane to build the pyramids.

21. What is an inclined plane?
22. How do you calculate the MA of an inclined plane?

25F THE WEDGE

The wedge is an inclined plane that moves, or is portable. Force is applied to the wedge, moving it lengthwise. It moves under or into a resistance. Once again, a smaller force acting over a longer distance is transformed into a larger force acting over a shorter distance.

Large wedges, axes, are used to split logs. Other examples of the wedge are knife blades, chisels, the teeth of saw blades, and vegetable peelers. In fact, most cutting instruments work on the principle of the wedge.

An axe is a large wedge.

23. What is a wedge?
24. Give some examples of wedges.

25G THE SCREW

The screw is an inclined plane that has been wound around a rod in a spiral. Like other simple machines, the screw is able to multiply effort force by acting over a long effort distance. **A small effort is needed to twist a screw into a wall because of the long distance through which the screw is turned.**

The distance between the ridges of the screw is called the PITCH of the screw. The ridges themselves are called the THREADS of the screw. If the distance between the threads is small, the pitch of the screw is also small. The smaller the pitch, the more times the screw must be turned to move the same distance forward. **The greater the number of turns—the effort distance—the larger the mechanical advantage of the screw.**

Screws come in many sizes, from the tiny screws used in eyeglass frames, watches, and cameras to the bolts holding truck engines together. Screw jacks are used to lift cars, trucks, and even houses.

A screw can be thought of as an inclined plane in a spiral.

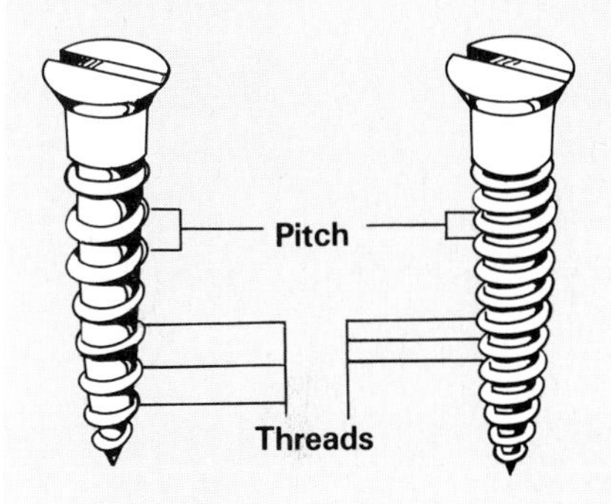

25. What is a screw?
26. What is pitch?
27. How is pitch related to the mechanical advantage of the screw?

25H MACHINES AND ENERGY CONSERVATION

Earlier in this chapter, you learned that simple machines can make work easier or faster. **Machines cannot increase the amount of work done.** The amount of work done by a machine, the energy it puts out, is limited. A machine cannot put out more work than is put into it. The energy balance is controlled by the Law of Conservation of Energy. No one has ever found a way to break this law of nature.

You are probably wondering why the work output does not at least equal the work input. The answer is friction. **Some energy is always lost**

to friction. If it were not for friction, the amount of work a machine could do would equal the amount of work put into the machine. However, output still could never exceed input. It's the law!

Each figure illustrates one of the six simple machines. Can you identify them?

28. How do simple machines affect the way work is done?
29. Why is the work that comes out of a machine less than the work that is put into it?

SUMMARY

VOCABULARY

simple machines
lever
wheel and axle
pulley
inclined plane
wedge
screw
fulcrum
resistance force
effort force
effort distance
mechanical advantage
gear
pitch
threads

KEY FACTS AND CONCEPTS

Simple machines increase the force provided by muscle power to make work faster or easier.

There are six kinds of simple machines.

The lever is a bar that is supported at one place while a force is applied at another place.

Levers are classified by where the fulcrum, resistance, and effort points are located on the bar.

The amount by which a simple machine multiples force is called its mechanical advantage, or MA.

Simple machines make work easier by using smaller forces over greater distances.

The wheel and axle is a combination of two different-sized wheels that rotate together.

Gears are wheels that can connect with one another.

The pulley can increase force, change direction, or both. There is the fixed pulley, the movable pulley, and the pulley system.

The mechanical advantage of a pulley system is equal to the number of supporting ropes used.

The inclined plane is any sloping surface used to make work easier.

The more gradual the slope of the inclined plane, the greater its mechanical advantage.

The wedge is a portable inclined plane.

The screw is an inclined plane that has been wound around a rod in a spiral.

The distance between the ridges of the screw is called the pitch.

The ridges themselves are called the threads.

Machines cannot increase the amount of work done.

The Law of Conservation of Energy states that work output cannot exceed work input.

Work output does not equal work input because some energy is always lost to friction.

CONCLUSION

Simple machines make work easier. They can change the amount of force applied, the direction the force takes, or both. Machines cannot increase the amount of work done because of friction. That is why machines are oiled and lubricated—to cut down on friction.

30. What is the KEY IDEA of this chapter?

CHAPTER

26 Heat Engines

Using Heat to Move Machines

26A INTRODUCTION

The simple machines you studied in Chapter 25 run on muscle power. However, muscle power alone could not do enough work to meet all of society's needs. Long ago, the problem arose of how to provide such basic necessities as housing and transportation to a large number of people. The problem was solved when people learned how to use heat to make things move. Machines that change heat energy to mechanical energy are called HEAT ENGINES.

Engines transform energy from fuels, steam, or from air or water under pressure into motion. The steam engine, for example, uses the pressure of steam to drive pistons. The steam comes from water heated by burning fuel. Steam was used to push the pistons in steam locomotives of the 19th century. Today, steam is used to turn the turbine blades of the ocean liner *Queen Elizabeth 2.*

Steam powers both the old steam locomotive and the modern ocean liner *Queen Elizabeth 2.*

SOME HEAT ENGINES

- Steam engine
- Steam turbine
- Gasoline engine
- Diesel engine
- Gas turbine

There are many different kinds of heat engines. STEAM ENGINES, STEAM TURBINES, GASOLINE ENGINES, DIESEL ENGINES, and GAS TURBINES are all heat engines. **Expanding heated gases supply the force that produces motion in each of these engines.**

1. What kind of machine changes heat energy to mechanical energy?
2. Name some different kinds of heat engines.

26B THE STEAM ENGINE AND STEAM TURBINE

The development of the steam engine in the 1700's made modern industry possible. One steam engine could do the work of hundreds of horses. But a steam engine does not create power. **It uses steam to change the heat energy released by burning fuel into mechanical energy to do work.** Another name for this kind of burning is COMBUSTION.

All heat engines run on the energy released during combustion. In steam engines and steam turbines, the fuel is burned outside the engine. That is why they are called EXTERNAL-COMBUSTION ENGINES.

Steam Engines. In a steam engine, steam under pressure pushes against a PISTON. **The piston is a disk of metal that slides back and forth inside a tube.** The tube is named by its shape, a CYLINDER. The piston separates the cylinder into two ends. Steam enters both ends of the cylinder through a valve. The valve controls the opening and closing of both ends of the cylinder.

The valve controls which end of the cylinder the steam will enter. As steam enters a cylinder, it pushes the piston. The valve allows steam to enter until the piston has traveled the length of the cylinder. Used steam escapes through an open valve at the other end of the cylinder.

Then the valves reverse the flow of steam. The piston is pushed back in the opposite direction. The back and forth motion of the piston is transferred to the ROTARY motion of a wheel.

The steam engine turns heat energy into motion. The connecting rod and flywheel change back and forth motion to rotary motion.

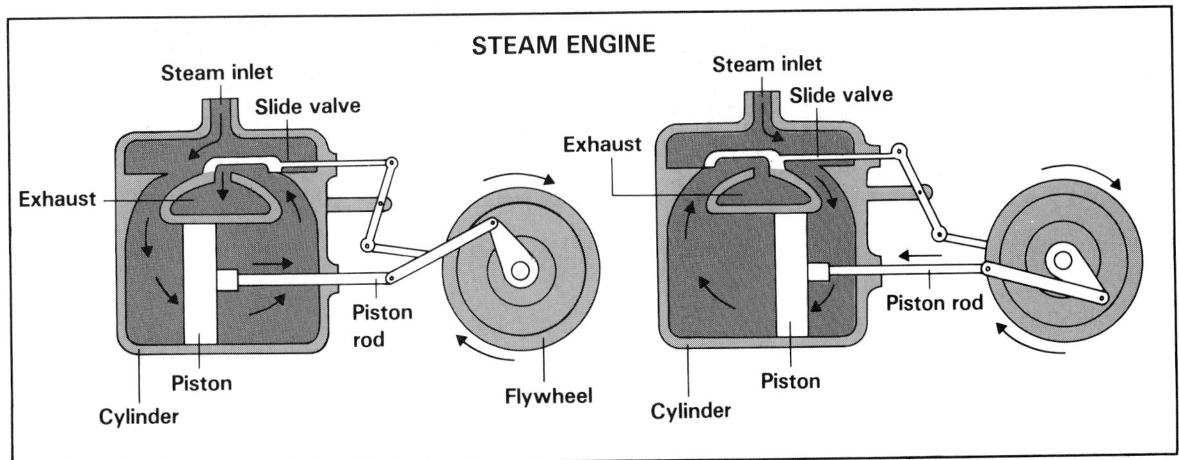

Energy is wasted in overcoming the inertia of pushing the piston and connected parts back and forth. An engine with all rotary parts is usually more efficient.

Steam Turbines. The steam turbine is a rotary engine. In this engine, steam is directed against blades or vanes set in a wheel. The expanding steam pushes the vanes and makes the wheel turn. **Most turbines have several wheels. The wheels gradually increase in size to make room for the expanding steam as it does its work.**

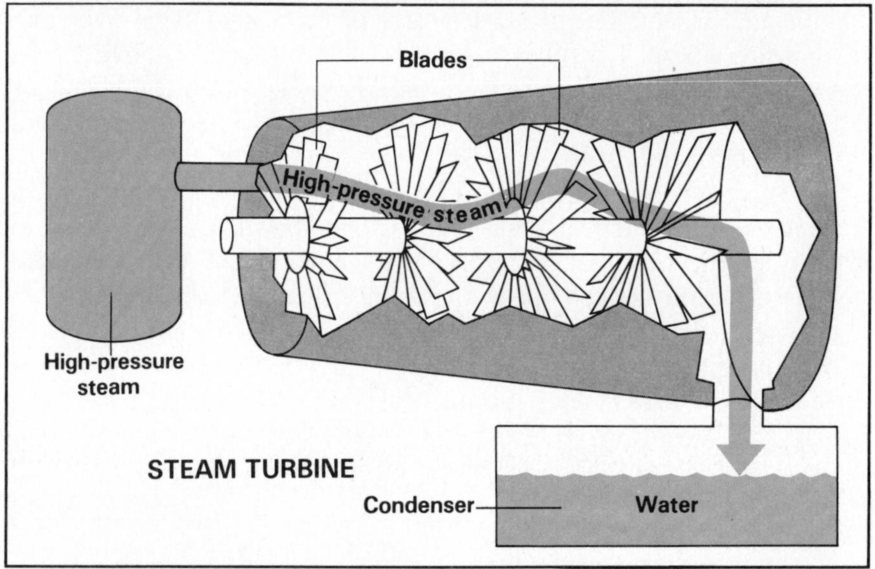

On the top is a photograph of a powerful steam turbine. On the bottom is a simplified drawing showing how the steam turbine works.

Steam turbines have replaced steam engines for many uses. The turbines are more efficient. They use less fuel to do as much work as a steam engine. More of the energy from fuel is turned into kinetic energy or motion. Less energy is wasted starting and stopping reciprocating parts.

Steam turbines are used in ships and power plants. The turbines in some ships and power plants use steam produced by nuclear reactors instead of by fire. The source of heat has no effect on how the turbine operates.

3. Where is fuel burned in an external-combustion engine?
4. What does steam push in a steam engine?
5. What does steam push in a steam turbine?
6. Why is a rotary engine more efficient than a reciprocating engine?

ACTIVITY: Making Your Own Steam Turbine

MATERIALS: Burner, test tube holder, soda straw, test tube, 2 cm × 30 cm cardboard strip, tape, rubber stopper, glass tubing, paper clip

a. Fold the cardboard strip back and forth into 12 sections, each 2.5 cm long.

b. Cut off a 3 cm section of soda straw. Tape the folds of the cardboard strip to form a six-bladed paddle wheel. The piece of soda straw should be in the middle with the wheel around it.

c. Straighten the paper clip and pass it through the straw in the wheel.

d. Put a small amount of water into the test tube. Carefully put the glass tube in the stopper. Use a few drops of glycerine or soap to lubricate the hole. Put the stopper and glass tube in the test tube.

e. Hold the test tube over the burner with the test tube holder. When the water boils, direct the glass tube toward the blades of the paddle wheel. **Do not point the tube at yourself or at anyone else.** Observe what happens.

---

7. What happens when the steam hits the blades of the wheel?
8. Where did the energy in the steam come from?
9. What form of energy does the heat energy in the steam take when it hits the paddle wheel?

26C THE GASOLINE ENGINE AND DIESEL ENGINE

Gasoline engines, diesel engines, and gas turbines are INTERNAL-COMBUSTION ENGINES. **They burn their fuel inside the engine.** The gasoline and diesel engines burn their fuel in a cylinder right next to the pistons they have to push. **Internal-combustion engines are more compact and lighter in weight than external-combustion engines.**

TWO KINDS OF ENGINES

External Combustion	Internal Combustion
Steam engine	Gasoline engine
Steam turbine engine	Diesel engine
	Wankel engine
	Gas turbine engine

Notice that the cylinder in a four-stroke cycle engine provides power one fourth of the time. As in the steam engine, back and forth motion must be changed to rotary motion.

Many gasoline and diesel engines work on a FOUR-STROKE CYCLE. *Stroke* means the up-and-down movements of the pistons. A four-stroke cycle engine has intake, compression, power, and exhaust strokes. **Each cycle accompanies a motion, or stroke, of the piston.**

HOW A FOUR-STROKE CYCLE GASOLINE ENGINE WORKS

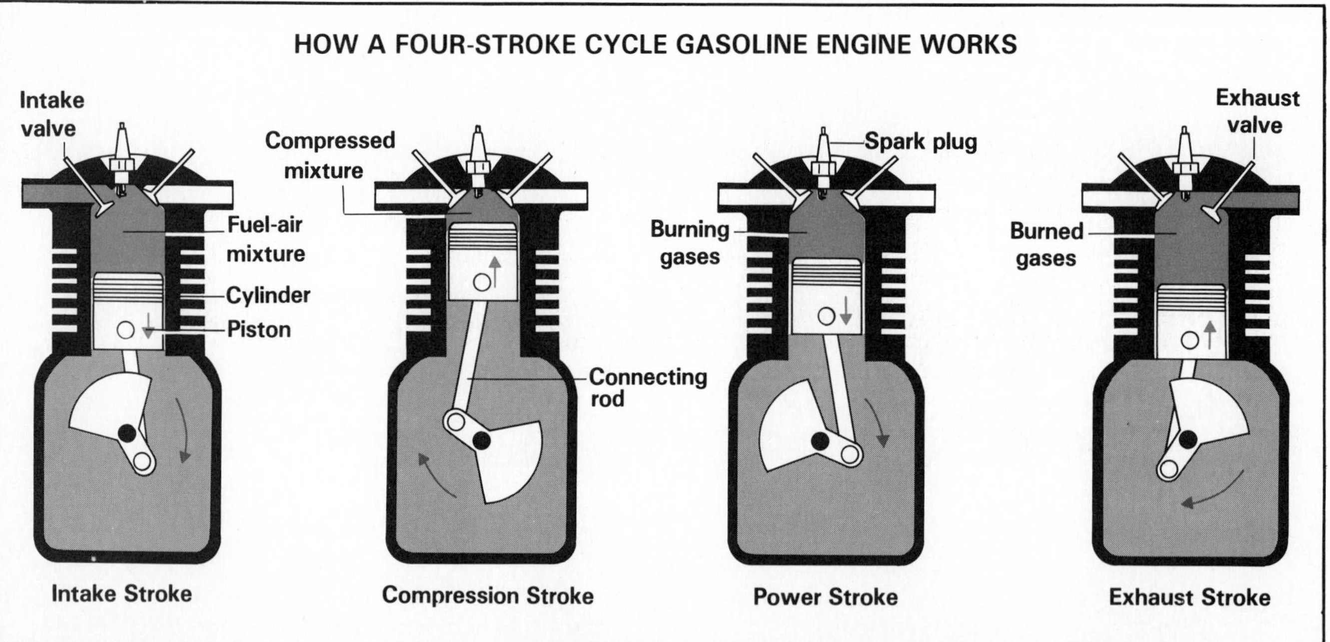

The first stroke of the cycle is the intake stroke. The piston moves downward, away from the valves. This lowers the pressure in the cylinder. Outside air rushes into the cylinder through the intake valve. In the gasoline engine, the air first passes through the CARBURETOR. **The carburetor adds gasoline to the air to make an explosive mixture that enters the cylinder.** The diesel engine has no carburetor, so only air enters at this time.

On the second, or compression, stroke, the valves close and the piston rises. The air or air and gasoline mixture is compressed. Diesel engines compress the air much more than gasoline engines do. The air in a diesel engine gets very hot.

The third stroke is the power stroke. In gasoline engines, a spark from the spark plug ignites the air and gasoline mixture. **Heat from the burning fuel makes the gas in the cylinder expand.** This pushes the piston down.

In diesel engines, a measured amount of fuel is sprayed, or injected, into the cylinder. The heat of compression ignites the fuel. Heat from the burning fuel expands the gases in the cylinder and pushes the piston down.

When the piston is down, the exhaust valve opens and the piston moves up the cylinder again. This is the exhaust stroke. The burned fuel and expanded gases are pushed out of the engine through the open valve. Then the exhaust valve closes, the intake valve opens, and the cycle starts again.

THE FOUR STROKES OF A FOUR-STROKE CYCLE ENGINE:

Intake
Compression
Power
Exhaust

In engines of more than four cylinders, power strokes overlap so that at least one cylinder is always providing power. The advantage of this is smoother operation. The disadvantage is having more pieces of metal that must stop and start. **Energy is wasted overcoming inertia.**

Many motorcycle engines work on a TWO-STROKE CYCLE. The strokes are called the intake-compression stroke and the power-exhaust stroke. In two-stroke cycle engines, the valves are replaced with holes, or ports, in the cylinder walls.

There are fewer moving parts in a two-stroke cycle engine than in a four-stroke cycle engine.

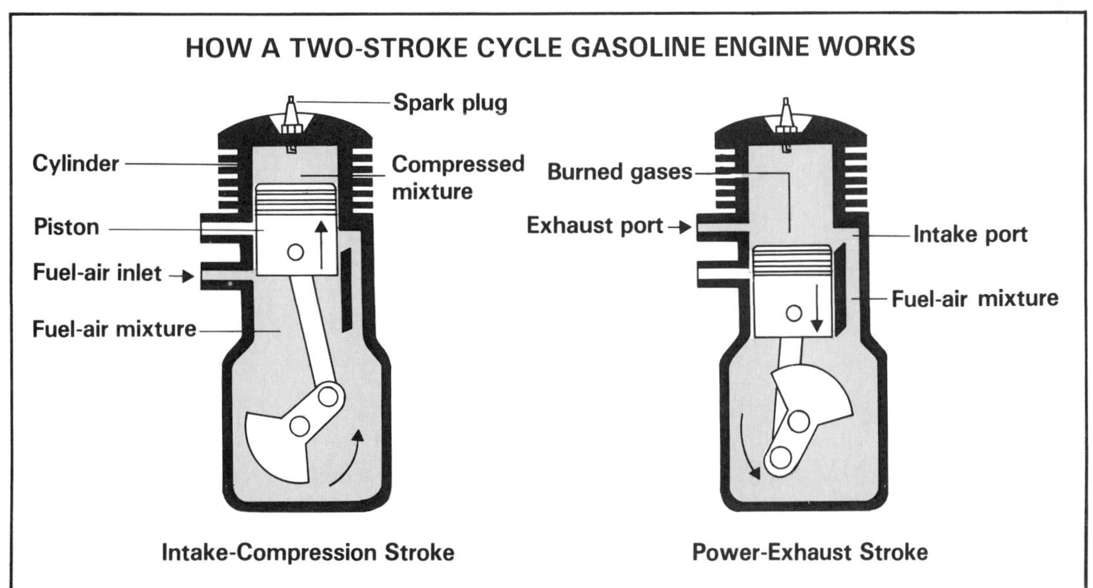

When the piston moves up the cylinder during the intake-compression stroke, it compresses the air and gasoline mixture in the cylinder.

When the piston comes down on the power-exhaust stroke, the air and gasoline mixture is forced through a port into the cylinder. As the piston uncovers the exhaust port, the gases escape. At the same time, a fresh mixture enters the cylinder through the intake port. The cycle is repeated.

The two-stroke cycle engine uses twice as many power strokes as the four-stroke cycle engine. This is an advantage in motorcycles where space is limited. **But the two-stroke cycle engine is not as efficient as the four-stroke cycle engine.** For one thing, the fresh air and gasoline mix with the exhaust gas. Thus, some fresh mixture is lost before it is burned.

Two-stroke cycle engines have been used in automobiles from time to time. At present, they are used primarily in motorcycles, chain saws, and other small-engine devices.

10. Where is fuel burned in an internal-combustion engine?
11. Name the strokes of the four-stroke cycle engine.
12. What happens during each stroke?
13. Explain the action of the two-stroke cycle engine.
14. What takes the place of valves in the two-stroke cycle engine?

26D THE ROTARY ENGINE

The rotary gasoline engine, or Wankel engine, has a rotor instead of a piston. The rotor is shaped like a triangle with bulging sides. **A Wankel engine operates more quietly and smoothly than a piston engine.** This is because it does not involve the back-and-forth motion of pistons. **A Wankel engine has fewer moving parts, weighs less, and is smaller than a piston engine of the same power.** Despite its many advantages, the Wankel engine still has some problems. Engineers are still trying to solve these problems.

A rotating triangle takes the place of pistons in a rotary engine.

Like the piston engine, the Wankel engine goes through a four-step cycle to produce power. These steps are intake, compression, power, and exhaust.

The rotor turns in a specially shaped chamber. As the triangular rotor turns, the corners of the rotor touch the walls of the chamber.

As the rotor turns, an intake port is uncovered. An air and gasoline mixture is drawn in. When the rotor covers the port, the mixture is compressed. A spark plug ignites the compressed mixture. **The heated, expanding gases move the rotor around.** The rotor turns until it uncovers the exhaust port and pushes the burned gases out. Then the exhaust port is covered, the intake port is uncovered, and the process starts again.

All three sides of the triangle go through this cycle. **It is as though there were three cylinders, each one giving a power stroke.** Wankel engines are used in such vehicles as airplanes, automobiles, boats, and trucks.

15. What replaces the pistons in the Wankel engine?
16. Describe the operation of a Wankel engine.

26E TIMING SYSTEMS

Steam engines, steam turbines, gasoline engines, diesel engines, and Wankel engines all need TIMING SYSTEMS. Valves must open and close at the right time. Spark plugs must fire at the right time. Fuel must be injected at the right time.

Rotating pieces of metal on a shaft open and close the valves. The ignition system ignites the fuel mixture in the different cylinders at different times. Fuel is sent to the cylinders either by a carburetor or by an injection pump. In either case, the amount of fuel sent to the cylinders is crucial because combustion depends upon a delicate balance of air and fuel. **An engine will not run well or at all if the timing of all the parts is not just right.**

Engineers are constantly working to improve the look and efficiency of cars. The car in this photograph is electric.

TIMING SYSTEMS COORDINATE

Valves
Ignition
Fuel delivery

17. Why do most engines need timing systems?

26F THE GAS TURBINE ENGINE

The gas turbine is an internal-combustion engine. As you know, that means that fuel is burned inside the engine. **Expanding heated gases push the blades of the turbine to produce motion.** There are two kinds of gas turbine engines. In TURBOJET engines, used in jet aircraft, the expanding gases blow out the rear of the engine to produce most of the motion. In TURBOPROP engines, used in propeller-driven aircraft, most of the motion is produced by the hot gases pushing the turbine blades.

The main part of a gas turbine engine is a long shaft with bladed wheels at both ends. When the shaft turns, large amounts of air are drawn in and compressed by the blades at the front of the engine. The air travels through a COMBUSTION CHAMBER where fuel is burned. **The heated, expanding gases push against the turbine blades at the rear of the engine before escaping.** An electric motor is used to start the shaft turning until the fuel is ignited.

Jets have replaced propeller planes for most commercial purposes.

The turbine blades in turbojet engines take just enough energy to run the compressor blades. Most of the energy is in the force of the jet of gas escaping from the rear of the engine. **The engine obeys Newton's third law of motion, which you studied in Chapter 24.** This law states that for every action there is an equal and opposite reaction. **The force of gases escaping from the rear of the engine pushes the engine forward with equal force.** This forward force is called THRUST.

In a turboprop engine, more energy is taken up by the turbine blades so less energy escapes through the exhaust opening. The turbine blades turn the propeller.

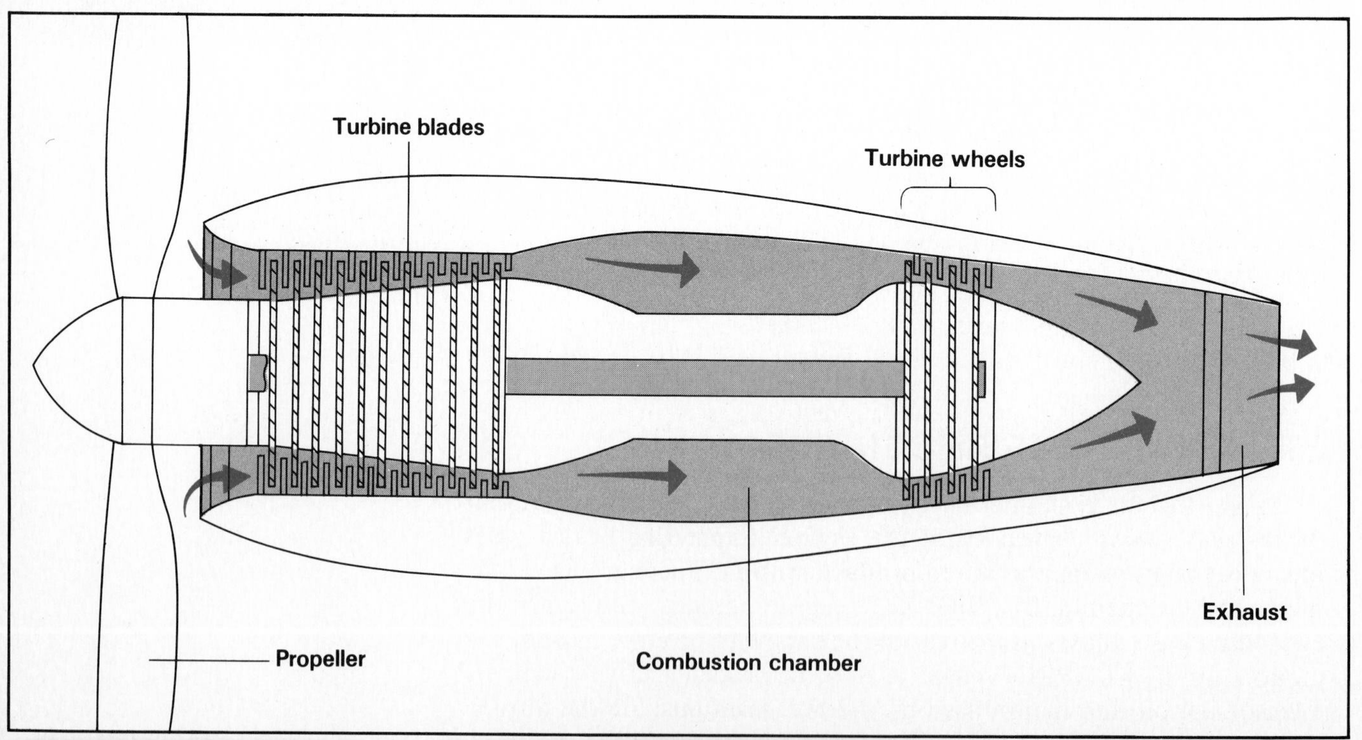

The turbine blades in turboprop engines take most of the energy from the hot gases. Turboprop engines have more turbine wheels than turbojet engines. **Only a small amount of thrust comes from the gases**

escaping from the engine. A set of gears reduces the speed of rotation of the engine shaft. These gears drive the propeller on turboprop aircraft.

Small gas turbines are used as power sources like any other internal-combustion engine. In these small engines, as much energy as possible is taken up by the turbine blades. The jet energy is not used at all. Some land vehicles are powered by small gas turbines. Gas turbines are also used to drive electrical generators and other stationary equipment.

> Turbojet engines get most of their power from the thrust of escaping gas. Turboprop engines get most of their power from gases pushing turbine blades.

18. How is air drawn into a gas turbine?
19. Where do the expanding, heated gases produce motion in a gas turbine?
20. How are turboprop and turbojet engines different?
21. How does the turbojet engine follow Newton's third law of motion?

SUMMARY

VOCABULARY

heat engine
steam engine
steam turbine
gasoline engine
diesel engine
gas turbine
combustion
piston
external-combustion engine
cylinder
rotary
internal-combustion engine
four-stroke cycle
carburetor
two-stroke cycle
timing system
turbojet
turboprop
combustion chamber
thrust

KEY FACTS AND CONCEPTS

Force from expanding gases, heated by burning fuel, moves heat engines.

Heat engines convert heat energy into mechanical energy.

External-combustion engines burn fuel outside the engine.

The tube-shaped space inside engines is called a cylinder.

The piston is a disk-shaped piece of metal that slides back and forth inside a cylinder. Valves control gases entering or leaving the cylinder.

Steam engines have pistons that move back and forth.

Energy is needed to overcome the inertia of the parts in steam engines.

In steam engines, steam under pressure pushes the piston to provide power.

Internal-combustion engines burn fuel inside the engine.

The four strokes of four-stroke cycle gasoline and diesel engines are intake, compression, power, and exhaust.

Two-stroke cycle engines combine these functions so that they have twice as many power strokes as the four-stroke cycle engine. Two-stroke cycle engines have openings, or ports, in the cylinder walls instead of valves.

The Wankel engine is a rotary gasoline engine.

Rotary engines have rotors that keep turning.

Many types of engines need timing systems to operate efficiently.

The gas turbine has a shaft with bladed wheels attached to each end. The front blades act as an air compressor.

In turbojet engines, the main thrust is caused by the reaction of the gases jetting out of the rear of the engine.

Turboprop engines take most of their energy from turbine blades and use it to turn propellers.

CONCLUSION

Motion is produced by the expansion of heated gases pushing something. All engines have this in common. The gases are heated by burning fuel. Until the engine was invented, people had to depend on the power of their own muscles or on animal, wind, and water power to do work.

22. What is the KEY IDEA of this chapter?

CHAPTER

27 Sound

The Molecules that Vibrate

27A INTRODUCTION

What is sound? You hear sounds all around you every day. An alarm clock may wake you up in the morning. This loud sound begins your day of sounds. Sounds range from the sound of your own breathing to the sound of traffic in the street. Despite the many differences between sounds, there are certain features that all sounds share.

One characteristic that all sounds have in common is that every sound is caused by VIBRATIONS. **Vibrations are the rapid back and forth motions of matter.** Motion is always involved in the production of sounds. **To start something moving, energy must be supplied.**

When vibrations reach your ear, nerve endings are stimulated. The nerves send impulses to your brain. Your brain translates the impulses into what you call sound.

The brain translates the vibrations of matter into sound.

1. Name and define one characteristic that all sounds share.
2. What happens when vibration reaches your ear?

27B FREQUENCY

One way to tell one sound from another is by the number of vibrations that a sound makes each second. This is called the FREQUENCY of the sound. **Frequency is measured in a unit called the hertz, abbreviated hz.** One hertz means one vibration is made each second. You can hear frequencies from about 20 to about 20,000 hertz. The lowest tone on a piano has a frequency of 27 vibrations a second, or 27 hertz.

There is wide variation among people's ability to hear sounds. Also, the ability to hear higher frequencies decreases with age. This is due partly to aging and partly to noise in the environment weakening people's ability to hear. Many people who work around noisy machinery, jet aircraft, or rock bands tend to lose their ability to hear certain frequencies earlier in life.

Some animals can hear sounds that humans cannot hear. Sound frequencies too high for the human ear are called ULTRASONIC. Such animals as dogs and bats can hear ultrasonic sounds. Dog whistles are ultrasonic.

In general, sounds with frequencies greater than 20,000 hertz are called ultrasonic sounds. Ultrasonic sound waves are used for many scientific and industrial purposes.

Ultrasonic waves are used by dentists to clean teeth.

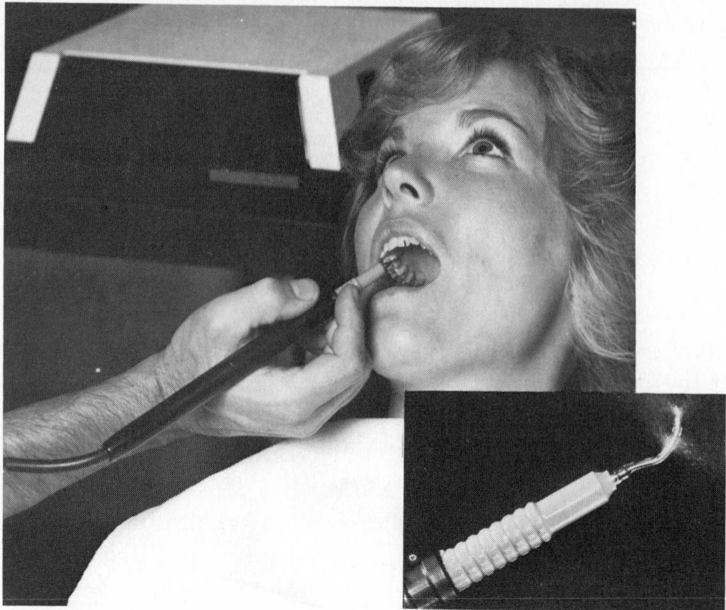

The frequency of a sound determines its PITCH. **Pitch is what is heard. Differences of frequency are heard as differences of pitch.** A higher frequency of vibration will cause you to hear a higher pitch. The word *pitch* is used by musicians to describe musical sounds. In fact, when people talk about hearing sounds, the word *pitch* is used rather than the word *frequency*.

3. Name one way you can tell one sound from another.
4. What does one hertz mean in terms of vibrations?
5. What are ultrasonic sounds?
6. What is pitch?

Even though these astronauts were standing next to each other on the moon, they had to use radios to communicate with each other.

27C HOW SOUND TRAVELS

So far in this chapter, you have learned that sound is caused by vibrations. For sound to occur, something must be made to vibrate and carry the vibrations. Sound will not travel in a completely empty space. Sound requires a MEDIUM. **A medium is a substance that will carry the sound, or vibrations.** The medium may be a solid, a liquid, or a gas.

Sound must have a medium to carry it. It will not travel in a vacuum. For example, there is no sound in outerspace. Two astronauts outside of their ship in space must use radios to speak to each other, even if they are only one meter apart!

Different mediums carry sounds at different speeds. Solids carry sound faster than liquids or gases. The speed of sound in steel, for example, is 5,200 meters a second. Liquids usually carry sound faster than gases. The speed of sound in water is about 1,500 meters a second. The speed of sound in air, a gas, is less than one fourth as fast.

It is the different properties of the mediums that determine how fast sound can travel through them. Three properties that control the speed of sound in a medium are density, elasticity, and temperature. Elasticity is the ability of a material to return to its original shape after it has been disturbed. The denser the substance, the lower the speed of sound. The more elastic the substance, the higher the speed. The warmer the substance, the higher the speed.

To illustrate how the speed of sound is affected by temperature, suppose it is 0° Celsius, or freezing, outside. Sound will move through the air at 331 meters a second. At 20° Celsius, room temperature, the speed would be 343 meters a second. On a warm day, 30° Celsius, the speed would increase to 349 meters a second. On a hot day, 40° Celsius, sound would move through the air at a speed of 353 meters a second.

7. What does sound require in order to occur?

8. Name the three mediums through which sound travels.

9. Name three properties that affect the speed of sound through a medium.

10. How does the density of a substance affect the speed at which sound travels through it? How does elasticity affect speed? How does temperature affect speed?

27D SOUND WAVES

When an object vibrates, it makes the surrounding air vibrate. The air vibrates because when the vibrating object moves outward, air molecules get squeezed together, or compressed. Then, when the vibrating object moves inward, air expands to fill the space just occupied by the vibrating object. Scientists call these compressions and expansions COMPRESSIONS and RAREFACTIONS.

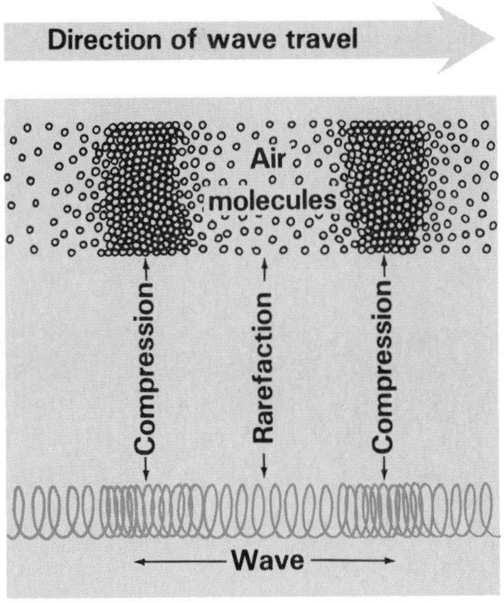

It is by these repeating compressions and rarefactions that vibration travels through the air. This repeating series of compressions and rarefactions make up SOUND WAVES. **Sound waves carry sound energy through the medium.** In sound waves, the distance from a point on one wave to the same point on the next wave is called a WAVELENGTH.

Sound moves through air, producing areas of compression and rarefaction.

Direction of wave travel

Air molecules

Compression

Rarefaction

Compression

Wave

A louder sound will have a greater crowding of air molecules in the compression stage than a soft sound. The molecules will be spaced farther apart in the rarefaction stage. Loud sounds have a greater AMPLITUDE than soft sounds. **The amplitude of a wave indicates how much the air molecules have spread apart and crowded together.**

To understand amplitude, imagine gently plucking the string of a violin. The string does not move very far and the sound is soft. The amplitude of the wave is not very great. Now imagine plucking the violin string with a great amount of energy. The string would move far from its normal rest position. The sound made would be loud. You could say that, in this case, the sound wave has a large amplitude.

Sound waves are LONGITUDINAL. **This means that the medium carrying the wave vibrates in the same direction as the wave moves.** For example, a sound wave moving through air molecules moves forward parallel to the movement of the air molecules. **The sound wave and the air molecules move in the same direction.**

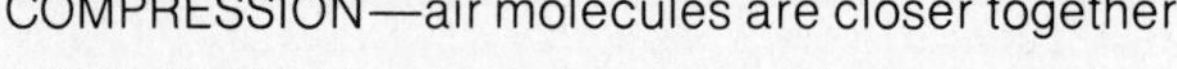

COMPRESSION—air molecules are closer together.

RAREFACTION—air molecules are farther apart.

WAVELENGTH—the distance from a point on one wave to the same point on the next wave.

AMPLITUDE—the amount of compression and rarefaction of the medium carrying the sound wave.

LONGITUDINAL WAVE—vibration of the medium in the direction the wave is moving.

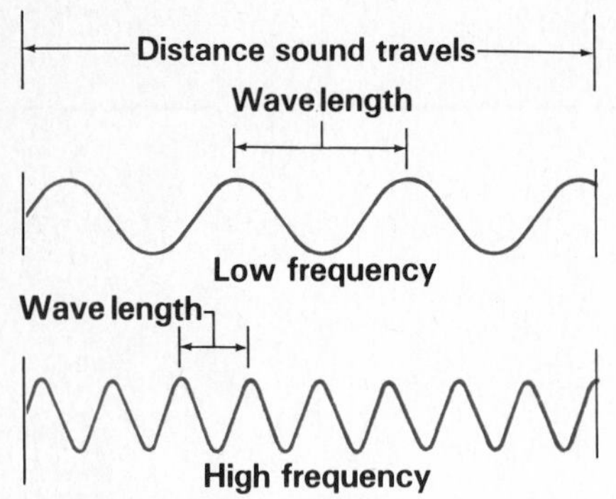

The higher the frequency, the shorter the wavelength.

11. What is a repeating series of compressions and rarefactions called?
12. What does amplitude mean?
13. Explain what is meant by sound waves being longitudinal.

27E MUSICAL SOUNDS

Either the vibrating strings, vibrating air, or vibrating surface of each of the three types of musical instruments produces the sounds you call MUSIC. **Music is made by a vibrating body that sends out regular vibrations at regular intervals. It is this regularity that distinguishes music from noise.** Musical sounds are made by three types of instruments: stringed, wind, and percussion. **Each instrument works on the principle of vibration.**

In stringed instruments, shortening the strings raises the pitch they produce. This photograph shows a sitar, a stringed instrument popular in India.

Stringed Instruments. With stringed instruments, the frequency, or pitch, of a vibrating string is determined by the tension, or pull, on the string. It is also determined by the thickness of the string and the length of the string. For example, the tighter a string is stretched, the faster it vibrates and the higher the pitch it produces. When a guitar is tuned, the strings are tightened or loosened until they vibrate at frequencies that will produce the right pitches. The pitches of the strings should match notes in the musical scale.

THE FREQUENCY OF A VIBRATING STRING IS

HIGHER when it is:	LOWER when it is:
Tighter	Looser
Shorter	Longer
Thinner	Thicker

Changes in temperature or humidity will disturb the tension, or tightness, of the strings. This is why guitarists, violinists, and other string players must tune their instruments so frequently.

The strings of the piano and harp are many different lengths and thicknesses to produce a wide range of frequencies. You could not get the varied pitches from these instruments that you do just by changing the tension on the strings. Some strings must be longer and thicker than others to produce the lower pitches.

There is another factor in the production of musical sounds. **Every object produces its own special sound.** This sound is the NATURAL FREQUENCY of the object. **If an object vibrates at its natural frequency due to the vibration of another object, the sound produced will be louder.** This effect on sound is called RESONANCE. The vibration of one object has caused another object to resonate. This amplifies sound.

Stringed instruments have strings stretched over some kind of resonance box or board. The wooden box or board resonates with the strings thereby amplifying the sound produced. In a piano, a large sheet of wood, called the sounding board, is located under the strings for resonance. The bodies of violins and guitars are resonance boxes.

If you look at the strings inside a piano, you will see that some are thick and some are thin. Some strings are long, and others are short. These differences in the strings produce differences in frequency, or pitch.

Wind Instruments. Wind blown into or through a tube produces the sound in wind instruments. Columns of air vibrate rather than strings. The frequency of the vibrations depends on the length of the column of air. The length of the column of air depends, of course, on the length of the instrument. **The longer the column of air, the lower the frequency.** Compare the low notes of the tuba with the high-pitched sound of the tiny piccolo. The column of air is much longer in the tuba. Therefore, the tuba is able to produce much lower notes than the piccolo.

If the tube or pipe of a wind instrument is closed at the bottom, the note produced has a wavelength four times the length of the tube or pipe. If the tube or pipe is open at both ends, the note has a wavelength twice the length of the tube or pipe. **The pitch of the sound depends upon the wavelength. All wind instruments work on this principle.**

SOUND-PRODUCING TUBE OR COLUMN

Both Ends Open	One End Closed
Soundwave length is twice the tube length.	Sound wavelength is four times the tube length.

Different notes, or frequencies, are made by wind instruments in at least three ways. **First, in many instruments, the length of the air column is changed by the musician's fingers on the instrument's holes and keys.** Pushing a key on a clarinet, for example, can shorten the air column. The wavelength of the sound is shortened, and the pitch is raised.

Second, the length of the air column in a wind instrument can be changed mechanically. Moving a slide on a trombone changes the length of the air column. When the slide is extended, the column of air is longer and the pitch is lower. Pulling the slide in shortens the air column and raises the pitch.

Third, in brass instruments such as the trumpet, the vibrating lips of the musician make the air columns vibrate. Lip pressure can break the column of air into vibrating sections, shortening the wavelength. In fact, before valves were invented, this was the only way trumpet players could play different notes.

Percussion Instruments. Percussion instruments are instruments that you strike to produce sound. A drum, for example, has a skin stretched tightly over a cylinder made of metal or wood. The musician strikes the skin causing it to vibrate. This produces the sound. The fact that a drum is hollow inside creates resonance.

Other percussion instruments include cymbals, bells, and chimes. Although different from the drum, these instruments also have to be struck to produce sounds.

MUSICAL INSTRUMENTS PRODUCE SOUND BY VIBRATING

Strings	Air Columns	Solid Surfaces
Violin	Trumpet	Drums
Guitar	Tuba	Bells
Cello	Trombone	Blocks
Harp	Flute	Triangle
Piano	Saxophone	Cymbal

14. What distinguishes music from noise?
15. With stringed instruments, what determines the pitch of a vibrating string?
16. Why are the strings in a piano different lengths and thicknesses?
17. What is natural frequency?
18. How does resonance affect sound?
19. What produces sound in wind instruments?
20. Why can the tuba produce lower notes than the piccolo?
21. How are different notes made by wind instruments?
22. What produces sound in percussion instruments?

27F HARMONICS AND OVERTONES

When a violin, an oboe, and a french horn play the same note they do not sound alike. **You can easily detect a difference in quality from one instrument to another.** The quality of a sound is called TIMBRE. It is timbre that enables you to recognize that a particular sound is coming from a violin and not a french horn. **Timbre is a result of the material and shape of a given instrument.**

The timbre of a musical tone is caused by the blending of many frequencies. **A vibrating object vibrates both as a whole and in parts.** That is, each half of the string, each third of the string, and each fourth of the string may vibrate separately. This is how the object produces many frequencies. When a string, for example, vibrates as a whole, it produces a FUNDAMENTAL TONE.

But at the same time as the fundamental tone is sounded, the string may be vibrating in parts. OVERTONES are produced when a string vibrates in parts. Overtones are also called HARMONICS of the fundamental frequency.

The first overtone is sounded when the string vibrates in two parts. This vibration has twice the frequency of the fundamental tone. **The second overtone is produced when the string vibrates in three parts.** The frequency of the second overtone is three times that of the fundamental tone.

ACTIVITY: Sounds from Strings and Tubes

MATERIALS: Book, soft drink bottle, 2 pencils, 2 rubber bands (1 thick, 1 thin), ruler, binder paper

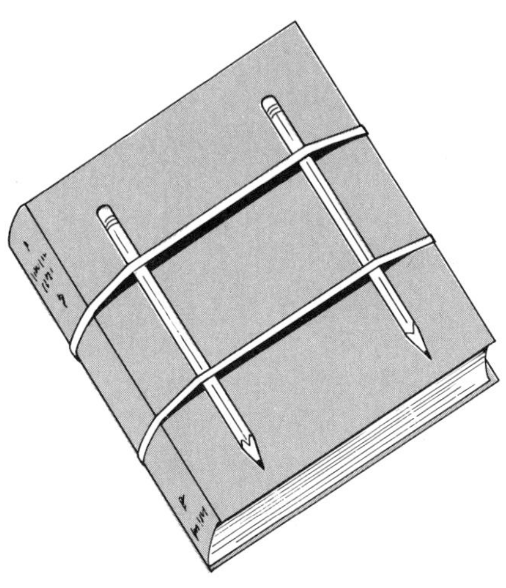

a. Put the rubber bands around the book as shown in the illustration above. Slip the pencils under the rubber bands. The pencils should be parallel to each other, 10 cm apart.

b. Pluck the thin rubber band between the pencils, and listen to the sound. Pluck the thick rubber band. Listen to the sound. Answer question 23.

c. Move one pencil so that the two pencils are 5 cm apart. Pluck the rubber bands again, and listen to their sounds. Answer question 24.

d. Pull one rubber band tight from the side opposite the pencils. Then pluck the rubber band and listen to its sound. Answer question 25.

e. Roll the sheet of binder paper into a tube about 3 cm in diameter. Use tape or a rubber band to hold the tube together. Blow across the end of the tube. Listen to the sound as you blow. Close one end of the tube with your hand, and blow across the other end of the tube. Listen to the sound. Answer question 26.

f. Blow across the mouth of the empty soft drink bottle. Listen to the sound. Fill the bottle half full with water. Blow across the mouth of the bottle again and listen. Answer question 27.

23. How does the pitch of the thick rubber band compare with the pitch of the thin band?
24. How does the pitch of the shortened rubber band compare with the pitch when it is longer?
25. How does the pitch of the looser rubber band compare with the pitch of the tightened rubber band?
26. How does the pitch of the open tube compare with the pitch of the closed tube?
27. How does the pitch of the half-filled bottle compare with the pitch of the empty bottle?
28. What happens to the pitch of the sound of a vibrating string as it is shortened? What happens when it is tightened?
29. If you have two strings of the same length and tension, but one is denser than the other, which will sound a higher pitch?
30. If you have eight empty soft drink bottles, describe how you would tune them to play music on them.

It is the combination of these overtones that gives a sound its quality, or timbre. The number and strength of the overtones is different for each instrument. This is why two different instruments playing the same note don't sound alike.

31. What is the quality of a sound called?

32. How does an object vibrate?

33. What is another word for overtones?

34. What are overtones?

35. How does the first overtone differ from the fundamental tone?

36. What gives a sound its timbre?

37. Why don't two different instruments playing the same note sound alike?

27G DECIBELS

The unit used to compare the intensity of sounds is the DECIBEL. The decibel is not the unit of loudness. Loudness depends on both the intensity and the frequency of sound. **The intensity of a sound depends on its energy.** The decibel can be used to compare the amounts of energy involved in the production of different sounds.

In the decibel system, a small increase in loudness is shown by a large increase in sound energy. For example, under normal conditions, a sound with an intensity of 0 decibels can just about be heard by the average person. A sound of 10 decibels has 10 times as much energy as a 0-decibel sound. However, a sound of 20 decibels has 100 times as much energy as a 0-decibel sound. And a sound of 30 decibels has 1,000 times as much energy as a 0-decibel sound. **But a sound with twice as much energy does not sound twice as loud, only somewhat louder.**

A sound of about 120 decibels would be very loud. It would hurt your ears. A jackhammer used to break up concrete is measured at between 100 and 110 decibels. A whisper is measured at about 20 decibels. The ordinary speaking voice has an intensity of about 60 decibels. So you see that much more energy goes into producing the normal speaking voice than in producing a whisper.

38. What does the decibel measure?

39. How much more energy does a sound of 20 decibels have than a sound of 10 decibels?

SUMMARY

VOCABULARY

vibrations
frequency
ultrasonic
pitch
medium
compressions
rarefactions
sound waves
wavelength
amplitude
longitudinal
music
natural frequency
reasonance
timbre
fundamental tone
overtones
harmonics
decibel

KEY FACTS AND CONCEPTS

Every sound is caused by vibrations.

The brain translates vibrations into sound.

The number of vibrations a sound makes each second is its frequency.

The frequency of a sound determines its pitch.

Pitch is what is heard.

Sound requires a medium, which is a substance that will carry sound.

The medium may be a solid, a liquid, or a gas.

Vibrations travel in a repeating series of compressions and rarefactions.

This repeating series of compressions and rarefactions make up sound waves.

The amplitude of a wave indicates how much the medium has moved from its normal rest position.

Sound waves are longitudinal.

Music is made by a vibrating body that sends out regular vibrations at regular intervals.

With stringed instruments, the pitch of a vibrating string is determined by the tension, the thickness, and the length of the string.

Every object produces its own special sound called its natural frequency.

The vibration of one object can cause another object to vibrate, or resonate.

Resonance amplifies sound.

In wind instruments, columns of air vibrate to produce sound.

The pitch of the sound depends on the wavelength.

Percussion instruments are struck to produce sounds.

The quality of a sound is called timbre.

Overtones, or harmonics, are produced when an object vibrates in parts.

A combination of overtones gives a sound its timbre.

The unit used to measure the intensity of sound is the decibel.

CONCLUSION

Every sound on the earth is caused by vibrations. When these vibrations reach the ear, they become nerve impulses. The brain receives them and translates them into the sensation of sound. The energy of vibrating matter is used to communicate.

40. What is the KEY IDEA of this chapter?

CHAPTER

28 Light Energy

Energy That Travels as Waves

Sunlight can be trapped by solar panels to produce heat. Solar panels are black because black absorbs light energy.

28A INTRODUCTION

Light is a form of energy. Like all forms of energy, light can do work. Light energy can cause changes.

LIGHT ENERGY CAN DO WORK

Light energy provides heat to warm the earth's surface.

Light energy causes leaves to produce food.

Light energy creates pictures on film.

Light energy makes objects visible.

Light energy produces electricity in a solar battery.

There are two sources of light: objects that give off light and objects that reflect light. In this chapter, you will study the properties of light and color.

THE TWO SOURCES OF LIGHT

DIRECT LIGHT	INDIRECT LIGHT
Objects That Give Off Light	**Objects That Reflect Light**
Electric light bulbs	Planets
Burning candles	Mirrors
Burning logs	Paper
Stars	Metal

1. Why is light a form of energy? Give some examples of the kind of work light energy can do.
2. What are the two sources of light? Give some examples.

28B LIGHT TRAVELS AS A WAVE

Light travels as a wave. To visualize a wave, imagine that you are holding one end of a rope and the other end is tied to a doorknob. If you stretch the rope and snap your wrist, a wave will travel down the length of the rope. Light travels in the same way.

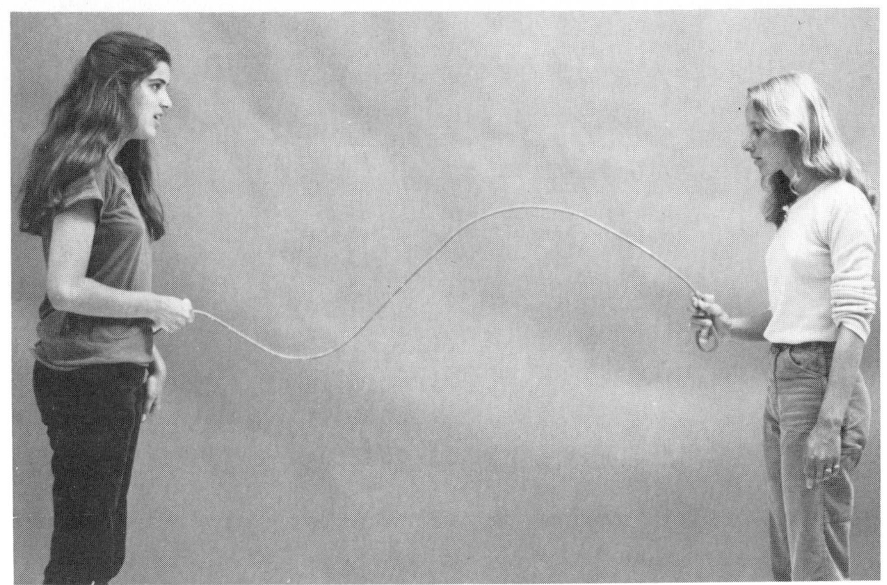

Light is a form of energy that radiates waves in all directions. Light waves travel much like ocean waves or ripples created in a still pond by a thrown pebble. The waves spread out in all directions. The parts of a wave have special names. The highest part of a wave is a CREST and the lowest part is a TROUGH. The height or depth of a wave is its AMPLITUDE. The distance between two waves is called the wavelength. **The wavelength is the distance between one point on a wave and the corresponding point on the next wave.**

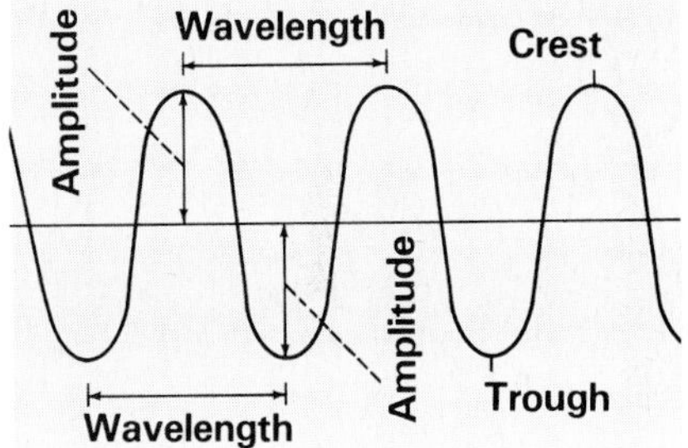

Wavelengths can differ. Imagine again that you have a length of rope. If you snap your wrist very slowly, the time between waves will be longer than if you snap your wrist quickly. Also, the distance between waves will be greater. How often you move your wrist up and down will determine the frequency of a wave. **Frequency is the number of waves produced in a given time.** Frequency is often measured in waves per second.

WAVELENGTH AND FREQUENCY ARE RELATED

The lower the frequency, the longer the wavelength.

The higher the frequency, the shorter the wavelength.

Some wavelengths are more than ten kilometers long. Radio waves have wavelengths that can measure ten kilometers. That is, it is ten kilometers from the crest of one wave to the crest of the next wave. But radio waves do not have much energy. You cannot get hurt if you stand in the path of a radio wave. In fact, radio waves will often fade. You may notice this with your car radio when you drive under a bridge or into a tunnel.

Some wavelengths are so short that twenty billion waves could fit in the space of one centimeter. X-rays and gamma rays, for example, have very short wavelengths but very high frequencies. Gamma rays come from radioactive atoms and can penetrate steel one meter thick. X-rays and gamma rays have a great deal of energy. They would damage your body if you were exposed to them for too long.

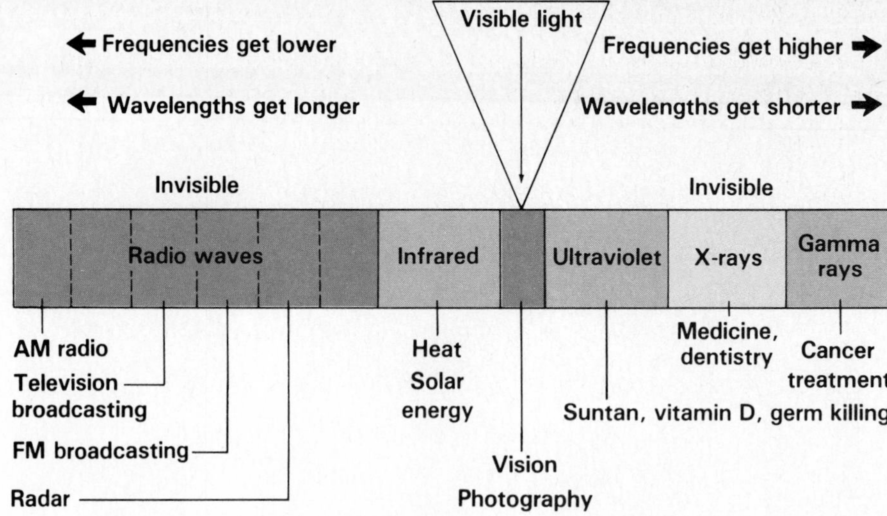

Energy waves make up the ELECTROMAGNETIC SPECTRUM. At one end of the electromagnetic spectrum are long radio waves. At the other end of the spectrum are short gamma rays.

The only part of the electromagnetic spectrum that you can see is known as the VISIBLE SPECTRUM. The visible spectrum appears as a band of colors because the eye sees the different wavelengths of light as different colors.

3. What is light? How does light travel?
4. What is a wavelength?
5. What is the frequency of a wavelength?
6. How are wavelength and frequency related?
7. What is the electromagnetic spectrum?
8. What kinds of energy waves are at opposite ends of the electromagnetic spectrum?
9. What is the visible spectrum?

A smooth surface reflects light in a regular pattern. A rough surface scatters light in all directions.

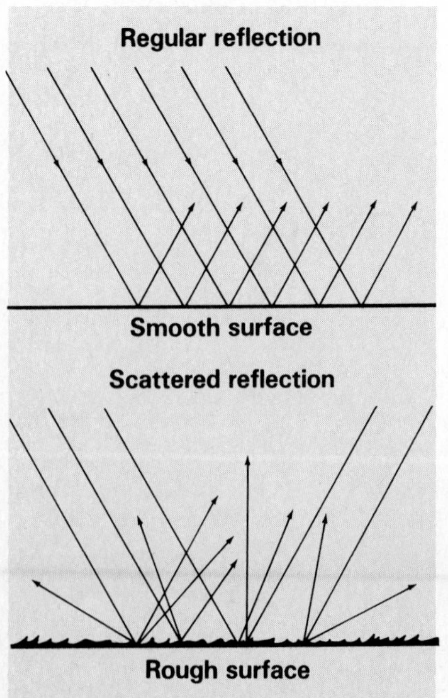

28C REFLECTION OF LIGHT

Light travels in a straight line. You must be standing in the path of light to see it.

When light falls on an object, the light can be absorbed, transmitted, or reflected. A dark coat will absorb light. A pair of glasses will transmit light. A mirror will reflect light. An object may do all three. A piece of paper can absorb some light, let some light pass through, and reflect some light.

The light you see coming from most objects is made up of rays of reflected light. Light is reflected when it bounces off a reflecting surface. Each leaf on a tree is a reflecting surface. When light falls on a leaf, the light is reflected to your eyes. The books on a shelf, the rug on a floor, the clothes on a person—you see all of these because of reflected light.

A reflecting surface can change the direction of light. The direction of change is determined by the type of reflecting surface. A reflecting surface can be smooth or rough. A smooth surface, like a mirror, will reflect light in a regular pattern. A rough surface, like a sidewalk, will reflect, or scatter, light in all directions.

The direction in which light is reflected is determined by the Law of Reflection. Light that strikes a surface is called incident, or incoming, light. The light that bounces off a surface is called reflected light. **According to the Law of Reflection, the angle at which light strikes a surface is equal to the angle at which it bounces off.**

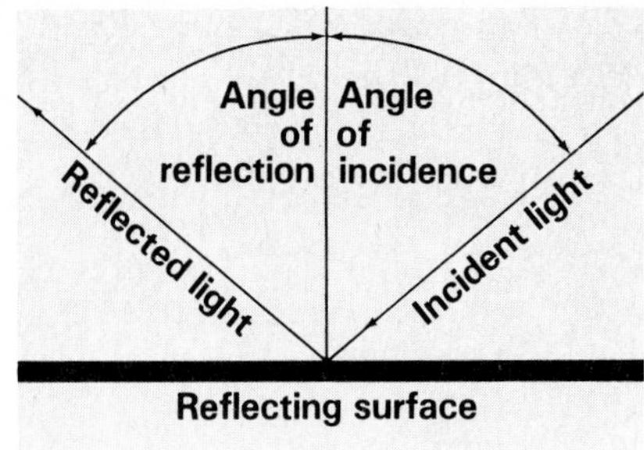

The angle of incidence equals the angle of reflection.

THE LAW OF REFLECTION

The angle of incident light is equal to the angle of reflected light.

The Law of Reflection applies under all conditions, whether the surface is smooth or rough. If you shine a flashlight on a polished automobile, the light will be reflected at an angle equal to the angle of incidence.

If you shine light on a rough surface, the reflected light is scattered. The light is sent off in all directions by the uneven surface. However, each angle of reflected light would be equal to the angle of incidence.

10. In what direction does light travel?
11. What is absorbed light? Give an example.
12. What is transmitted light? Give an example.
13. What is reflected light? Give an example.
14. Explain why you can see objects around you.
15. Explain how a reflecting surface can change the direction of light.
16. Explain the Law of Reflection.
17. Explain how the Law of Reflection works when light strikes a rough surface.

ACTIVITY: The Law of Reflection

MATERIALS: Mirror, ruler, protractor

In this activity, you will study the Law of Reflection.

a. Draw two lines, one dashed and one solid, to form an angle smaller than a right angle.
b. Place a mirror at the point where the two lines meet, so that the dashed line and its reflection appear as a continuous straight line.
c. Looking into the mirror, line up your ruler with the reflection of the solid line. Make a drawing of this line along the edge of the ruler.
d. Measure the angles on each side of the dashed line with a protractor. Answer question 18.
e. Repeat steps a to d, changing the size of the angle each time. Answer question 19.

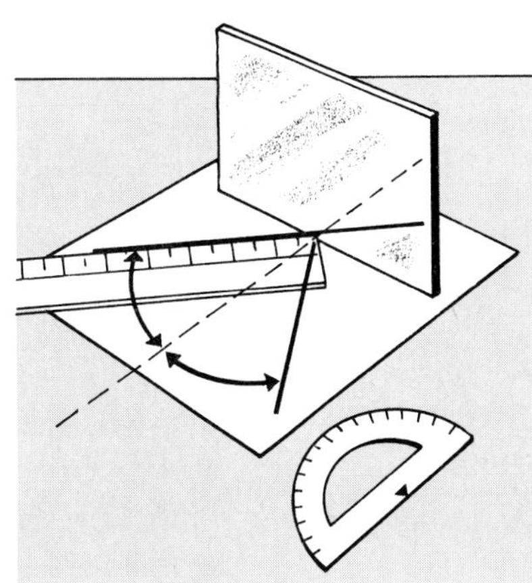

18. What angle did you measure on each side of the dashed line?
19. What angle did you measure on each side of the dashed line?
20. What law have you just verified?

28D MIRRORS AND REFLECTED LIGHT

Mirrors are the most common reflecting surfaces. A mirror is usually a piece of glass backed by silver and black paint. Mirrors can have three kinds of reflecting surfaces: flat, curved outward, or curved inward. A mirror with a flat surface is called a PLANE mirror. A mirror that curves outward is a CONVEX mirror. A mirror that curves inward is called a CONCAVE mirror.

The shape of the mirror determines what happens to reflected light. But remember that the Law of Reflection remains the same regardless of the shape of the mirror.

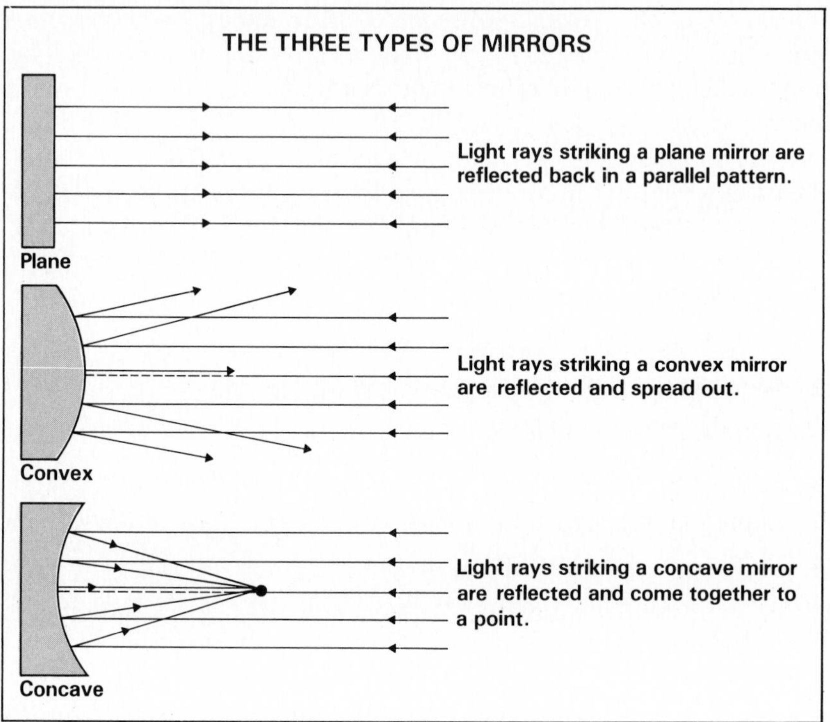

THE THREE TYPES OF MIRRORS

Name of Mirror	Shape of Mirror	Effect on Light
PLANE	Flat	Reflects light back to where it came from
CONVEX	Curved outward	Reflects light and spreads it out
CONCAVE	Curved inward	Reflects light to a point

Mirrors can form two types of images: a VIRTUAL IMAGE and a REAL IMAGE. A virtual image seems to come from inside or behind the mirror. All three types of mirrors can form a virtual image. A real image is formed when the image and the object are on the same side of the mirror. Concave mirrors can form a real image.

Plane Mirror. A plane mirror produces a virtual image. The image appears to be the same distance behind the mirror as the object is in front of the mirror. Of course, there is no image behind the mirror. It only appears that there is. The image in a plane mirror is erect, or right-side-up. The image also appears to be the same size as the object.

Plane mirrors have a flat surface. They are used when you want an undistorted image, such as in a bathroom, beauty salon, or clothing store.

Convex Mirror. A convex mirror is curved outward like the backside of a spoon. Convex mirrors produce a virtual image. That is, the image appears to be inside the mirror. The image is also erect and smaller than the object, and appears to be closer than the object actually is.

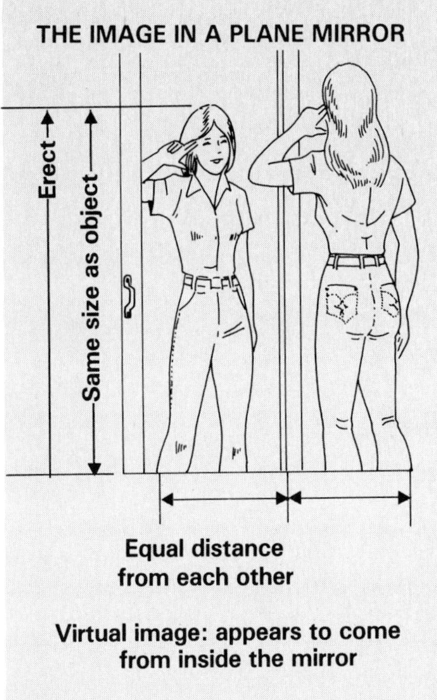

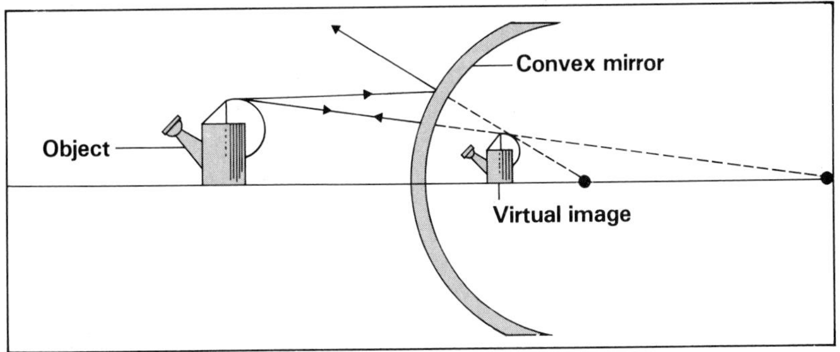

Convex mirrors produce a virtual image. Follow the three lines and note that the Law of Reflection holds true.

Convex mirrors are used as automobile rearview mirrors and as security mirrors in stores. Although convex mirrors give a distorted indication of distance, they allow a person to see a wide area. Convex mirrors are often found in amusement parks. People stand before a convex mirror and see themselves stretched out of shape.

Concave Mirror. A concave mirror is curved inward like the bowl of a spoon. The rays of light that strike a concave mirror are reflected and come together to a point called a FOCAL POINT. The position and size of the image depends on the position of the object in relation to the focal point.

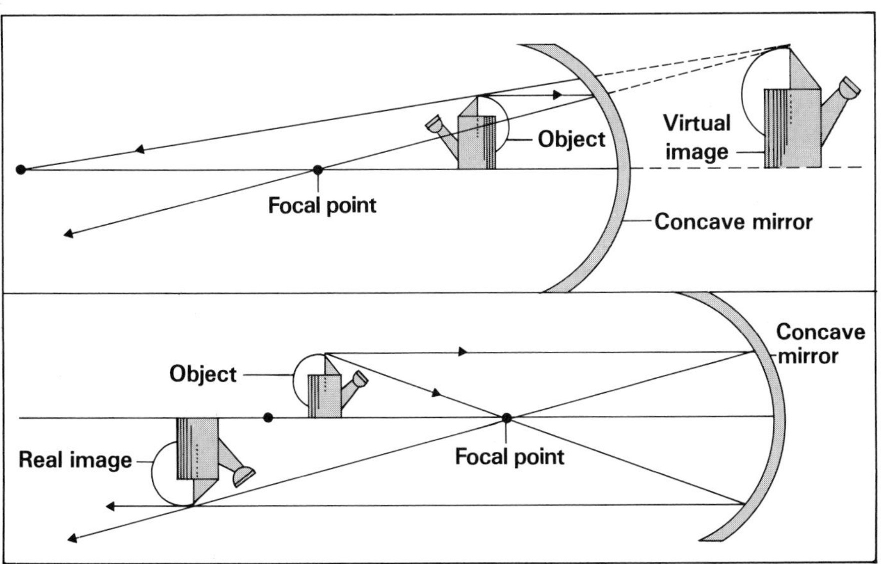

The images in a concave mirror depend on whether the object is inside or outside the focal point.

The position and size of the image in a concave mirror depends on the location of the object in relation to the focal point.

If you look at your face in the bowl of a spoon, for example, you will be outside the focal point. Therefore, your image will be real, inverted, or upside-down, and smaller. It will also appear to be closer than your face actually is.

If an object is inside the focal point, its image will be virtual, larger than the object, and erect. Also, the image appears to be further away than the object actually is. There will be no image at all if the object is at the focal point.

Concave mirrors are used as flashlights, car headlights, and searchlights. The bulbs in these lights are placed at the focal point, and the light is reflected out in a strong beam. Concave mirrors are also found in amusement parks. People who stand before a concave mirror see themselves short and round.

21. Describe the three types of mirrors.
22. What is the difference between a virtual and a real image?
23. Name some properties of a plane mirror.
24. Name some properties of a convex mirror.
25. Name some properties of a concave mirror.

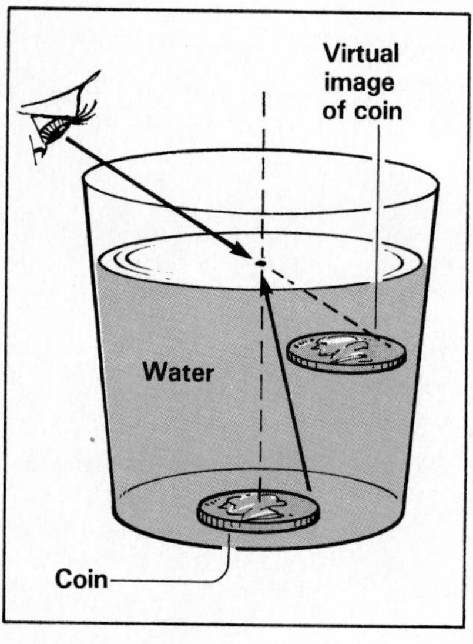

28E REFRACTION OF LIGHT

Light travels through air at a speed of 299,727 kilometers per second. If light could bend around the earth, it would circle the earth about seven and one-half times in one second. **When light travels through a transparent substance, it slows down and bends.** The bending of light as it passes from one substance to another is called REFRACTION.

You can see the refraction of light if you place a fork in a glass of water. Look at the fork from the side of the glass, and note how the fork appears to be broken at the surface of the water.

There are other ways to see the refraction of light. Place a coin at the bottom of a glass. Lower your head until you can no longer see the coin. Have someone fill the cup with water. You will be able to see a virtual image of the coin because the light falling on the coin has been refracted.

The amount that light is refracted or bent when it enters a substance is called the index of refraction. The more light is slowed down, the greater the index of refraction.

Transparent Substance	Speed of Light	Index of Refraction
Air	299,727 km/sec	1.00
Water	225,000 km/sec	1.33
Glass	200,000 km/sec	1.50

26. What happens to the speed of light when it passes through a transparent substance? What do you call this?

27. Explain why a straw looks broken in a glass of water.
28. What is the index of refraction? Give some examples.

28F LENSES AND REFRACTED LIGHT

A LENS is a transparent substance that is used to refract light. Lenses are found in eyeglasses, cameras, and microscopes. Lenses may bring light rays together or separate them. Unlike mirrors, lenses do not form images by reflecting light. **Lenses produce images by refracting light.**

Lenses are usually made from glass that is shaped by grinding and then polished. **The two types of lenses are concave and convex.**

A concave lens bends and spreads apart light rays. If you look through a concave lens, you will see a virtual image. It will be erect and smaller than the object. Concave lenses are used in eyeglasses to help nearsighted people see objects that are far away.

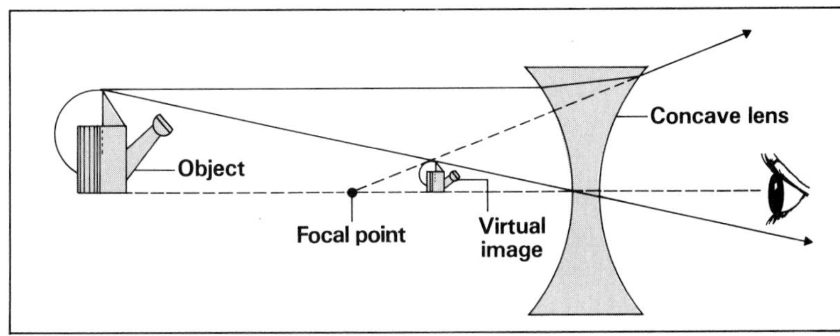

You must look through a concave lens to see the virtual image.

A convex lens can form two kinds of images. A convex lens bends light rays to meet at a focal point.

If the object is far from the lens, the image will be inverted and smaller. If the object is close to the lens, the image will be erect and larger.

Convex lenses are used in eyeglasses to help farsighted people see objects that are close by. Reading glasses are convex lenses.

A convex lens can produce two kinds of images.

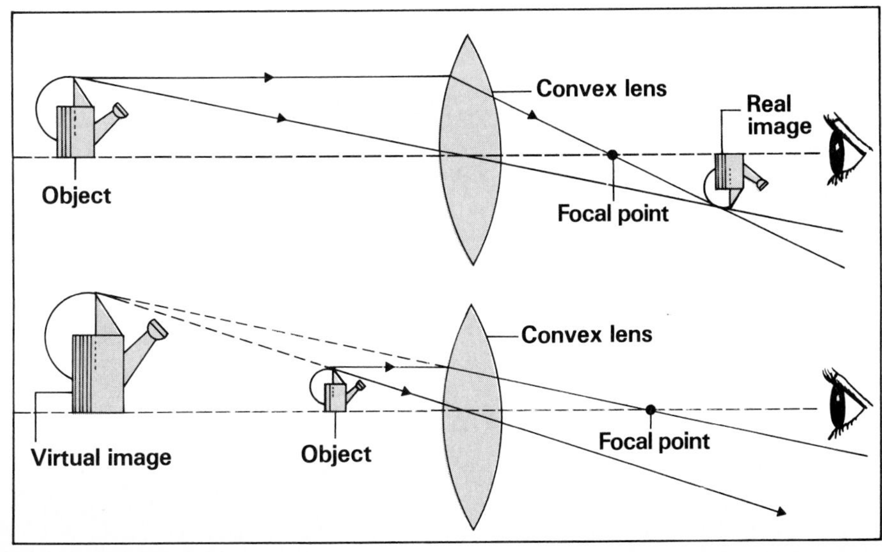

29. What is a lens? How are lenses used?
30. How does a concave lens differ from a convex lens?
31. Name three properties of concave lenses.
32. Name three properties of convex lenses.

28G LIGHT AND COLOR

A PRISM is a special type of lens with three sides like a triangle. **When white light is passed through a prism, the white light is broken into the visible spectrum.** The colors of the visible spectrum are red, orange, yellow, green, blue, indigo, and violet. Thus, white light is really a mixture of all colors.

A prism is able to break white light into the colors because the index of refraction is different for each color. When white light goes through a prism, it is refracted twice, once when it enters the prism and again when it leaves the prism. The double refraction separates white light into the various colors.

Red light is refracted the least because it has the largest wavelength. It is slowed the least and is bent the least. Violet light is refracted the most because it has the shortest wavelength. It is slowed the most and is bent the most.

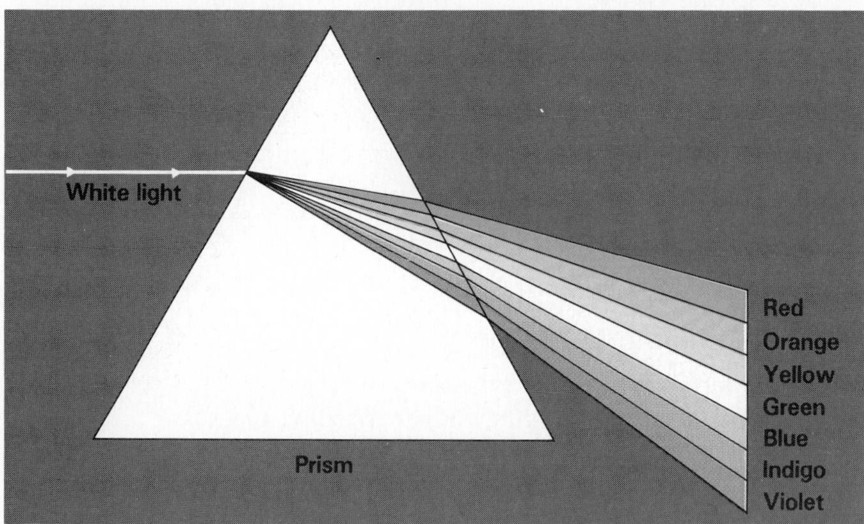

A prism breaks white light into the colors of the visible light spectrum.

The color of an object is the color of the light it reflects. When white light hits a green leaf, only the green light is reflected. All the other colors are absorbed. Your eyes see the reflected green light.

If an object does not reflect light, it will look black. If an object reflects all light, it will look white.

33. How does a prism break up light?
34. What is the visible light spectrum?
35. Why is a red apple red?
36. Why are some solar heaters black?
37. What is color?
38. What is light?

SUMMARY

VOCABULARY

crest
trough
amplitude
electromagnetic spectrum
visible spectrum
plane
convex
concave
virtual image
real image
focal point
refraction
lens
prism

KEY FACTS AND CONCEPTS

Light is a form of energy that radiates waves in all directions.

The wavelength is the distance between one point on a wave and the corresponding point on the next wave.

Frequency is the number of waves produced in a given time.

Wavelength and frequency are related.

All of the energy waves found in nature make up the electromagnetic spectrum.

The visible spectrum is the only part of the electromagnetic spectrum you can see.

Light travels in a straight line.

An object can absorb, transmit, or reflect light.

The light you see coming from most objects is made up of rays of reflected light.

The Law of Reflection states that the angle of incidence is equal to the angle of reflection.

The direction in which light is reflected is determined by the Law of Reflection.

The shape of a mirror determines what happens to reflected light.

A virtual image appears to come from inside or behind a mirror.

A real image is on the same side of the mirror as the object.

The bending of light as it passes from one substance to another is called refraction.

Lenses produce images by refracting light.

The two types of lenses are convex and concave.

A prism is able to break white light into colors because the index of refraction is different for each color.

The color of an object is the color of the light it reflects.

CONCLUSION

Light is a form of energy that radiates waves in all directions. When light strikes an object, it can be absorbed, transmitted, or reflected. The light you see coming from most objects is made up of rays of reflected light. The color of an object is the color of the light it reflects. Mirrors are excellent reflecting surfaces. Lenses transmit light. The shape of a mirror or lens will determine how the light rays will be bent. The bending of light is determined by the Law of Reflection and the index of refraction.

39. What is the KEY IDEA of this chapter?

CHAPTER

29 Electrical Energy

The Most Common and Convenient Type of Energy

29A INTRODUCTION

You need energy because energy powers all the parts of the complex society in which you live. The energy you use comes from two sources: prospecting and processing. Most of the energy you use has been obtained from prospecting. This is energy obtained as raw materials, such as wood, coal, and oil. However, prospected energy is becoming scarce and expensive to obtain.

THE TWO SOURCES OF ENERGY

Prospecting	Processing
Wood	Electricity
Coal	Nuclear
Oil	Light

Energy prospecting is giving way to energy processing. As old sources of raw materials run out, new sources of energy will be manufactured products. Thus, much of the search for energy is taking place far from forests, mines, and wells. **The search for the energy of the future is taking place in laboratories.**

Most of the energy that is produced today comes from prospected fuels like coal, oil, natural gas, and uranium. These fuels are used to make or process electricity.

Electrical energy must be made and then transported to the user.

Electricity is an example of processed energy. Electricity is not mined from the ground or pumped from a well. It is produced by burning raw materials, such as coal or natural gas. The energy from the coal or gas is converted, or processed, into electrical energy.

Electricity is the most common and convenient type of energy to use. In this chapter, you will study how electrical energy is produced and the energy sources used to produce electricity.

1. What are two sources of energy? Give examples of each.
2. What is prospected energy? What is its future?
3. What is processed energy? What is its future?
4. Why is electricity a form of processed energy?
5. What is the source of most of the energy used today?
6. What is the most common and convenient form of energy used today?

29B PRODUCING ELECTRICAL ENERGY

Electricity is produced in a POWER PLANT. Despite the large size of a power plant, what goes on inside is quite simple. Electricity is produced when a wire is moved through a magnetic field. In a power plant, a generator is used to produce electricity. A generator is a machine that has wires coiled inside a magnet. **When the coils of wire in a generator spin, electricity is produced.**

A turbine is used to spin a generator. You studied turbines in Chapter 26. A turbine is a wheel with blades on it. When the blades on the wheel turn, the generator is turned. Four traditional sources of prospected energy are used in a power plant to turn a turbine.

In a power plant, prospected energy is converted into electrical energy. This plant burns natural gas or fuel oil to produce electricity.

SOURCES OF ENERGY USED TO PROCESS ELECTRICITY

WATER: obtained from rain water
COAL: prospected from mines
NATURAL GAS: prospected from wells
URANIUM: prospected from mines

The oldest form of energy used to produce electricity is rain water stored behind dams. The water that falls inside a dam is used to spin the turbine blades which, in turn, spin the generator to produce electricity. Because a dam is dependent on a supply of water, producing electricity from falling water is no longer popular.

Most power plants today turn their turbines with steam. Coal and natural gas are used to produce heat to boil water into steam. The steam turns the turbine blades, which then turn the generator to make electricity. The electricity is then sent over transmission wires to homes and businesses by a utility company.

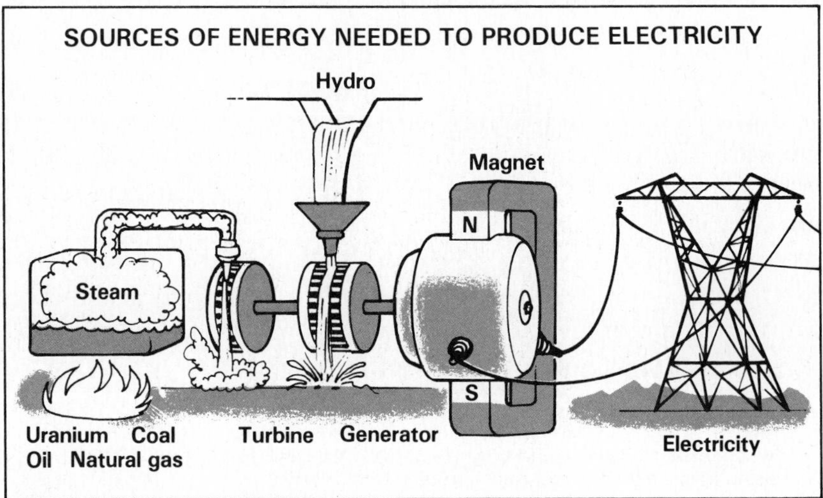

7. Why is energy needed to process electricity?
8. Explain how electricity is produced.
9. Name four sources of energy used by a power plant.

29C NUCLEAR ENERGY

Uranium is a traditional source of energy. It has been used in power plants to produce electricity since 1957 when the first NUCLEAR POWER PLANT was built in Pennsylvania. There are seventy-four nuclear power plants in twenty-six states producing eleven percent of the nation's total electricity. Although they are expensive to build and some people are concerned with how safe they are, nuclear power plants can generate electricity more cheaply than coal and, in some places, natural gas.

The energy for a nuclear power plant comes from the nucleus of a uranium atom. As you learned in Chapter 21, the neutrons and protons that make up the nucleus of an atom are held together by nuclear force. **Nuclear force is the energy that holds the nucleus of an atom to-**

gether. In some atoms, like uranium, the nucleus does not have enough nuclear force to hold itself together. When this is the case, the nucleus is said to be unstable.

You may recall from Chapters 20 and 21 that an atom with an unstable nucleus is radioactive. In the process of becoming more stable, the nucleus releases some of its energy. The release of energy from a radioactive atom is called radiation. The radiation can be in the form of particles, high-energy waves, heat, or light.

In a uranium atom, the particles of radiation can be neutrons. These neutrons can fly around with a great amount of energy. In flying around, a neutron can slam into and penetrate the nucleus of another uranium atom causing it to split. The splitting of an atom is called NUCLEAR FISSION. **Energy is produced during nuclear fission. It is this energy that can be controlled and used in a nuclear power plant.**

If the energy of a splitting atom is not controlled, stray radiation can be released. Radiation can be harmful. Radiation can burn or penetrate the human body, cause cell damage, and even change the genes. Genetic damage is serious because it affects future generations of people.

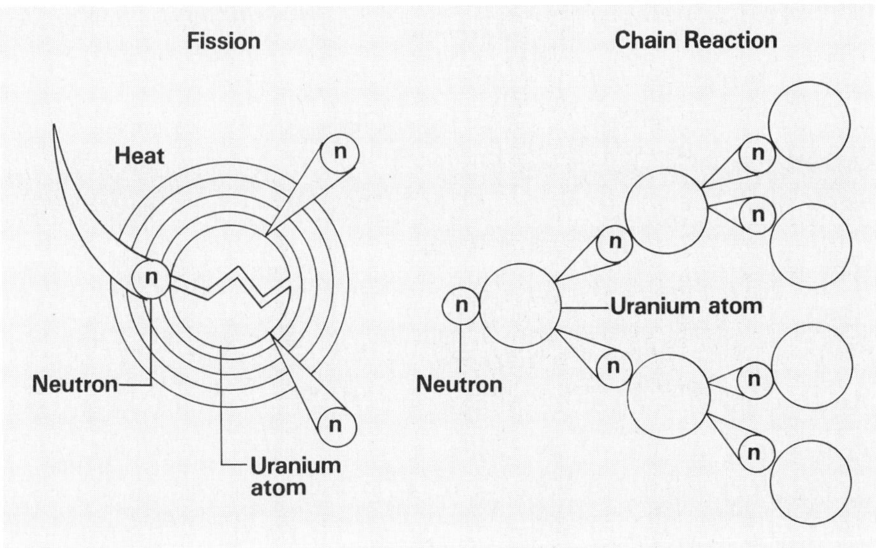

In a nuclear power plant, the source of heat to boil water is the process of atomic fission. The heat that results from the fission of uranium is used to produce steam to generate electricity.

This photo shows a nuclear engineer inserting fuel into a nuclear reactor.

ACTIVITY: Reducing Your Energy Bill

MATERIALS: None

Energy is a major cost in your life. When you add up the cost for gasoline, natural gas, and electricity, your energy costs can be more than what you pay for food, clothing, or shelter. This activity is divided into three parts: (1) How to Read a Utility Bill, (2) How to Calculate the Amount of Energy You Use, and (3) How to Reduce Your Utility Bill.

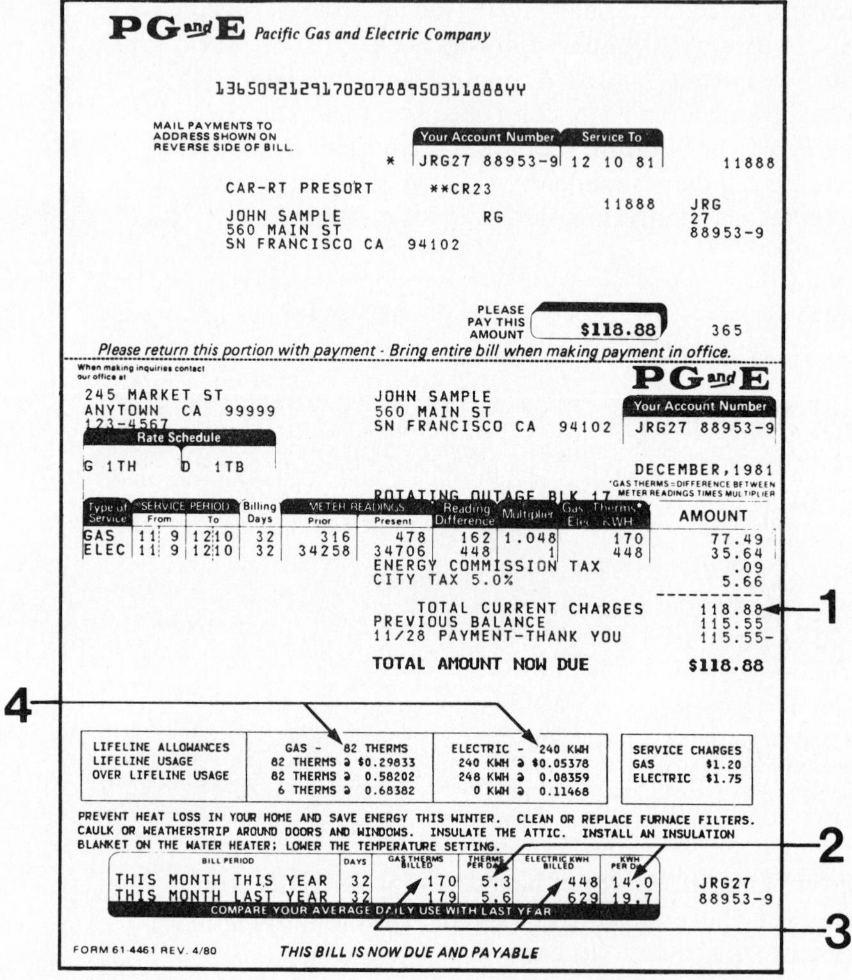

PG and E *Pacific Gas and Electric Company*

136509212917020788950311888YY

MAIL PAYMENTS TO ADDRESS SHOWN ON REVERSE SIDE OF BILL.

Your Account Number	Service To
JRG27 88953-9	12 10 81

11888

CAR-RT PRESORT **CR23

JOHN SAMPLE RG 11888 JRG 27 88953-9
560 MAIN ST
SN FRANCISCO CA 94102

PLEASE PAY THIS AMOUNT **$118.88** 365

Please return this portion with payment - Bring entire bill when making payment in office.

When making inquiries contact our office at
245 MARKET ST
ANYTOWN CA 99999
123-4567

JOHN SAMPLE
560 MAIN ST
SN FRANCISCO CA 94102

PG and E

Your Account Number: JRG27 88953-9

Rate Schedule: G 1TH D 1TB

DECEMBER,1981

ROTATING OUTAGE BLK 17

*GAS THERMS = DIFFERENCE BETWEEN METER READINGS TIMES MULTIPLIER

Type of Service	Service Period From	Service Period To	Billing Days	Meter Readings Prior	Meter Readings Present	Reading Difference	Multiplier	Gas Therms* Elec KWH	AMOUNT
GAS	11 9	12 10	32	316	478	162	1.048	170	77.49
ELEC	11 9	12 10	32	34258	34706	448	1	448	35.64
					ENERGY COMMISSION TAX				.09
					CITY TAX 5.0%				5.66
					TOTAL CURRENT CHARGES				118.88
					PREVIOUS BALANCE				115.55
					11/28 PAYMENT-THANK YOU				115.55-
					TOTAL AMOUNT NOW DUE				**$118.88**

LIFELINE ALLOWANCES	GAS - 82 THERMS	ELECTRIC - 240 KWH
LIFELINE USAGE	82 THERMS @ $0.29833	240 KWH @ $0.05378
OVER LIFELINE USAGE	82 THERMS @ 0.58202	248 KWH @ 0.08359
	6 THERMS @ 0.68382	0 KWH @ 0.11468

SERVICE CHARGES
GAS $1.20
ELECTRIC $1.75

PREVENT HEAT LOSS IN YOUR HOME AND SAVE ENERGY THIS WINTER. CLEAN OR REPLACE FURNACE FILTERS. CAULK OR WEATHERSTRIP AROUND DOORS AND WINDOWS. INSULATE THE ATTIC. INSTALL AN INSULATION BLANKET ON THE WATER HEATER; LOWER THE TEMPERATURE SETTING.

BILL PERIOD	DAYS	GAS THERMS BILLED	THERMS PER DAY	ELECTRIC KWH BILLED	KWH PER DAY
THIS MONTH THIS YEAR	32	170	5.3	448	14.0
THIS MONTH LAST YEAR	32	179	5.6	629	19.7

COMPARE YOUR AVERAGE DAILY USE WITH LAST YEAR

JRG27 88953-9

FORM 61-4461 REV. 4/80 *THIS BILL IS NOW DUE AND PAYABLE*

How to Read a Utility Bill

a. Find the following numbered parts on the utility bill shown, and answer questions 10 to 13 that follow.

1— This is the charge for one month of gas and electricity.

2— These two numbers show the average amount of gas therms and electric kilowatt-hours used each day.

3— These two numbers show the total amount of gas and electricity used during the billing period.

4— These numbers show the unit cost of gas and electricity. The cost increases as you use more units of energy.

10. What is the total energy bill for a billing period of one month?
11. What is the average amount of gas and electricity used each day?
12. What was the total amount of gas and electricity used during the billing period?
13. What would the charge have been if 340 kwhs had been used?

How to Calculate the Amount of Energy You Use

By keeping a record of your monthly utility bills and a worksheet on the use of your appliances, you can reduce your utility bill. You can calculate the amount of electricity you use in a month with a chart like the one shown. A sample of the calculations is also shown.

Sample electric worksheet

Appliances (Complete for only those appliances used)	Kilowatt hours used	Multiply	Frequency of use	Multiply	Number of uses	Multiply	Days used per month	Equals	Kilowatthours per month	Multiply	Enter cost per kilowatt hour 14 ¢ and convert from cents to dollars (9.5¢ = $.095) (Enter this amount in each box below)	Equals	Estimated cost per month
Refrigerator-Freezer (16 cu. ft.)	5.0		daily	X		X	30	=	150	X	$ .14	=	$ 21.00
Dishwasher	1.0	X	avg. # of loads per month 25					=	25	X	$ .14	=	$ 3.50
Hair Dryer (blower)	1.25	X	avg. # of hrs. for days used .5			X	15	=	9.4	X	$ .14	=	$ 1.32

- b. Create a worksheet like the one shown by selecting the electric appliances you have from the following list.

Appliance	Kilowatt-hours Used	Appliance	Kilowatt-hours Used
Water heater	16.0	Oven	1.3
Refrigerator-Freezer, 16 cu. ft.	5.0	Microwave	1.5
		Television	.23
Refrigerator-Freezer, 22 cu. ft.	7.0	Stereo	.10
		Hair dryer	1.25
Freezer	5.1	Toaster	1.2
Dishwasher	1.0	Electric blanket	.75
Clothes washer	.25	Vacuum cleaner	.75
Clothes dryer	4.0	Iron	1.0
Lighting	.001	Portable heater	1.5
Range top burner	1.25		

c. Contact your utility company or look at your utility bill for the cost of electricity per kilowatt-hour. Place this number in the next-to-last column.

d. Complete your worksheet.

How to Reduce Your Utility Bill

-Check for drafts and leaks around doors and windows. To do this, hold a piece of plastic wrap up near a window or door.
-Open drapes facing the sun for warmth.
-Close drapes over large glassed areas to keep out drafts.
-Turn off pilot lights on furnaces during the off-season.
-Wrap the water heater in an insulating blanket.
-Fix dripping faucets.
-Use heavy quilts on beds instead of electric blankets.
-Fill the dishwasher completely before operating.
-Turn off the dishwasher after the final rinse and before the drying cycle starts.
-Vacuum the refrigerator coils and condensers every month.
-Clean the lint trap of the clothes dryer after each use.

e. List ten more energy tips that can reduce your utility bill.

When a uranium atom splits, heat and more neutrons are released. These neutrons can then split more uranium atoms, making more heat and neutrons. This process in which atoms are continually splitting and releasing heat is called a CHAIN REACTION.

A chain reaction can be controlled in a nuclear power plant. The device that controls and produces heat is called a NUCLEAR REACTOR.

In a nuclear power plant, heat is generated by the fission of uranium in a reactor. The heat is used to boil water into steam. The steam turns a turbine, which turns a generator.

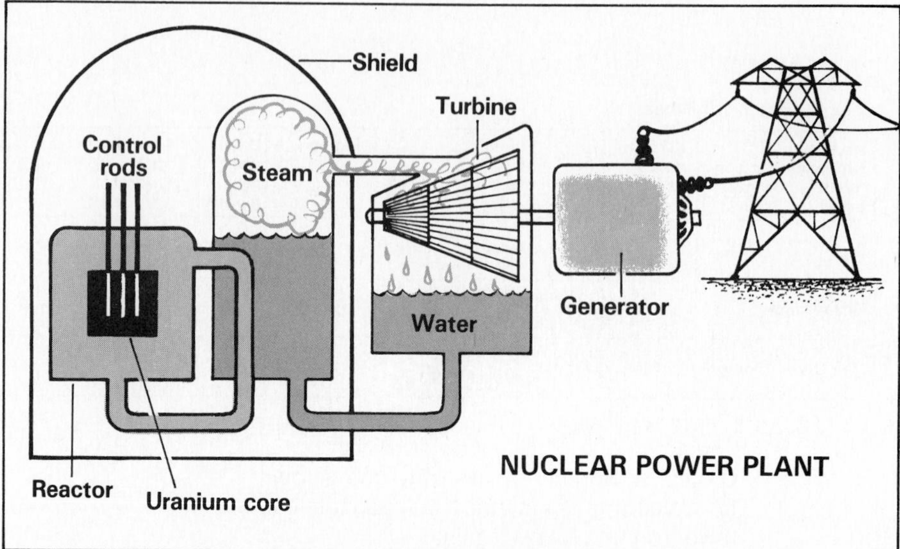

PARTS OF A NUCLEAR REACTOR

ENERGY SOURCE: Uranium 235 or Plutonium 239, which produce heat by fission, are the sources of energy.

CONTROL RODS: By inserting or withdrawing the rods, the rate of fission can be controlled.

SAFETY SHIELD: This material surrounds the reactor and prevents any radiation from leaking into the atmosphere.

A liquid that flows through a set of pipes is pumped through the reactor to absorb heat. This hot liquid (300° Celsius) is pumped to a heat exchanger where it is used to boil water into steam to turn the turbines. **Thus, nuclear energy is converted to heat energy in a reactor.**

14. What is the source of energy in a nuclear power plant?
15. What is a nuclear power plant?
16. What is an atom's nuclear force?
17. What is a radioactive atom?
18. What is radiation?
19. What are the dangers of radiation?
20. Explain the process of atomic fission.
21. What is a chain reaction?
22. What is a nuclear reactor?
23. How does a nuclear reactor control the rate of fission?
24. How does a nuclear power plant produce electricity?

29D THE NUCLEAR ENERGY CONTROVERSY

The reason you go to school is to acquire the necessary knowledge to help you make decisions. The ability to make decisions is an important life skill.

People are already making decisions about using nuclear energy to generate electricity.

THE NUCLEAR ENERGY CONTROVERSY

Those who say that nuclear energy is safe claim that:

1. Nuclear energy will be needed when the sources of coal, oil, and natural gas run out.
2. It is cheaper to generate electricity with nuclear energy than with coal or natural gas.
3. Nuclear power plants are clean. They do not produce pollution the way coal and oil do.
4. All power plants are safe regardless of how they are fueled. Considering the dangers from mining for coal and drilling for oil, nuclear power is safer than electricity generated by coal or oil. Electricity generated from natural gas is the safest.
5. Some twenty-four million people are already using electricity generated by nuclear power plants. Several New England states and several large cities get more than half of their electricity from nuclear power. It would be costly to change to some other way of generating electricity.
6. Nuclear power plants are built with many safety systems. There are backup systems should a system fail. This is what happened at Three Mile Island. There was no serious accident.
7. Nuclear power plants have an excellent safety record. After twenty-five years of operation, no one has been harmed or has died from radiation from a nuclear plant.

Those who say that nuclear energy is dangerous claim that:

1. Nuclear power plants produce radiation. Should the radiation leak, it could cause death or birth defects.
2. Nuclear power plants present a potential danger. There has been one accident already at Three Mile Island when the fuel became very overheated.
3. Nuclear power plants require huge amounts of water to cool their reactors. If this hot water is dumped into rivers or oceans, THERMAL POLLUTION may result. **Thermal pollution results when the water temperature of an environment changes and the ecology of an area is upset.**
4. The cost of building a nuclear power plant is very high, and this cost is passed on to the consumer.
5. Nuclear reactors produce radioactive wastes. This is the biggest problem with nuclear power plants. When the nuclear fuel is used up, the remaining waste remains highly poisonous for many years. The problem with long-term, safe storage of radioactive nuclear wastes has not yet been solved.
6. Radiation from nuclear wastes can cause bone and lung cancer.
7. The transportation of nuclear wastes to storage areas is very dangerous. People do not want trucks carrying nuclear wastes driving through or near their cities and towns.

In the debate over nuclear energy, you may often hear the word MELTDOWN. **A meltdown means that the nuclear fuel in the reactor would become hot enough to melt.** Proponents of nuclear power claim that safety measures would prevent this from happening. Opponents say that it could happen and the first time it did happen, deadly radiation would be spread.

Can a nuclear power plant explode like a bomb? Most scientists and engineers agree that there is little chance of an explosion. The nuclear fuel is too spread out in the reactor. It is not packed together closely enough to create what is called a critical mass.

The major problem with nuclear energy is the disposal of the nuclear wastes. Nuclear waste is usually a form of plutonium. This plutonium may be dangerous for thousands of years. Presently, nuclear wastes are sealed in containers and then left for storage in isolated areas or buried deep in the earth's crust. Many people object to this because no one knows how the earth will change over thousands of years. If some nuclear waste were to leak, the cost in lives and money would be greater than the value of the power generated.

This photo shows a storage area for nuclear waste.

The question of nuclear power safety and of how to provide energy for living things is a complicated issue. Energy does not just exist for the taking. The sources of prospected energy are becoming increasingly scarce. The energy for the future will have to be processed. You will study some of these new and alternate sources of energy for the future in Chapter 42.

25. Briefly state the arguments in favor of nuclear energy.
26. Briefly state the arguments against nuclear energy.
27. What is a meltdown?
28. What is the major problem with nuclear energy?
29. What is the most common form of energy used today?
30. What will the future source of energy be?

SUMMARY

VOCABULARY

power plant
nuclear power plant
nuclear fission
chain reaction
nuclear reactor
thermal pollution
meltdown

KEY FACTS AND CONCEPTS

Energy is needed to keep life going.
The two sources of energy are prospecting and processing.
Most of the energy used today is from prospected fuels.
Most of the energy that will be used in the future will have to be processed.
Electricity is the most common and convenient form of energy used today.
Electricity is produced in a power plant.
A generator is used to produce electricity.
Energy is needed to turn a turbine, which then turns a generator.
Nuclear fission is used to produce energy in a nuclear power plant.
In a nuclear power plant, a chain reaction produces heat, which is used to boil water into steam to turn the turbine.
A nuclear reactor is used to control a chain reaction.
Nuclear energy is converted into heat energy in a nuclear reactor.
The use of nuclear energy is controversial. The major concern is safety.
There have been no major accidents with nuclear power plants since the first one opened in 1957.
The major problem with nuclear energy is the disposal of nuclear wastes.

CONCLUSION

Electricity is the most common and convenient form of energy used today. To generate electricity in a power plant, water, gas, coal, or uranium is used as fuel. However, these forms of energy are becoming scarce. In the future, alternate sources of energy and new ways of generating energy will have to be found.

31. What is the KEY IDEA of this chapter?

UNIT **FOUR**

Energy and Change

SCIENCE COMPETENCIES

Unit 4 will help you to master two LIFE SKILLS:

RESPECTING THE EARTH—How to Cope with Environmental Changes

UNDERSTANDING NATURAL PROCESSES—How to Conserve the Earth's Resources

CHAPTER

30 Landforms

The Structure of the Earth

30A INTRODUCTION

In the early 1950's, scientists made an amazing discovery. They discovered that the ocean bottom was not flat. By sending out high frequency sound waves from ships and recording the sound waves that bounced back from the ocean floor, scientists found that the bottom of the ocean has different LANDFORMS. **A landform is a constantly changing feature on the earth's surface.**

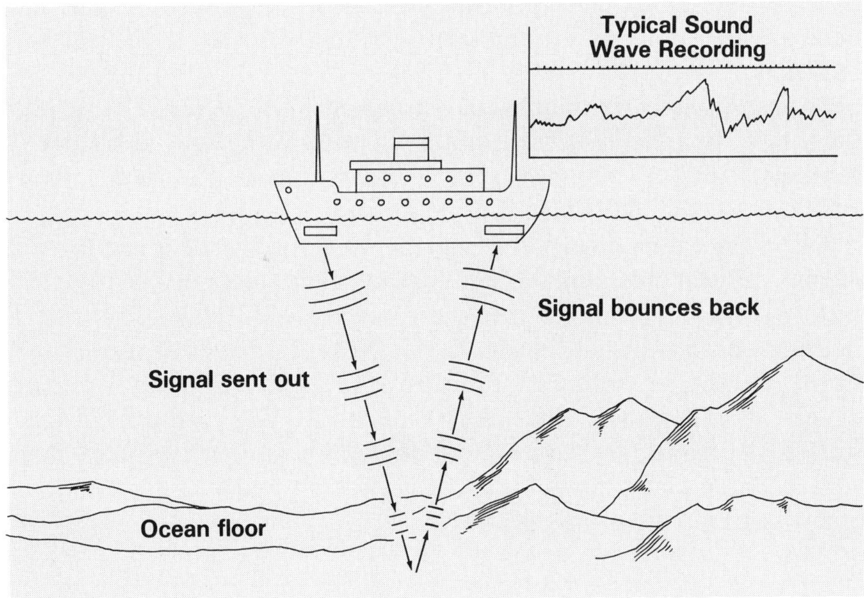

Ships bounce sound waves off the ocean floor. The resulting maps reveal surprising features on the ocean floor.

The ocean floor has mountain ranges, canyons, ridges, and plains. These are the same landforms that are found on continents. But the ocean floor has even greater mountain ranges, deeper canyons and ridges, and flatter plains than the continents have. Some of the earth's most impressive scenery is beneath the ocean.

DIFFERENT LANDFORMS

On the Continents	Edge of the Continents	Beneath the Ocean
Mountains	Shorelines	Mountains
Plains		Trenches
Plateaus		Continental Shelves
		Plains

The earth's surface is varied. It has been shaped over millions of years by geologic forces. Some forces build up the land while others wear it down. Forces that build up or lift the land are called CONSTRUCTIVE FORCES. Such forces come from within the earth. Forces that wear down the land are called DESTRUCTIVE FORCES. These forces come from the atmosphere.

In this chapter, you will study how the earth's landforms are the result of constructive and destructive forces.

1. What is a landform?
2. What did scientists discover about the ocean floor?
3. Name the two forces that produce different landforms.

30B THE EARTH'S CRUST

Over the years, many ideas that explained the shape of the earth's surface were proposed and discarded. In 1915, Alfred Wegener, a German scientist, proposed that all the continents were once part of one great landmass. **Wegener believed that the landmass broke apart millions of years ago, and the continents gradually drifted to their present positions.**

Wegener's idea was not widely accepted until the 1960's. At that time, new discoveries caused many scientists to accept his theory of continental drift. Today, Wegener's theory is part of a larger theory known as PLATE TECTONICS.

According to the theory of plate tectonics, you live on a moving slab of rock called a crustal plate. Fewer than twenty plates cover the entire earth's surface, forming a thin sheet called the CRUST. The crust is floating on denser rock in the earth's MANTLE, which moves very slowly. Geologists, scientists who study the earth, think that heat from the earth's core causes currents in the mantle. The currents cause the rock in the mantle to rise or sink, dragging the floating plates along with it. Some plates carry the great masses of land you live on, while others lie beneath the great ocean floors.

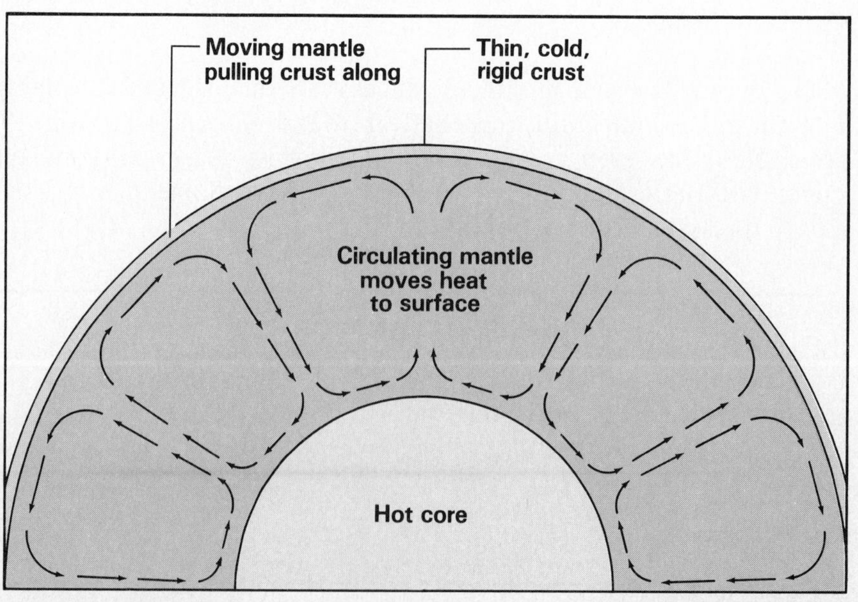

Heat energy is moved from the earth's core to the crust by slowly moving rock in the mantle. When the mantle moves against the thin, rigid crust, it breaks into plates and is pulled along by the rock in the mantle.

The theory of PLATE TECTONICS states that the continents ride on crustal plates being pulled across the earth by moving rock in the earth's mantle.

ACTIVITY: Making a Cross Section Model of the Earth

MATERIALS: Paper (11 meters long), meter sticks, markers

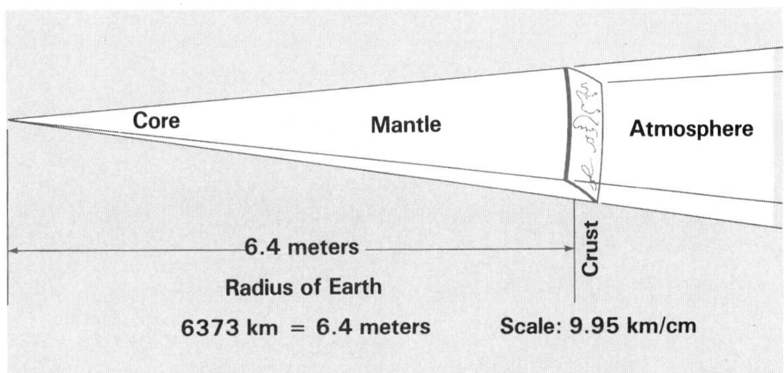

In this activity, you will make a model of a portion of the earth. The model will help you understand the size of the crust and the landforms that make up its surface.

---

a. Use a length of paper 9 meters long, or tape together 9 pieces of newspaper to make one long strip.

b. Draw a wedge like the one shown in the drawing above. It should stretch about 7 meters along your strip of paper.

c. Leave about 2 meters of paper beyond the crust so that you can add the atmosphere when you study weather in Chapter 34.

d. Use the information in the table below to fill in your model. When you finish, you will have a basic model of the earth.

e. Draw models of the crust showing where crustal plates are pulled apart and where crustal plates collide.

---

4. What does the model show about the size of the crust in relation to the size of the earth?
5. How much difference is there between the top of the highest mountain and the bottom of the deepest trench on your model? What is the distance on the real earth?
6. Do you think you could see a person on your model?

The Earth's Crust

The crust at its thinnest point beneath the oceans is about 10 km thick. Scale = 1.0 cm

The crust at its thickest point beneath the continents is about 48.3 km thick. Scale = 4.8 cm

The Earth's Surface

The highest point on the surface of the earth (Mount Everest) is 8.832 km above sea level. Scale = 0.99 cm

The deepest point on the earth (Mariana Trench in the Pacific) is 10.4 km below sea level. Scale = 1.0 cm

The mantle is about 2896 km thick. Scale = 21.9 m
The outer core is about 2092 km thick. Scale = 2.1 m
The inner core is about 1384 km thick. Scale = 1.39 m

All changes on the earth take place where a constructive or destructive force meets a part of the earth. The meeting place is called an INTERFACE. There are two major kinds of interfaces. One interface occurs where the earth meets the destructive forces in the atmosphere. You live at that interface. The other interface occurs where two crustal plates meet.

Constructive forces that build up the earth's surface usually act at the interface between two plates. When rock in the mantle moves up, it pulls the crust apart. As the plates separate, molten rock moves up from the mantle, filling the break and forming new crust. When two plates collide, one slab is forced down under the other. Such collisions cause volcanic eruptions and raise new mountains.

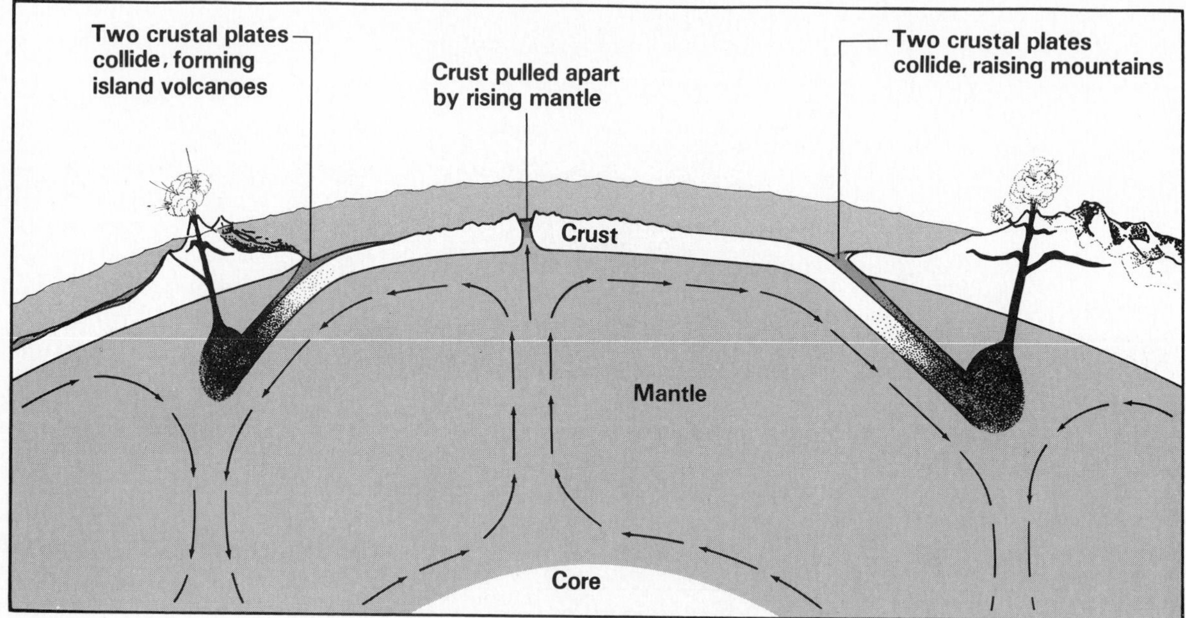

Geologists think that collisions of crustal plates over millions of years have created the great landmasses. There are seven such landmasses, called CONTINENTS, that make up almost one third of the earth's surface. The remainder of the earth is covered by water.

Most landforms have been created by a combination of constructive and destructive forces. In the following sections of this chapter, you will look at some of those landforms.

7. How does the theory of plate tectonics explain moving continents?

8. What is an interface?

9. What kind of force acts at the interface between the earth's surface and the atmosphere?

10. What kind of force acts at the interface between two crustal plates?

30C MOUNTAINS

As you know, continents have major features called landforms. **Each type of landform has characteristics that distinguish it from the others.** Constructive forces build and raise the landforms, while destructive forces wear them away. As a result, landforms are slowly being changed all the time.

ACTIVITY: Currents in the Earth

MATERIALS: Model of the earth, heat source, Pyrex container, food coloring, sawdust or light plastic beads

This activity will help you understand how currents move in the earth's mantle and how they affect the crust. Use your imagination to extend what you observe in your model of the earth.

---

a. Fill the container with water and place it over your heat source. Do NOT turn on the heat.
b. Let the container sit without disturbing it for several minutes.
c. Carefully add some of the food coloring to the container without churning the water.
d. Float some of the sawdust or beads on the water's surface.
e. Turn the heat on slowly.
f. Draw a picture of what you see as the water warms.
g. After the water has been heated, turn off the heat. Write a paragraph describing the behavior of the water and sawdust or beads during the heating process.

---

11. Where did the heated water go? Why?
12. What did the moving surface do to the sawdust or beads? Why?
13. How do the currents in the water and movement of the sawdust or beads relate to the earth's mantle and crust? Explain your answer using the diagram you drew in step f.

MOUNTAINS are the most impressive of all landforms. **Mountains are complicated masses of rock that rise more than 1,000 meters above the surrounding land.** They may stretch for several thousand kilometers where two crustal plates have collided. There are many old belts, or ranges, of mountains all over the world and new mountains are being raised all the time.

As soon as mountains are raised above the land surface, destructive forces begin wearing them down. After millions of years, the mountains are often so badly worn down that only traces of them remain.

Mountains are formed in different ways. With some ranges, such as the Appalachians, constructive forces bent and crumpled the rocks. Such bent and crumpled rocks are called FOLDED MOUNTAINS. In the Appalachians, the folds have worn away and have formed long ridges and valleys. Today, the Appalachian Mountain range stretches from Canada to Georgia along the east coast of the United States.

In the western United States, greater forces produced a range of complex mountains. **The stronger forces first folded and then broke the rocks into large blocks.** The resulting mountain range formed from a jumble of broken, folded, and shattered rock.

Farther west, constructive forces broke and lifted gigantic masses of rock in large pieces. The great raised blocks of rock are called BLOCK MOUNTAINS. One such block is the Sierra Nevada Mountain range in California.

This block mountain range was formed when constructive forces lifted a single block of rock.

A third type of mountain is formed by volcanic eruptions. Rock from the earth's surface melts when it is trapped between two colliding plates and is carried down into the earth. The molten rock moves up along cracks in the overlying rock. When it reaches the surface, the molten rock, called LAVA, erupts to form VOLCANIC MOUNTAINS. The Cascade Mountains in the northwestern United States are an example of volcanic mountains.

MOUNTAIN LANDFORMS

Folded Mountains
Complex Mountains
Block Mountains
Volcanic Mountains

14. What two features separate mountains from other landforms?
15. Name three different types of mountains.
16. What kind of force raises mountains?

30D PLAINS AND PLATEAUS

Both PLAINS and PLATEAUS are flat landforms. Plains are made of sand, silt, and clay laid down by streams. **Plains are usually very wide and flat or gently rolling landforms.** Some plains have formed next to mountains. These plains were made from the material produced as the mountains were worn down. This kind of plain is found from the Rocky Mountains to the Mississippi River.

Other plains have formed where streams run into the ocean. As the debris the streams were carrying collects, a wide, flat coastal plain grows at the land's edge. The Atlantic Coastal Plain, for example, forms much of the eastern edge of North America.

Plateaus, like plains, are wide and flat or gently rolling landforms. **Plateaus are often old plains or ocean bottoms that have been raised by constructive forces.** Unlike the forces that raise mountains, the forces that raise plateaus seldom do more than gently warp the land. **So plateaus are high, flat or gently rolling landforms.**

The most famous plateaus in the United States are the Colorado Plateau and the Applachian Plateau. Both are made of thousands of meters of flat rock.

Each plateau is being eroded by water. In Colorado, the Colorado River has cut into the Colorado Plateau and formed the Grand Canyon. In West Virginia, many rivers and streams have cut into the Applachian Plateau, forming steep-walled valleys. The rivers will eventually wash away both plateaus altogether. Millions of years from now, only a hill or two will remain.

Thousands of years ago, solid rock filled the Grand Canyon. The Colorado River wore away the rock bit by bit.

17. What is a plain?
18. What is a plateau?

30E THE EDGE OF THE LAND

A special landform, called a SHORELINE, forms where land and ocean meet. Waves pound the shore day and night. Currents move great masses of sand along the coast. Rivers bring still more sand as they flow into the ocean. **The beach that forms at the boundary between land and water changes very rapidly.** Storms bring even faster and more obvious changes, sometimes even wiping away beaches. But the beach is only one small part of the shoreline.

When flat ocean floors are raised up out of the sea, they form a special kind of shoreline. **As the ocean bottom is lifted from the sea, waves carve cliffs into the edge of the land.** The waves slowly straighten the shoreline, building a narrow beach at the base of the cliffs.

When the land sinks beneath the sea, another special kind of shoreline forms. **When land is flooded, the ocean fills valleys, leaving hills as points of land sticking up out of the sea.** The waves wear away the

points of land and carry the debris into the areas between the points called bays. With time, the points are worn away and the bays fill with sand. Finally, the shoreline is changed into a straight, sandy beach.

When a flat, sandy coastal plain sinks beneath the sea, shallow river valleys are flooded. As the currents shift sand from the coastal plain, a long, bar-shaped strip of sand forms. As years pass, the sandy strip grows longer and higher until it forms a barrier between the land and sea. Then, what began as a sand bar has become a barrier island. Some of the most famous barrier islands stretch along the Atlantic coast. They are broken here and there by inlets that let water move from the marshes to the sea.

19. What is the difference between the two shorelines that may form when land sinks beneath the sea? Describe how each might look.

20. Name some destructive forces that change shorelines.

21. Describe the difference between a shoreline rising from the sea and one sinking into the sea.

30F LANDFORMS BENEATH THE SEA

When scientists discovered landforms on the ocean floor, they opened many new avenues for exploration. Constructive and destructive forces are also at work on the ocean floor. **Where crustal plates are being pulled apart, great mountains are forming on the sea floor.** Molten rock moving up between the plates forms the mountains. The Mid-Oceanic Mountain Ridge was formed in this way and is the world's largest mountain system. It stretches more than 64,000 kilometers through the Atlantic, Pacific, and Indian Oceans. The undersea mountains are 2 to 3 kilometers high and as much as 1,000 kilometers wide.

Where crustal plates have collided, deep trenches have formed on the ocean floor. **Trenches form where one crustal plate plunges slowly underneath another.** The deepest known spot in all the oceans is near the island of Guam in the Pacific Ocean. There, in a spot called Challenger Deep in the Mariana Trench, the ocean is more than eleven kilometers deep.

Chains of volcanoes also form on the ocean floor. **The volcanoes form where sand and mud are carried deep into the crust by a plunging crustal plate.** Heat and pressure deep within the crust cause the mud and sand to melt. When the melted rock moves up to the ocean floor, it erupts to form undersea volcanoes. Chains of volcanic islands, like the islands of Japan, dot the Pacific Ocean.

Ocean floor maps show the diversity of landforms on the sea bottom. This drawing shows a section of the Mid-Oceanic Mountain Ridge.

VOLCANIC ISLANDS form where two crustal plates collide.

Other volcanic islands form where a crustal plate passes over a "hot spot" in the mantle. The Hawaiian Islands are still forming today over such a hot spot. Where ancient volcanic islands have been worn flat by wave action their flat tops form sea mounts. Often, living corals build ring-shaped islands of living rock on the sea mounts that dot the Pacific Ocean.

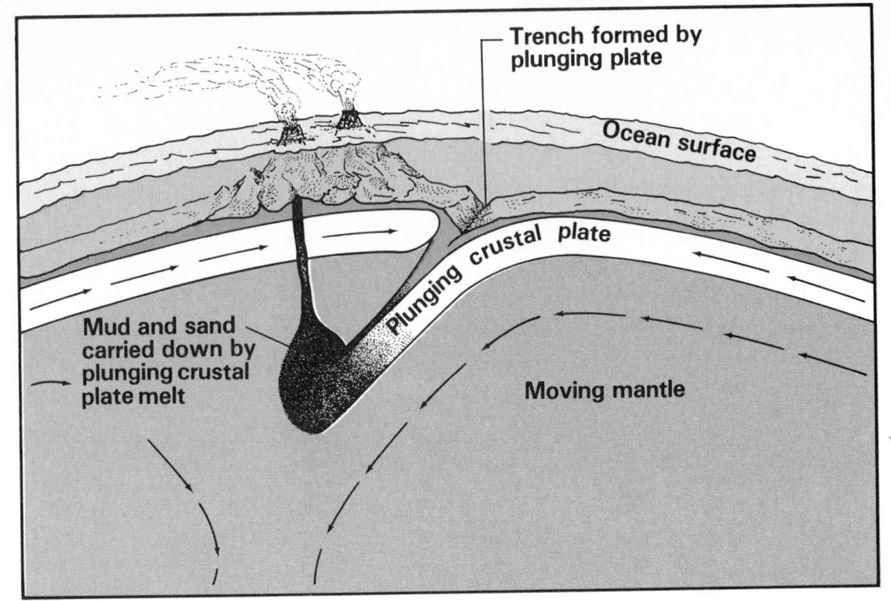

Volcanic islands are produced when sand and mud, which have been carried deep into the crust by a plunging plate, melt. The newly melted rocks move upward and erupt to form volcanoes on the sea floor.

Along the edges of most continents, mud and sand from the land are deposited in the sea. **Over millions of years, the deposits have formed wide, gently sloping shelves.** These landforms are CONTINENTAL SHELVES. At the edges of continental shelves, the sea floor slopes steeply down into the ocean. Such slopes border continental shelves around the world.

Beyond the continental slope, wide, flat, or gently rolling plains spread out deep beneath the ocean surface. ABYSSAL PLAINS are like plains on land in that they cover wide areas and are only interrupted by occasional ridges or canyons. Unlike plains on land, however, abyssal plains are under nearly five kilometers of ocean water.

22. What causes trenches and chains of undersea volcanoes to form?
23. What are continental shelves and where do they form?
24. What are abyssal plains and how are they like plains on land?

SUMMARY

VOCABULARY

landform
constructive forces
destructive forces
plate tectonics
crust
mantle
interface
continent
mountains
folded mountains
block mountains
lava
volcanic mountains
plains
plateaus
shoreline
continental shelf
abyssal plain

KEY FACTS AND CONCEPTS

The earth's surface has been shaped over millions of years by geologic forces.

Constructive forces build up the land, while destructive forces wear it down.

According to the theory of plate tectonics, you live on a moving slab of rock called a crustal plate.

All changes on the earth take place where a constructive or destructive force meets a part of the earth.

Constructive forces that build up the earth's surface usually act at the interface between two crustal plates.

Geologists think that collisions of crustal plates have created great landmasses.

Each type of landform has features that distinguish it from the others.

Mountains are complicated masses of rock that rise more than 1,000 meters above the surrounding land.

Plains are usually very wide and flat or gently rolling landforms.

Plateaus are high, flat or gently rolling landforms.

Shorelines form where land and ocean meet.

Landforms are created on the sea floor where crustal plates collide or are pulled apart.

The earth's surface is covered with a wide variety of landforms.

CONCLUSION

The earth's surface is made up of a variety of landforms. The interaction of constructive and destructive forces with the earth's surface produces such landforms as mountains, plains, plateaus, shorelines, and ocean trenches. Each landform affects the lives of the people who live on or near it. Studying landforms can help you understand how the earth changes and how those changes affect your life.

25. What is the KEY IDEA of this chapter?

CHAPTER

31 The Rock Cycle

The Changing Earth

31A INTRODUCTION

The earth is constantly changing. Changes on the earth can be observed as part of a process called the ROCK CYCLE. There are three kinds of rocks in the rock cycle: IGNEOUS, METAMORPHIC, and SEDIMENTARY. **The processes of the rock cycle change rocks from one form to another.**

In May of 1980, a volcano called Mt. Saint Helens erupted. Volcanic eruptions are one part of a large process called the rock cycle.

THE THREE KINDS OF ROCK

IGNEOUS: cooled magma

METAMORPHIC: existing rock changed by heat and pressure

SEDIMENTARY: small pieces, or sediments, of rock cemented together.

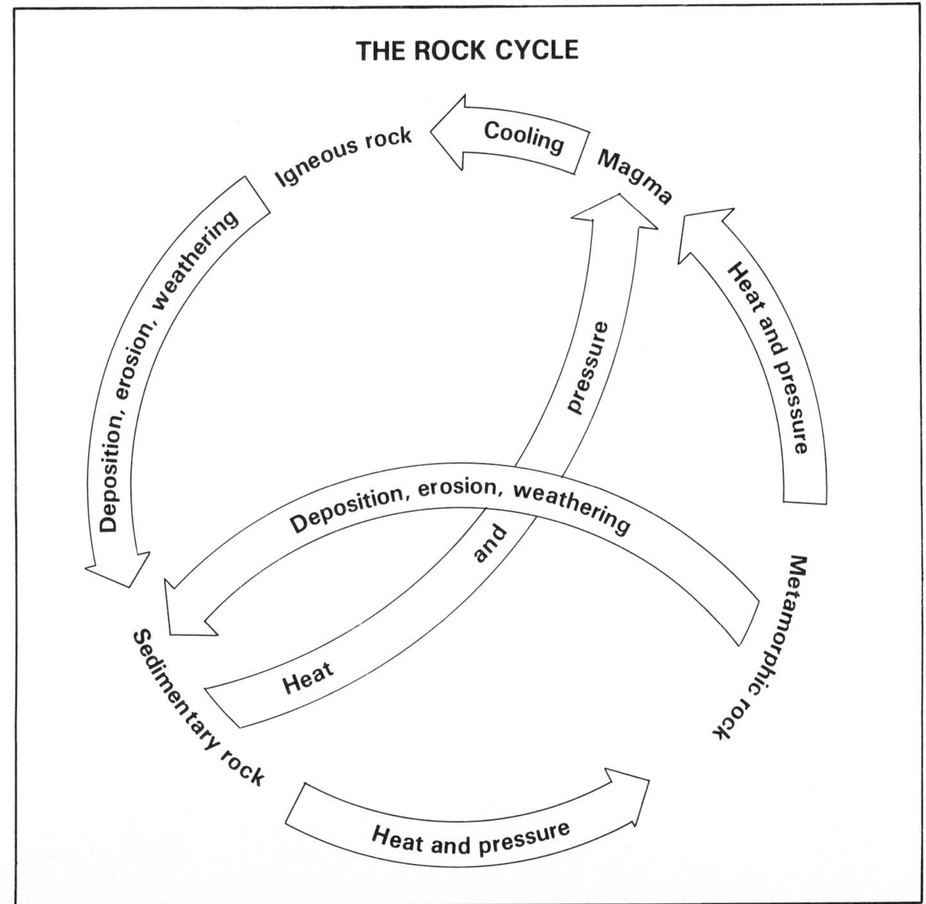

For millions of years, the materials that form the earth's crust have moved through the rock cycle. When molten rock, or MAGMA, cools and hardens, it forms igneous rock. Magma reaches the earth's surface as lava. **Lava is the liquid rock that pours out of volcanoes.**

The forces that form volcanoes also bend, fold, and metamorphose, or change, rock. Metamorphic rock may be formed from igneous, sedimentary, or other metamorphic rocks.

The same forces that form volcanoes also raise the land and expose rocks to destructive forces. Destructive forces wear down the rocks. The resulting sand and mud are pressed and cemented together to form sedimentary rocks.

The three kinds of rock are changed from one form to another by constructive and destructive forces. Destructive forces wear down rocks while constructive forces build them up. The same force can also act either constructively or destructively, depending on other factors.

CONSTRUCTIVE AND DESTRUCTIVE FORCES AND PROCESSES	
Heat	Weathering
Freezing	Erosion
Pressure	Deposition

Every step in the rock cycle changes the rocks that form the earth's crust and its landforms. In some places, new rock is formed. In other places, crustal rock is destroyed. In still other places, rocks are changed into new forms. **The constructive and destructive forces that form different kinds of rocks give the earth its different features.**

In this chapter, you will see how rocks are changed into different forms by forces in the rock cycle. You will be studying the different kinds of rock formed by these forces.

1. Explain the rock cycle.
2. Name the process in the rock cycle in which heat and pressure change the form of a rock.
3. What forces in the rock cycle wear away rock, forming sand and mud?
4. What do the processes in the rock cycle do to rocks in the earth?
5. What two major forces play a role in the rock cycle?

31B MAGMA

Magma is molten rock under the earth's surface. It can form in either of two ways. First, when two crustal plates collide, sand, mud, and silt are carried deep into the earth. There, in the earth's crust and upper mantle, it is very hot and the pressure is great. **Thus, the sand, mud, and silt are melted together to form magma.**

Another way magma is formed is when two crustal plates are pulled apart. Hot rock from the mantle then moves up to the earth's surface.

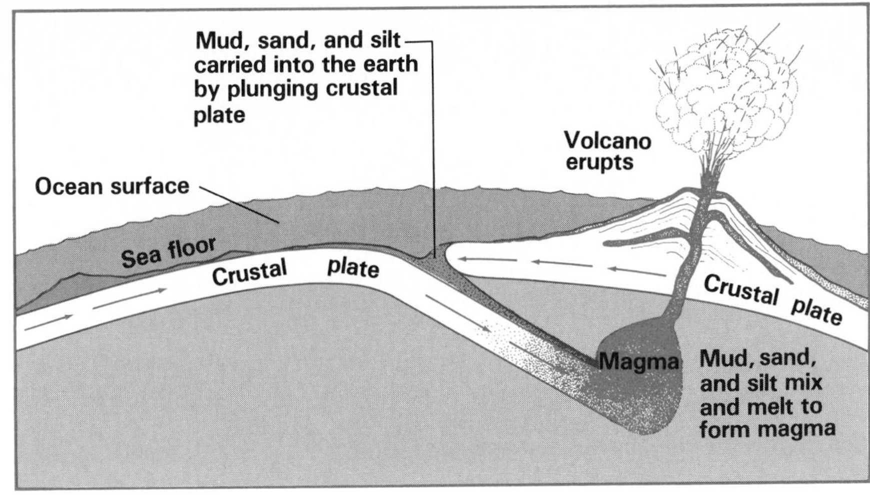

These photos show the three different types of volcanic mountain. The top photo shows a shield cone, the middle a cinder cone, and the bottom a composite cone.

As the pressure lessens on the hot rock, it melts. This hot, liquid rock is magma.

When magma reaches the earth's surface, it erupts. **Volcanoes are mountains formed by erupting magma, or lava.** Some kinds of lava flow smoothly over the land. Other kinds form a crust. The lava flowing underneath this crust breaks it into jagged blocks.

Chemical compounds that form in the magma are called minerals. **The kind of volcanic mountain built by an eruption depends on the minerals in the magma.** When magma is made from iron-rich minerals, it forms basalt. **Basaltic magma flows freely.** Volcanoes built from basaltic magma are wide and flat. Such volcanoes are called SHIELD CONES.

When magma is made from granite-like rocks, it behaves like sticky taffy. **Eruptions of granite-like magma are often explosive.** Explosive eruptions produce great amounts of dust and ash. The ash forms a steep-sided CINDER CONE.

Sometimes a volcano will change character. One eruption may produce smooth-flowing lava. The next eruption may be an explosion, sending clouds of dust and ash into the air. Such alternating eruptions build tall, strong COMPOSITE CONES with layers of lava and ash.

DIFFERENT KINDS OF ERUPTIONS FORM DIFFERENT KINDS OF VOLCANOES

Eruption Style	Lava Type	Volcano
Quiet	Basaltic	Flat shield cone
Explosive	Granitic	Steep cinder cone
Combination	Mixture of basaltic and granitic	Steep composite cone

6. Describe the two ways in which magma forms.

7. Draw pictures of the three different kinds of volcanic mountain. Describe the kind of eruption that produces each type of volcano.

31C IGNEOUS ROCKS

As you learned in the Introduction, igneous rocks are formed from magma that has cooled and hardened. **To be more specific, igneous rock forms when the minerals in magma crystallize.** The minerals crystallize until all of the hot, liquid magma becomes hard rock.

Igneous rocks are made of tightly interlocking crystals. The crystals can be large or small depending on how long it took the rock to harden.

Granite is a common igneous rock made of large crystals. The crust of the earth under the continents is made of granite. **A common igneous rock made of small crystals is basalt.** Basalt can be found beneath most of the world's ocean floors. Many islands, such as the Canary and Hawaiian Islands, were formed from basalt.

8. Describe how igneous rock forms.
9. How does igneous rock fit into the rock cycle?

31D EARTHQUAKES

Constructive forces may fold, break, or change the character of rocks. Motion within the earth slowly shifts the crust, building up tremendous forces between crustal plates. Large masses of rock are often caught and squeezed between two plates. When this happens, the rock often responds by folding up like an accordian. Later, when the rocks are raised to the surface, you can see the bends and folds. **Bent and folded rocks are common features of mountains all over the world.**

This photo shows a series of folds that were raised to the earth's surface. Erosion wore away the softer rock, leaving ridges and valleys.

If the forces pushing on a mass of rock become too great, the rock may break. A break in a large mass of rock is called a FAULT. The pressure of the pushing forces is relieved when rocks move along the fault. Because the rocks are pressed tightly together, they move in short jumps. The jumping rocks shake the land causing vibrations called EARTHQUAKES.

Earthquakes shake a wide area of land. The land moves simultaneously up and down, from side to side, and back and forth. Every day, somewhere on the earth, an earthquake occurs. Fortunately, most of them occur in deserted areas. But when an earthquake shakes a city, buildings can be destroyed and lives are often lost.

10. What is a fault?

11. How are faults and earthquakes related?

31E METAMORPHIC ROCK

The forces that fold and fault large masses of rock also cause them to change character. Such changes are called METAMORPHISM. The word *metamorphism* means "changed form."

Pressure causes the mineral grains in a rock to change shape or line up in layers. High temperatures far beneath the earth's surface cause chemical compounds in the rocks to change. As a result, the rocks change form. Rocks that have been changed from one type into another are called metamorphic rocks.

The longer rock is exposed to heat and pressure, the more it changes. Different kinds of rock change in different ways.

Mud and silt buried and dried near the earth's surface is called shale, a sedimentary rock. Shale can be changed by heat and pressure into slate, a metamorphic rock. You probably have seen slate used to make decorative flagstones for pathways and gardens.

Another example of metamorphism is sandstone changing under heat and pressure into the metamorphic rock quartzite. Sandstone is made up of quartz. During metamorphism, the quartz grains in sandstone change in size and shape to become quartzite.

The igneous rock granite can be changed by heat and pressure to form the metamorphic rock gneiss (produced like the word *nice*). Granite contains the minerals quartz, feldspar, and mica. Metamorphism causes the feldspar and quartz crystals to form layers. Between these layers, shiny mica crystals form in wavy bands. This new rock is called gneiss. Some forms of gneiss are used to pave roads.

The sedimentary rock shale can be changed by heat and pressure into the metamorphic rock slate.

Sandstone, which is made up mostly of quartz, can be changed by heat and pressure into the metamorphic rock quartzite.

The igneous rock granite can be changed by heat and pressure into the metamorphic rock gneiss.

If the heat and pressure that cause metamorphism become too great, the rock will melt. Then, the molten rock is no longer metamorphic but has been changed to magma.

12. Give three examples of metamorphic rocks.
13. What forces are primarily responsible for metamorphism?
14. How does metamorphic rock fit into the rock cycle?

31F SEDIMENTARY ROCKS

When rock is exposed at the earth's surface, the destructive forces of weathering break down the rock. Processes of erosion carry away the resulting mud, silt, and sand. When these sediments reach the ocean or some other low place, they are deposited in layers. **As time passes, the layers are buried and cemented together, forming sedimentary rock.** Seventy-five percent of all rocks are sedimentary rocks.

These large sandstone formations are located in Bryce Canyon, Utah.

The kind of sedimentary rock that forms depends on what kind of sediments collect. Sedimentary rock tells geologists a great deal about what happened in a certain place millions of years ago.

One kind of sedimentary rock is sandstone. Where wind or water deposits layers of sand, the grains of sand become cemented together by minerals. Sandstones form from the sand on beaches and deserts. Such deserts as the Sahara and Gobi have large sand dunes that have changed to sedimentary rock.

Another kind of sedimentary rock is a conglomerate. Conglomerates form where rivers slow down enough to deposit a bed of boulders and gravel. When the rock particles, sand, and mud are cemented together, they form a conglomerate.

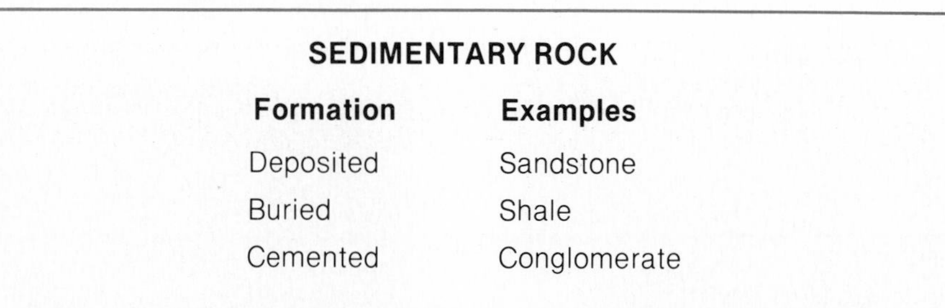

SEDIMENTARY ROCK

Formation	Examples
Deposited	Sandstone
Buried	Shale
Cemented	Conglomerate

The "cement" that holds grains of sand, pebbles, or mud together in a sandstone or conglomerate can be made from different substances. Substances such as limestone, iron oxide, or small particles of clay can act like cement to hold rocks together. But each substance works the same way. Each fills the spaces between the grains in a rock to hold it together.

Because sedimentary rocks are formed in places where plants and animals live, they often contain FOSSILS. **Fossils are rocks that contain the preserved remains of plants or animals.**

Swamps, river valleys, and continental shelves support large communities of living things. As they die, the plants and animals are buried by sand and mud. Water seeping through the ground carries minerals that replace the dead plant or animal tissue. **In a process that takes many years, the plant or animal remains are replaced by mineral matter and preserved as a fossil.**

ACTIVITY: The Rock Cycle

MATERIALS: Rock samples, weathered rock, sand, silt, mud samples, poster board, cards, markers, tape or glue

In this activity, you will learn to identify igneous, metamorphic, and sedimentary rocks. You will also place them in their proper places in the rock cycle.

a. Separate the rock samples into three groups. Each group should look different.
b. Look up the rock groups and use the information you find to label your groups as igneous, metamorphic, or sedimentary.
c. Using the drawing on page 211 as a guide, draw a poster of the rock cycle.
d. Write short paragraphs on cards describing each step in the rock cycle. Fasten the completed paragraphs to your chart.
e. Put the igneous, metamorphic, and sedimentary rocks in their proper places. Do the same for the weathered rock, sand, silt, and mud.
f. Label each place where something happens at an interface.
g. Label the type of force involved at each step in the rock cycle.

15. Why do you think fossils are found in sedimentary and not metamorphic rocks?
16. Can you think of a place where old rocks are destroyed by melting? Where rocks are metamorphosed? Where rocks are raised and folded or faulted? Explain your answers.

Fossils preserved in sedimentary rock tell the story of life on the earth millions of years ago. Fish and shell fossils show that a sandstone was once part of an ocean floor. Swampy plant fossils tell of mud flats and river valleys. Plants, trees, fish, snails, dinosaurs, and many other fossils provide a history of life on earth. **Geologists are still exploring the rocks and making new discoveries about the history of the earth.**

This photo shows the fossil of a reptile that was similar to the alligator of today.

17. How is a sedimentary rock formed?
18. Name two kinds of sedimentary rock and describe how each is formed.
19. How are plant and animal remains changed into fossils?
20. What can fossils tell geologists about the history of life on the earth?
21. How does sedimentary rock fit into the rock cycle?

SUMMARY

VOCABULARY

rock cycle
igneous
metamorphic
sedimentary
magma
shield cone
cinder cone
composite cone
fault
earthquake
metamorphism
fossil

KEY FACTS AND CONCEPTS

The earth is constantly changing.

The processes of the rock cycle change rock from one form to another.

For millions of years, the materials that form the earth's crust have moved through the rock cycle.

Every step in the rock cycle changes the rocks that form the earth's crust and its landforms.

The constructive and destructive forces that form different kinds of rocks give the earth its different landforms.

Magma is molten rock under the earth's surface.

Volcanoes are mountains formed by erupting magma, or lava.

The kind of volcanic mountain built by an eruption depends on the minerals in the magma.

Igneous rocks form when the minerals in magma crystallize until all of the hot liquid becomes rock.

Rocks may be folded or faulted by constructive forces.

The movement of rocks along faults causes earthquakes.

Heat and pressure change rock in a process called metamorphism.

When destructive forces break down rock, the sediments may be deposited, buried, and cemented to form sedimentary rock.

The kind of sedimentary rock that forms depends on what kind of sediment collects.

Fossils preserved in sedimentary rock tell the story of life on the earth millions of years ago.

CONCLUSION

The rock cycle is a never-ending process that changes rocks in different ways. Constructive and destructive forces cause those changes. As the rocks are changed, landforms are created and destroyed. The continual recycling and reshaping of the crust has produced the land on which you live.

22. What is the KEY IDEA of this chapter?

CHAPTER

32 Weathering and Erosion

Activity on the Earth's Surface

32A INTRODUCTION

Last night as you slept, the earth changed. Slow but steady processes were changing rock into soil. Wind shifted sand and soil particles. Glaciers ground up the rock beneath them. Streams washed away soil, and gravity pulled rocks down mountains.

The land changes slightly every day due to the work of destructive forces. The forces work at the interfaces between the earth and the atmosphere and the earth and the ocean. The landforms you studied in Chapter 30 are produced—land is raised by constructive forces and is reshaped by destructive forces.

As you know from Chapter 31, the interaction of forces that causes rocks to change and creates landforms is known as the rock cycle. In this chapter, you will learn how destructive forces help create the landforms you live on. Two of these forces are WEATHERING and EROSION.

DESTRUCTIVE FORCES

WEATHERING: breaks down rock into soil

EROSION: moves rock and soil particles from one place to another

1. Where do destructive forces work?
2. Name two destructive forces.

32B WEATHERING

Rocks are exposed to air and water. On land, rocks are heated by the sun or frozen on cold days. Beneath the sea, rocks are dragged along the ocean floor by currents. These conditions cause rocks to change.

The processes which change rocks are called weathering. **Weathering causes rocks to break into fragments and change form. The final result of weathering is soil.**

The weathering process is divided into two parts—PHYSICAL and CHEMICAL WEATHERING. **Physical weathering breaks rock into smaller pieces.** One of the main causes of physical weathering is the formation of ice in cracks within rocks.

Most rocks have cracks between mineral grains. Water flowing over the rocks seeps into the cracks. When the water freezes and expands, it breaks the rocks apart. In this way, even mountains are broken into piles of smaller rocks. But this takes millions of years.

Other forces contribute to physical weathering. Rocks are worn down when wind blows sand grains over their surfaces. Tree roots push into cracks and cause rocks to split. Waves pound rocky shores, wearing rocks down. All these forces combine to reduce big rocks to small rocks.

Chemical weathering changes the mineral composition, or makeup, of rocks. Chemical weathering takes place at the surface of rocks. **Physical weathering reduces a rock's size but increases its surface area. So physical weathering creates a larger surface area on which chemical weathering can occur.**

Chemical weathering works in different ways. **One of the main causes of chemical weathering is the dissolving action of water.** Some minerals in rocks dissolve in water and are washed away. This may

ACTIVITY: Physical Weathering and Surface Area

MATERIALS: Modeling clay, plastic knife, metric ruler

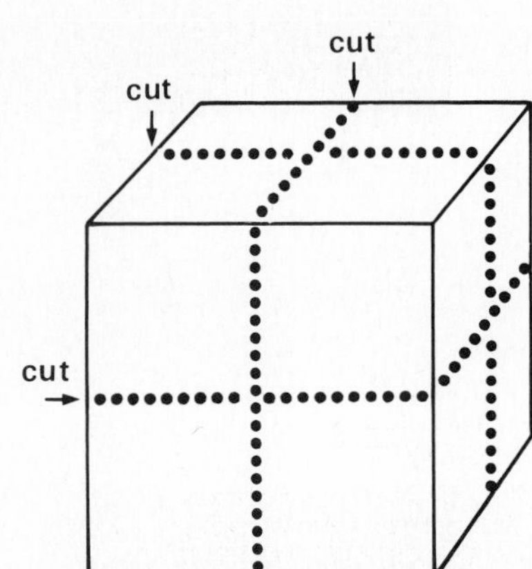

Step	Length of One Side	Area of One Side	Number of Blocks	Total Surface Area of All Blocks	Volume of One Block
c	8 cm	cm^2		cm^2	cm^3
f	cm	cm^2		cm^2	cm^3
g	cm	cm^2		cm^2	cm^3

In this activity, you will investigate physical weathering. You will learn how it increases the surface area on which chemical weathering can occur.

a. Make a cube using the modeling clay supplied by your teacher. The cube should be 8 cm on each side.
b. Determine the surface area of the cube. Do this by multiplying the area of one side by the number of sides (6).
• c. In your notebook, draw a table like the one shown above.
d. Physically weather your cube by cutting it in half three times—front to back, side to side, and top to bottom.
e. Count the number of blocks and determine the total surface area for all the blocks. Record your answer in question 3.
f. Record the data in your table.
g. Cut (physically weather) each block as you did the first time. Calculate the total surface area for all the blocks, and record the data in your table.

3. How many blocks did your "physical weathering" produce? How did the volume of a single block change?
4. What happened to the total surface area as the blocks were cut (weathered)?
5. What do you think happens to the surface area of a rock when physical weathering breaks it into several pieces?
6. Since chemical weathering works at the surface of rocks, what do you think physical weathering does to the rate of chemical weathering?

cause the remaining rock to crumble. For example, when rain falls, it combines with carbon dioxide in the air and forms a weak acid. When the rain falls on rocks made of limestone, it slowly dissolves the rock. In some places, the dissolved limestone has created large underground spaces called CAVERNS.

Some minerals combine with water in a chemical weathering process called HYDRATION. **Hydration changes hard minerals, like feldspar and mica, into softer clay minerals.**

OXIDATION is another chemical weathering process. Oxidation occurs when oxygen combines with another substance and forms a new substance. For example, when oxygen combines with the iron in rocks, iron oxide, or rust, forms. Rust dissolves in water and is much softer than the original rock.

Weathering is a very slow process. It takes many thousands of years for a rock to disintegrate. **Many more years are needed to change the minerals in rock into water-soluble forms.**

Chemical weathering produced this cavern by dissolving limestone.

7. What does weathering do to rock?
8. Describe some processes that physically weather rock.
9. Describe two chemical weathering processes.

Bridges must be constantly repainted to protect them against oxidation.

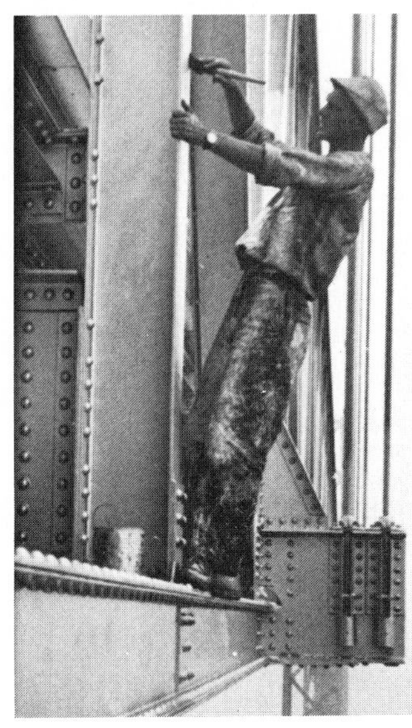

32C SOIL

Soil is the end product of the weathering process. When it is not carried away by water or wind, soil builds up over rock as it weathers. Weathering forms soil in layers. The bottom layer contains broken rocks produced by physical weathering and some changed minerals. Closer to the surface, soil contains only chemically weathered minerals. The clay, silt, and sand in this layer will not support life and are easily washed away.

The upper layer of soil mixes with dead plant and animal material. This layer is called TOPSOIL. **Topsoil is usually dark in color because of the decayed plant material and supports the growth of plants.** Small animals, such as worms and snails, live in the topsoil layer.

New soil is produced very slowly. **People depend on topsoil to grow food and plants for clothing, housing, and fuel. Where topsoil has been carried away by erosion, plants do not grow well.** You can protect topsoil by helping to prevent erosion. One way you can prevent erosion is by planting grass and other ground covers that keep soil in place. Your efforts will help ensure that the soil will be protected.

10. Which layer of soil supports plant life? Why?
11. Why must you help protect topsoil?

32D EROSION

The major destructive force that shapes the earth's surface and recycles weathered rock is erosion. **Erosion is the name for a group of processes that move weathered material from one place to another.** Each process picks up material in one place and deposits it in another. All the processes of erosion wear away the land surface. Given enough time, they can wear any land surface down to sea level.

PROCESSES OF EROSION

GRAVITY: pulls rocks and soil down hills

MOVING ICE: grinds up rock and carves mountains

RUNNING WATER: washes away soil and carries it to the sea

WIND: blows away loose sand and silt in dry areas

There are four major agents of erosion: gravity, moving ice, wind, and running water. Gravity pulls rocks and soil downhill. Moving ice grinds up rock. Wind blows away loose sand and silt, and running water washes away soil. Each process works in a different way and produces different results. **As they work, the processes of erosion shape the land surface raised by constructive forces. The result is the landscape on which you live.**

12. What is erosion?

13. Name four processes of erosion and tell what each does to the earth's surface.

14. What is the result of erosion?

32E GRAVITY AND MOVING ICE

All over the earth, the force of gravity is pulling rocks and soil downhill. On cliffs, rocks pushed outward by freezing water eventually tumble down the steep slopes. Rain-soaked soil, or mud, slides downhill, sometimes pushing over houses and blocking roads. Even particles of soil move downhill. On cold mornings, the particles are lifted on tiny spires of ice above the frozen soil. The particles slide downhill as the soil thaws in the morning sun. With such movement going on all over the earth, gravity moves many tons of rock each day.

In high mountains and colder regions of the earth, moving ice is an important agent of erosion. In these places, snow falls faster than it melts. As snow piles up, its weight changes the snow flakes into a mass

The rocks at the base of these cliffs were pulled down by gravity after they were pushed out by the freezing and thawing of water.

of solid ice and a GLACIER forms. **A glacier is a very slow-moving sheet of ice.** Gravity slowly pulls the glacier downhill.

The glacier in this photo is gouging out a valley and grinding up rock in its path.

Glaciers moving down mountainsides gouge out U-shaped valleys. **As the ice moves, it grinds up the rock in its path and carries it downhill.** The air warms as the glacier moves down the mountain until the ice begins to melt. The melting glacier deposits mounds of broken rock and gravel. Water from the melting glacier then spreads out the finely-ground rock.

Active mountain glaciers grind down mountains, leaving only U-shaped valleys and sharp ridges behind them. The ground rock and sand produced by the glaciers weathers into large deposits of mud, sand, and scattered boulders. These deposits, called Glacial Till, surround eroded mountains. They form wide plains in the midwestern United States. Because of the flatness of these plains, they are used for farming and sheep grazing.

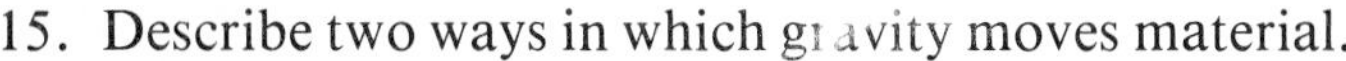

15. Describe two ways in which gravity moves material.
16. How do glaciers erode mountains?

32F WIND AND RUNNING WATER

In dry regions, the wind is a powerful destructive force. The wind erodes the land in two ways. First, the wind, blowing over the land, picks up fine, loose sand and silt. The wind carries the sand and silt until it slows down. Then the sand and silt are deposited. In Missouri, thick layers of silt, eroded from the Great Plains, have been deposited by the wind. In other areas, the wind builds great piles of sand called DUNES. The dunes shift and change shape with the wind, causing problems when people try to build houses or roads.

Dunes are formed by windblown sand.

The second way that the wind erodes the land is by grinding down rock surfaces. The process, called ABRASION, occurs when sand grains are blown by the wind against rocks. The flying sand grains polish and wear away the rocks. In desert regions, polished rocks stand as evidence of the wind's eroding power.

In areas where there is more rainfall, running water is the dominant process of erosion. As it flows downhill toward the sea, running water dissolves weathered minerals. The water also carries mud and sand and rolls larger rocks along stream bottoms.

Where the water slows to enter lakes and seas, it leaves behind the material it picked up from the land. This material forms large, fan-shaped DELTAS. Many farming regions are located on deltas because the soil is rich and the water is plentiful.

Streams flow rapidly in high mountain areas. They cut sharp V-shaped valleys with many waterfalls and rapids. As a stream flows toward the sea, it is joined by other streams and grows in size. The growing river cuts a wider valley. Closer to sea level, the river begins to wander in a widening, flat valley called a FLOOD PLAIN. **Many people have settled on flood plains because farming is easier on flat land.** The disadvantage of living on flood plains is that they are often flooded.

When people build or farm on a flood plain, flooding becomes a serious problem.

Water also shapes the land when it seeps into the earth. In areas where limestone lies under the surface, water may dissolve the rock and form caverns.

But in most places, water seeping into the earth is put to use by people. You may pump drinking water from a well or use water provided by a city water system. **In either case, the water began as rain and was filtered by seepage through the earth.** Then the water was pumped to the surface for your use.

All the processes of erosion are destructive forces. Gravity, glaciers, wind, and running water change the shape of the earth every day. The landforms they create affect the way you live.

17. Describe two ways in which wind erodes the land.
18. What special kind of landform is built by the wind?
19. Describe two ways in which running water erodes the land.
20. How does a valley change as a stream flows through it from the mountains to the sea?
21. Why do people farm on deltas and flood plains?
22. Why is underground water important to you?
23. What do forces of erosion create? How do they do this?

SUMMARY

VOCABULARY

weathering
erosion
physical weathering
chemical weathering
caverns
hydration
oxidation
topsoil
glacier
dune
abrasion
delta
flood plain

KEY FACTS AND CONCEPTS

The earth changes slightly every day due to the work of destructive forces.

Physical weathering breaks rocks into smaller pieces.

Chemical weathering changes the mineral composition of rocks.

Soil is the end product of the weathering process.

Erosion is a group of processes that move weathered material from one place to another.

Gravity pulls boulders, rocks, and sand down hills.

In cold regions, glaciers grind up rock and carve U-shaped valleys in mountains.

In dry desert areas, wind blasts rocks with sand and builds dunes.

Where water is plentiful, streams erode hills and mountains, building wide, flat deltas and flood plains.

The processes of weathering and erosion are destructive forces that form one part of the rock cycle.

CONCLUSION

The processes that weather and erode the surface of the land produce a variety of landforms. They also create places to live and the soil on which you depend for food. The destructive forces are part of the rock cycle that you may observe firsthand.

24. What is the KEY IDEA of this chapter?

CHAPTER

33 Natural Resources

Using the Earth

The waters of Lake Powell fall through Glen Canyon Dam in Utah generating electricity for people to use.

33A INTRODUCTION

Behind the high concrete wall of Glen Canyon Dam in Utah lie the quiet waters of Lake Powell. Inside the dam, water from the lake falls almost one hundred meters to turn a turbine and generator. Then the water rushes out and down the Colorado River. The energy of the falling water is changed into electricity that lights homes and schools. Falling water is one of many NATURAL RESOURCES that you use every day.

A natural resource is something provided by the earth that meets a need. Natural resources come in many forms. Resources are minerals dug from the earth and made into wire, chemicals, and many other products. Resources are trees grown in forests to be cut and sawed into lumber for houses. Resources are sunlight and water. **Everything you wear, eat, or use begins as a resource provided by the earth.**

NATURAL RESOURCES

Renewable	Nonrenewable
Sunlight	Coal
Plants	Oil
Animals	Metals
Soil	Nonmetals

Some resources can be replaced in your lifetime. A forest can be cut down and replanted. Water used to generate electrical power can be replaced by rainfall. Those resources that can be replaced are called RENEWABLE resources.

Other resources can never be replaced. Such resources are said to be NONRENEWABLE. Once a deposit of coal has been mined and burned, it can never be mined again. Oil pumped or minerals mined from the ground cannot be replaced. They, too, are nonrenewable resources.

In this chapter, you will study natural resources. You will learn how people obtain resources for their use. You will also learn why the earth is running out of some resources and what you can do to help stop this from happening.

1. What is a natural resource?

2. What is the difference between a renewable resource and a nonrenewable resource?

33B EARTH MATERIALS

Many of the things you depend on every day are made from EARTH MATERIALS. **Anything that is taken from the earth and used is an earth material.** With the exception of soil, all earth materials are nonrenewable resources. In millions of years, the processes of the rock cycle, which you studied in Chapter 31, will create new deposits. But the resources are needed today, not in millions of years. Therefore, as far as you are concerned, earth materials can be taken from the earth only once.

Geologists use what they know about the earth in their search for earth materials. They know that minerals have collected in certain places by different processes. For example, coal, oil, and natural gas began as plants in ancient swamps where dinosaurs roamed. When the swamps were buried by layers of mud and sand, the plants were changed to coal, oil, and natural gas. Where the layers were folded and faulted, pockets of oil and gas collected. So geologists search for folded and faulted sedimentary rocks formed from swamps. When they find such rocks they drill, hoping that oil and gas are still trapped in the rocks.

The oil and gas being removed from the earth today began as plants and animals in ancient swamps. Oil and gas are nonrenewable resources.

EARTH MATERIALS

Petroleum	Ore
Coal	Metals
Oil	Nonmetals
Natural Gas	

Geologists search the earth for ores and petroleum. ORE is an earth material. **Ores are concentrations of minerals deposited in the earth.** Many different mineral ores are mined and used by people.

There are two kinds of ore, METALLIC and NONMETALLIC. Metallic ores are mined and refined to produce metals like copper, iron, and zinc. Nonmetallic ores are also mined. They are used to make many different things. The mineral quartz is made into glass, limestone is made into cement, and phosphate is made into fertilizer. Dozens of minerals are mined and used for special purposes.

Copper ore, a nonrenewable resource, is mined at Utah's Bingham Canyon, shown in this photo. What are some uses for copper?

The second major kind of earth material that geologists search for is PETROLEUM. **Petroleum includes coal, oil, and natural gas.** After coal is mined, it is burned in power plants to generate electricity. Some coal is also used to make chemicals, plastics, and medicines.

Oil and natural gas are taken from wells drilled in the earth. Before it can be used, the oil and gas must be refined. The refining process separates oil and gas into gasoline, fuel oil, asphalt, and many other products. Refining also removes water and impurities. After refining, most oil and gas is burned to generate electricity, run engines, and heat homes. Like coal, oil and gas are also used to make plastics, paints, rubber, medicine, and many other products.

3. What is an ore?
4. Why are most earth materials nonrenewable resources?
5. What are the major kinds of ores?
6. Name three products you use every day. What nonrenewable resources were used to make them?

33C RENEWABLE RESOURCES

Renewable resources can be replaced after they are used. Some, such as sunlight, are replaced immediately. Others, such as soil, require many years to be replaced. There are six kinds of renewable resources that people use. They are: water, solar energy, wind, geothermal energy, soil, and living organisms.

One group of renewable resources produces energy. Falling water, sunshine, wind, and geothermal energy are all used to produce electricity or heat. Falling water inside a dam turns generators and produces electricity. Wind also generates electricity by turning windmills. Sunshine is used to change water to steam. Geothermal energy, or energy of steam from within the earth, is also used to generate electricity.

Another group of renewable resources provides food and fulfills other needs. Rain water, for example, collects underground. People use the water and return it to the ground or to rivers where it flows to

ACTIVITY: Refining by Distillation

MATERIALS: Heat source, flask with stand, rubber stopper, tubing, test tube, beaker, ice

This activity will help you understand one way that resources are processed. Oil must be refined before it can be used. Refining separates the oil into different materials. Oil is refined by heating and cooling. The process is called distillation. In this activity you will distill water.

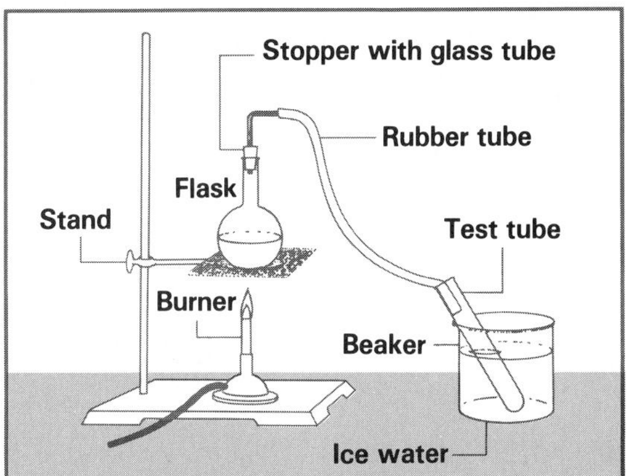

a. Put the equipment supplied by your teacher together as shown in the drawing.
b. Pour the colored water into the flask.
c. Put the stopper into the neck of the flask and the other end of the tube in the test tube.
d. Heat the flask slowly and observe what happens.

7. What happens to the colored water as the flask is heated?
8. Where did the water that changed to steam go?
9. What happened to the coloring material in the water?
10. How do you think other materials like oil might be distilled?

the sea. When the water evaporates, it goes into the air and later returns to the earth as rain.

Soil is a renewable resource. The top layer of soil, or topsoil, is used by growing plants both for support and as a source of water and mineral nutrients. When a plant dies, it falls to the earth and begins to decay. Burrowing animals, such as earthworms, eat decaying plant material. As they digest the dead plant material, their droppings enrich the soil. Thus, the materials taken from the soil are returned and reused.

Living organisms provide resources. Plants are grown and harvested to provide lumber, fiber for clothing, food, and many other products. After a crop is harvested, the land may be replanted.

Animals are also a renewable resource. Fish reproduce and are harvested from the sea. Cattle, hogs, and sheep are raised and used for food and to produce materials such as leather and wool.

The crops and animals on this farm are renewable resources.

Each renewable resource can be replenished. Some resources are replaced in seconds. Others take days, years, or centuries. A few are replaced without any effort on your part, while others are dependent on your efforts. **Your life depends in some way on each resource and its renewal.**

11. What are the two major groups of renewable resources?

12. Give two examples of renewable energy resources. How long do you think it would take to replenish each of them?

13. Name three things you use every day and the renewable resources that are used to make them.

33D CONSERVATION OF EARTH MATERIALS

You use more of the earth's resources than anyone who lived before you. Until the last 200 years, there were not very many people on the earth. Most people lived simple farming lives and used few of the earth's resources. But when people learned to use machines and to cure sickness, they began to live longer and use more resources. There are so many people living today that we may run out of some resources.

The only way for people to preserve the earth's resources is to practice CONSERVATION. **Conservation is a group of activities designed to protect the earth's resources.** Of course, if people did not use resources they could not live. So conservation is really the wise use of resources.

CONSERVATION METHODS

1. Controlled Use
2. Recycling
3. Alternate Sources

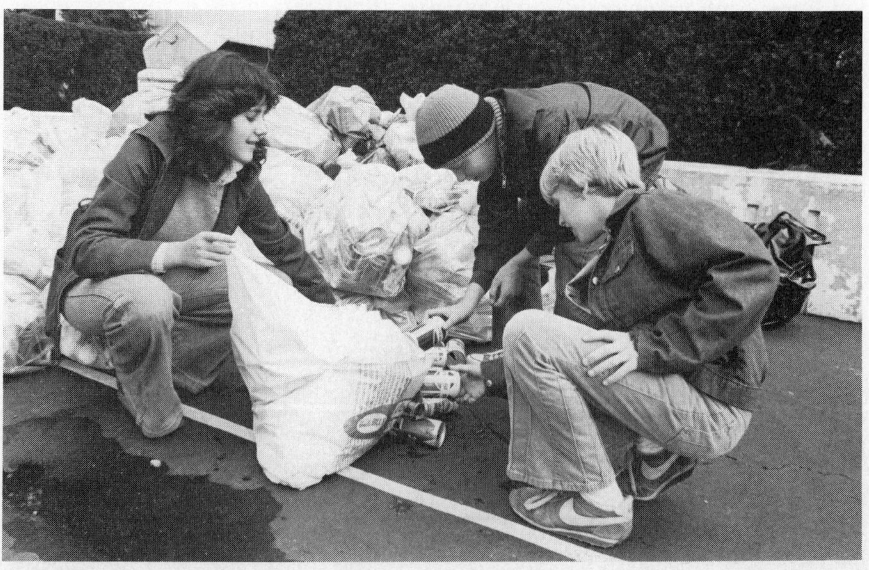

These students are helping to conserve natural resources by recycling nonrenewable earth materials.

There are three basic ways to conserve the earth's resources. The first is CONTROLLED USE. When the use of a renewable resource is controlled, people use less than the earth can replace. Cutting more wood than can be grown will destroy a forest. Controlled cutting and replanting will ensure a continuous supply of wood. **Controlled use gives the earth time to replace a resource.**

For nonrenewable resources, the only way for people to conserve is to RECYCLE. You recycle when you return aluminum cans to the store. The cans are melted down and made into new products. Recycled materials may be used two, three, or more times. **Recycling helps conserve by reducing the need to mine an earth material.**

Some resources, like petroleum, are rapidly being used up. Controlled use and recycling will help, but the best way to conserve is to find an ALTERNATE RESOURCE. **An alternate is a substitute.** Alcohol, made from grain, may be an alternate for gasoline. The energy of sunlight may be an alternate for heating oil or natural gas. Many new alternate sources are developed every year. But to be effective, the alternate sources must be used by a large number of people.

ACTIVITY: Conservation of Resources

MATERIALS: Poster board, markers

In this activity, you will create a list of resources, show how they are used, and show how they might be conserved. Your teacher will divide you into groups and give each group a set of materials.

- a. Draw a line down the center of your poster.
  b. Label the left side "Renewable Resources" and the right side "Nonrenewable Resources."
  c. Divide each side into three columns. Label one column "Resource", one "Use", and one "Conservation Method".
  d. Use the books and other resources in your classroom to fill in the table. Try to list at least ten resources on each side of your chart.

14. What kind of conservation method works best for renewable resources?
15. What kind of conservation method works best for nonrenewable resources?
16. How do the students in your group think you could conserve resources most effectively?

Conservation depends on people like you. You can help save the earth's resources by recycling materials and using only what you need. Without conservation, the world may run out of some resources in your lifetime.

17. What does the word *conservation* mean?
18. Name the three major ways to conserve resources.
19. Why must you help conserve the earth's resources?
20. Describe some ways you can help conserve resources.

SUMMARY

VOCABULARY

natural resources	ore	conservation
renewable resources	metallic	controlled use
nonrenewable resources	nonmetallic	recycle
earth materials	petroleum	alternate resource

KEY FACTS AND CONCEPTS

A natural resource is something provided by the earth that meets a need.

Renewable resources can be replaced.

Nonrenewable resources cannot be replaced.

Anything taken from the earth and used is an earth material.

Earth materials include petroleum and ores of metals and nonmetals.

Ores are concentrations of minerals deposited in the earth.

Petroleum includes coal, oil, and natural gas.

Conservation is the wise use of resources.

Conservation includes controlled use, recycling, and the use of alternate sources.

Controlled use gives the earth time to replace a resource.

Recycling helps conserve by reducing the need for an earth material.

An alternate source is a substitute for a resource.

Conservation depends on you.

CONCLUSION

The earth provides everything you need for life. Its natural resources provide fuel, food, clothing, and housing. In order to ensure that there will be resources for the future, you must use resources wisely. Conservation is up to you!

21. What is the KEY IDEA of this chapter?

CHAPTER

34 The Atmosphere

A Changing Ocean of Air

34A INTRODUCTION

This photo of the earth was taken by *Apollo 16* astronauts from the moon.

The earth is surrounded by a layer of air called the ATMOSPHERE. **The atmosphere is a mixture of gases, water vapor, dust, and chemicals.** The atmosphere provides the oxygen and carbon dioxide that all living things must have. Changes in the atmosphere produce WEATHER. **The behavior of the atmosphere affects you every day.**

THE ATMOSPHERE

1. Makes life possible
2. Produces weather
3. Affects the way you live

Weather consists of the day-to-day changes in the atmosphere. Thunderstorms, hail, rain, snow, and wind are parts of what makes up the weather. Longer trends in the way the atmosphere behaves are called CLIMATE.

Climate varies depending on where you live. Some areas of the earth have lots of rain and snow, while others are very dry. Some parts of the earth are hot, and others are cold. Tourists lie in the sunshine of a Florida winter, for example, while people are skiing or shoveling snow in Colorado. Climate controls the way people live and the kinds of things they do.

WEATHER: day-to-day changes in the atmosphere
CLIMATE: long-term weather trends

1. What is the atmosphere?
2. Why do you depend on the atmosphere for life?
3. How is climate different from weather?
4. How does weather affect your life?

34B WHAT IS AIR?

Air is a mixture of gases. Most air is a mixture of nitrogen (78%) and oxygen (21%). The other one percent is made up of argon, carbon dioxide, and small amounts of many other gases. Air also contains some water in gas form, or water vapor. The amount of water vapor in the air varies as conditions in the atmosphere change. In a given amount of air, up to four percent of the air may be water vapor.

In addition to gases and water vapor, air usually contains dust, ash, and chemicals. The dust may be soil or pollen lifted by the wind. Salt spray from the ocean is also carried in the air. The ash comes from erupting volcanoes and from smoke from forest fires. In recent years, chemicals from factory smokestacks and cars have been added to the air.

POLLUTION is caused by unnatural chemicals in the air. **Industrial chemicals along with car exhaust and smoke cause pollution.** The chemicals often mix with water vapor in the air and form weak acids. These acids can cause paint to peel from buildings. Many pollutants can kill plants and damage your lungs.

When pollutants get trapped near the ground, a dangerous mixture of smoke and fog called SMOG results. Smog often gets so thick over large cities that people have difficulty breathing. New York and Los Angeles, for example, have had serious air pollution problems. Many industries and cities spend billions of dollars every year to improve the quality of the air. Their efforts should result in a healthier environment for everyone.

AIR IS MADE OF:

Gases:	Oxygen
	Nitrogen
Water vapor:	Water
Dust:	Pollen
	Smoke
Pollutants:	Chemicals

The atmosphere presses down on the earth because of gravity. Gravity pulls each molecule of air toward the earth. Air is pulled down with the greatest force, or pressure, at sea level. Air pressure changes according to the air's temperature and height above sea level. Air pressure also changes as storms move through the atmosphere. **In fact, meteorologists measure air pressure to forecast storms.**

ACTIVITY: Measuring Air Pressure

MATERIALS: Clean glass jar, balloon, soda straw, glue, cardboard, markers

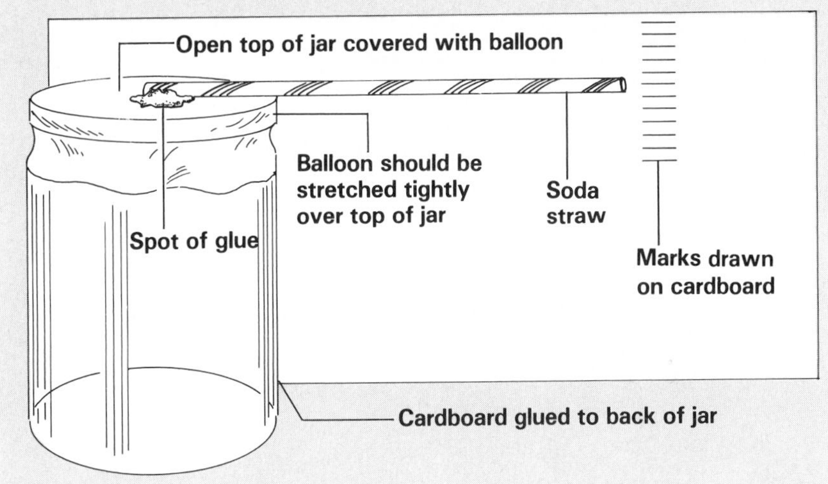

In this activity, you will build a device called a barometer. Barometers are used to measure air pressure. Once you have made your barometer, you will use it to measure changes in the atmosphere.

a. Stretch the balloon tightly over the open top of the jar.
b. Put a spot of glue in the exact center of the balloon.
c. Place one end of the soda straw in the glue.
d. Mark a scale on the cardboard.
e. Glue the cardboard to the back of the jar as shown in the drawing.
f. Construct a chart in your notebook. The chart should show the air pressure measured by your barometer. It should also show wind speed and direction, clouds, and rain or snow.
g. After several days, study your chart and then answer the following questions.

5. How does your barometer work?
6. How are changes in air pressure related to the weather?

Three physical factors—temperature, humidity, and air pressure—affect the way the air behaves. **Temperature is the amount of heat energy in the air.** It affects air pressure. Temperature also controls the amount of water vapor the air can hold.

The amount of water vapor in the air is called humidity. It determines whether clouds can form and if rain will fall. Lastly, it is changes in air pressure that cause winds to blow.

Temperature, humidity, and pressure describe the atmosphere's condition. Meteorologists use these three factors in forecasting the weather.

7. Name and describe three materials found in air.
8. What is air pressure?
9. Describe pollution and its effects.
10. What are the three physical factors that describe the condition of the atmosphere?

34C THE STRUCTURE OF THE ATMOSPHERE

The earth's "ocean" of air is not the same from top to bottom. Meteorologists have divided the atmosphere into layers. Each layer behaves in a different way. The bottom layer is called the TROPOSPHERE. The troposphere begins at the earth's surface and is about eighteen kilometers high. **All weather occurs in the troposphere.**

The second layer is called the STRATOSPHERE. The air's temperature is fairly constant from the bottom to the top of this layer. The stratosphere is about thirty-two kilometers thick and has only a few thin clouds.

Above the stratosphere is the EXOSPHERE. The exosphere is almost 482 kilometers thick. It stretches upward until the air thins out to the vacuum of space.

ACTIVITY: A Model of the Atmosphere

MATERIALS: Earth model from Chapter 30, markers, paper

In this activity, you will finish the model you began in Chapter 30. When you are finished, you will have a model of the earth. Your model will stretch from the center of the earth to the edge of space.

a. If you did not leave 2 m of paper beyond the earth's surface when you began your model, add it now.

b. Use your markers to add the following information.
The troposphere is about 18 kilometers thick. Scale = 1.7 cm
The stratosphere is about 32 kilometers thick. Scale = 3.2 cm
The exosphere is about 482 kilometers thick. Scale = 89 cm

c. Use section 34C to add more information to your model.

11. How does your size compare to the size of the earth and its atmosphere?
12. What happens to the atmosphere as you move away from the earth's surface?
13. Where does the weather that affects you occur?

When the sun shines on the earth, the atmosphere is heated. The air near the equator is heated more than the air near the North and South Poles. The heated air moves toward the poles while the cooler air moves toward the equator. As the earth rotates, it churns the air forming WIND BELTS. Wind belts stretch around the earth. **In a wind belt, winds blow primarily from one direction.**

WIND BELTS

Causes: Heat from the sun
Rotation of the earth

Effect: Move air around the earth

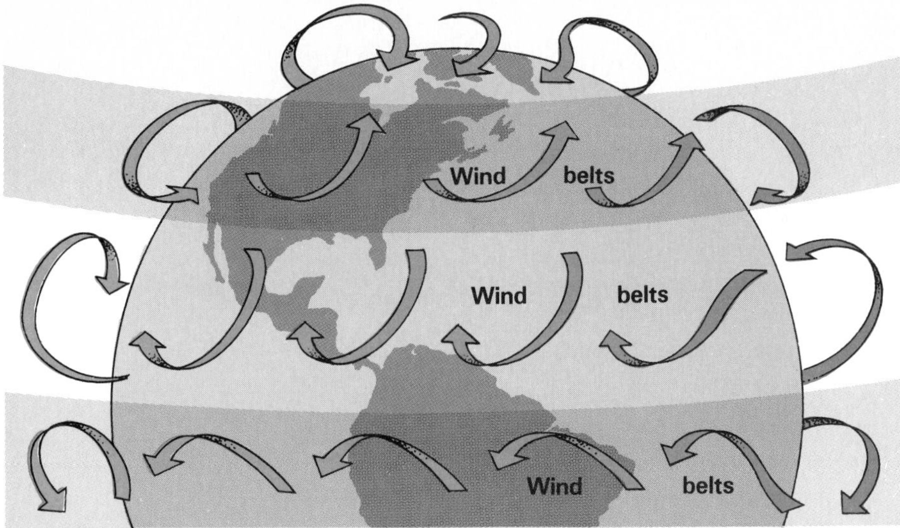

The sun's energy and the earth's rotation combine to cause belts of wind that circle the earth.

In the days of sailing ships, sailors used wind belts to help them go from one place to another. But if they sailed into a region between two belts, they could get trapped. Between wind belts the wind may shift rapidly from one direction to another or not blow at all.

JET STREAMS blow above the wind belts at the upper edge of the troposphere. **Jet streams are narrow bands of wind moving very fast.** They often blow faster than 300 kilometers per hour. **Storms on the surface of the earth tend to follow the paths of jet streams.** The rushing jet streams pull the storms along.

14. Name three layers in the atmosphere.
15. Which layer in the atmosphere contains all your weather?
16. How do winds behave between wind belts?
17. What are jet streams? How do they move storms?

34D CLOUDS

CLOUDS form when water vapor changes from a gas to a liquid, or condenses. **The water vapor condenses around small particles like smoke and dust.** As molecules of water vapor attach themselves to each particle, they form tiny drops of liquid water. **Millions of tiny water drops floating in the air form a cloud.** If you have ever walked in fog you have seen a cloud at ground level.

Clouds take many forms depending on how the air is moving. However, there are three basic types. Clouds are named according to their shape and height. Clouds composed of flat, smooth layers that cover the whole sky are called STRATUS clouds. They form when a layer of air is cooled without being mixed by the wind. When rain falls from stratus clouds it tends to be light and steady.

CUMULUS clouds are formed by rising air. They have flat bottoms and are very puffy. In fact, the word *cumulus* means "piled up" or "puffy." Cumulus clouds usually indicate fair weather. In very moist air, cumulus clouds may grow to greater heights. They are then called congested clouds.

When a stratus cloud produces rain or snow, it is called a nimbostratus cloud. If a cumulus cloud gets large enough to produce rain, it

Clouds are categorized based on their height and shape.

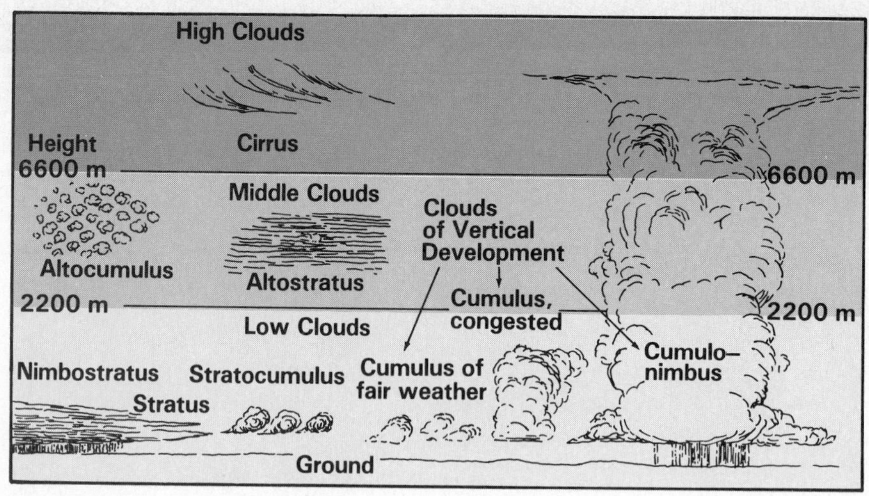

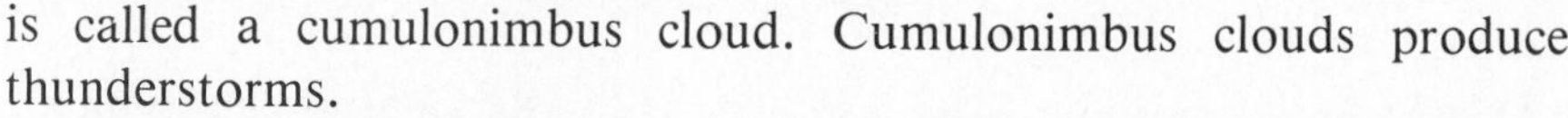
is called a cumulonimbus cloud. Cumulonimbus clouds produce thunderstorms.

Some clouds form close to the earth. **Clouds that form at lower levels are called altostratus and altocumulus.** They indicate what kind of weather is on the way.

CIRRUS clouds form far up in the troposphere. They are thin, wispy clouds made of ice crystals. Cirrus clouds often indicate the coming of rain or snow.

These photos show the three types of clouds. The first photo is of stratus clouds, the second is of cumulus, and the third is of cirrus.

Level	Wispy	Flat	Fluffy
High:	Cirrus		Cumulonimbus
Middle:		Altostratus	Altocumulus
			Cumulonimbus
Low:		Stratus	Cumulus
		Nimbostratus	Cumulonimbus

18. When do clouds form?
19. What is a cloud?
20. Describe the three basic types of cloud.
21. What type of weather is usually associated with each type of cloud?

34E PRECIPITATION

When the tiny water drops that form clouds become heavy enough, they fall from the clouds as PRECIPITATION. Precipitation takes many forms. **The kind of precipitation that falls is controlled by the air temperature.**

When the air temperature is above freezing, water drops fall to the ground as rain. Rain falling through cold air near the ground may freeze when it strikes the earth. Such freezing rain coats power lines, roads, and trees with ice. If raindrops freeze in the air, they fall to the ground as sleet.

Snow is made of tiny, six-sided ice crystals. Snow forms if water in a cloud condenses when the temperature is below freezing. Snowflakes often grow as they fall by bumping into each other. When the air is very cold, snow is usually light and fluffy. If the temperature is near freezing, the snow is wet and sticky. The weight of wet snow can pull down trees and power lines.

Snowflakes form when water vapor condenses and freezes one molecule at a time.

Hail is a special kind of precipitation. **Hail forms only in cumulonimbus, or thunderstorm, clouds.** Each hailstone is a layered ball of ice. Hailstones are formed when drops of water freeze in a cloud. Because of the upward movement of wind, the hailstone is kept above the freezing level for a long time. As more water droplets hit the hailstone and freeze, new layers of ice are added on. **When the hail finally falls, it does great damage.**

22. What is precipitation?
23. How does snow form?
24. Explain how a hailstone forms.

Hail damage to a cornfield is shown in this photo. A magnified hailstone is shown in the photo at the top right.

SUMMARY

VOCABULARY

atmosphere
weather
climate
pollution
smog
troposphere
stratosphere
exosphere
wind belt
jet stream
cloud
stratus
cumulus
cirrus
precipitation

KEY FACTS AND CONCEPTS

The earth is surrounded by a layer of air called the atmosphere.

The atmosphere is a mixture of gases, water vapor, dust, and chemicals.

Short-term events in the atmosphere are called weather.

Long-term events in the atmosphere are called climate.

Weather and climate affect your life every day.

Pressure, temperature, and humidity describe the condition of the atmosphere.

Three layers in the atmosphere are the troposphere, the stratosphere, and the exosphere.

All weather occurs in the troposphere, which is the layer nearest the earth.

Wind belts move air over the earth.

Jet streams are narrow bands of high-speed wind.

Clouds form when water vapor condenses around small particles of dust and smoke in the air.

Clouds take many forms.

There are three basic cloud types—stratus, cumulus, and cirrus.

The kind of precipitation that falls from a cloud is controlled by the air temperature.

CONCLUSION

You depend on the atmosphere for life. The moving winds and conditions in the troposphere form clouds and precipitation called weather. Weather and climate determine the kind of house you live in, clothes you wear, food you eat, and activities you engage in.

25. What is the KEY IDEA of this chapter?

CHAPTER

35 Weather

The Churning Atmosphere

35A INTRODUCTION

At any given moment, more than one hundred STORMS are taking place on the earth. **Storms are violent disturbances in the atmosphere.** Storms are the most dangerous and feared of all kinds of weather.

There are several different kinds of storms, but they all have one thing in common. **Storms move heat energy in the atmosphere from one place to another.** The amount of energy involved controls the size of a storm. The most common storms, called cyclonic storms, move moderate amounts of energy. They cause winds that stir the air and produce rain or snow. But when a great deal of heat energy is involved, storms may become violent. Violent storms can destroy homes and threaten lives. **Whether they are moderate or violent, storms affect what you do and what you wear from day to day.**

Storms create most of the weather that affects you every day. In this chapter, you will learn about the different kinds of storms. You will

CYCLONIC STORMS are moderate storms that cause changes in day-to-day weather.

VIOLENT STORMS include hurricanes, tornadoes, and thunderstorms and can be very dangerous.

find out how meteorologists forecast storms and what to do when a violent storm is nearby. Most important, you will see how storms create weather that controls your life.

1. What is a storm?
2. Describe the two different kinds of storms. How are they different?
3. What causes storms?
4. How do storms affect your life?

35B AIR MASSES

When a large mass of air stays in one place over the earth, it takes on the properties of the region. An AIR MASS is a large body of air with the same temperature and moisture throughout. An air mass over the North Pole would get slowly cooler, while one over the equator would get warmer. An air mass sitting over land will dry out, while one over the ocean will soak up moisture. Warm and cool air masses are always present in the atmosphere.

When an air mass is moved by wind belts or jet streams, it meets other air masses that are warmer or cooler. The boundary between two air masses with different temperatures and moistures is called a STATIONARY FRONT.

When the air masses moving on opposite sides of a stationary front mix, the warmer air is forced upward. This forms an area of low pressure. **Storms are areas of low pressure in the atmosphere.**

In the large air masses on either side of a stationary front, air pressure is usually higher than normal. Air flowing away from the center of the air mass moves clockwise. As it moves along one side of the station-

A stationary front is the interface between two air masses. When winds begin to blow along a stationary front, a cyclonic storm may form.

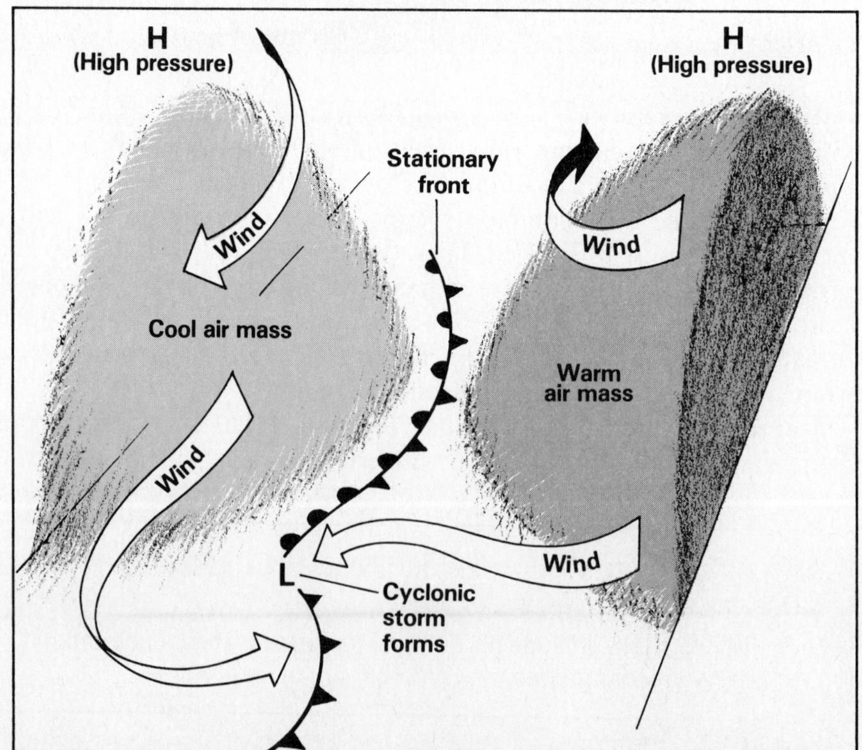

ary front into a developing center of low pressure, the air is turned in a different direction. So the air starts to move counterclockwise. **Thus, a cyclonic storm is an area of low pressure with winds blowing counterclockwise around its center.**

Air flowing into a cyclonic storm is lifted into the atmosphere by the decreasing pressure. The moisture in the air condenses and forms precipitation, releasing heat energy. The heat energy causes the air to expand, lowering the pressure. The decreasing air pressure pulls more moist air into the storm, keeping it alive.

5. Describe an air mass.
6. What causes air masses to move? What happens when they move?
7. Describe a stationary front.
8. How do cyclonic storms form along stationary fronts?

35C CYCLONIC STORMS

When a cyclonic storm develops as a low pressure area between two air masses, COLD and WARM FRONTS are formed. As the wind begins blowing around a cyclonic storm, cooler air from one air mass is pushed under the other. The new boundary is called a cold front. Warmer air from the other air mass is blown up and over the cooler air forming a warm front. **Weather that affects you usually occurs near a warm or cold front.**

A cold front is a boundary where cooler air moves under warmer air. The cool air pushes the warmer air upward and cumulus or cumulonimbus clouds form. Showers and thunderstorms result as the warm, moist air is lifted into the atmosphere. Cold fronts usually move more rapidly than warm fronts. Consequently, the showers or thunderstorms along a cold front last only a short time.

A warm front forms where warmer air is pushed up and over cooler air. Along warm fronts, the air is lifted slowly and stratus clouds form. The clouds often stretch far ahead of the front. They begin as high cirrus clouds and gradually change to altostratus and stratus as the front approaches. The rain or snow that comes with a warm front is usually slow and steady, often lasting for several days.

Cyclonic storms normally last from seven to ten days. During that time, wind belts and jet streams move the storm across the earth's surface. As the storm moves, the cold front slowly catches up with the warm front. On the fifth or sixth day, the cold front collides with the warm front and an OCCLUDED FRONT is formed.

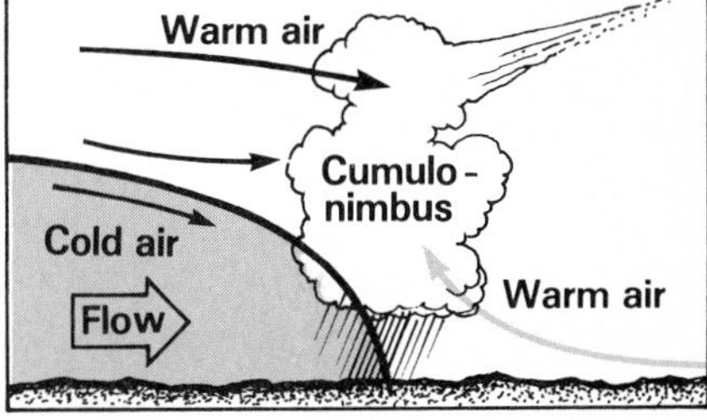

Cold fronts move rapidly, with brisk winds and showers or thunderstorms.

Warm fronts move slowly, with lowering clouds and steady rains.

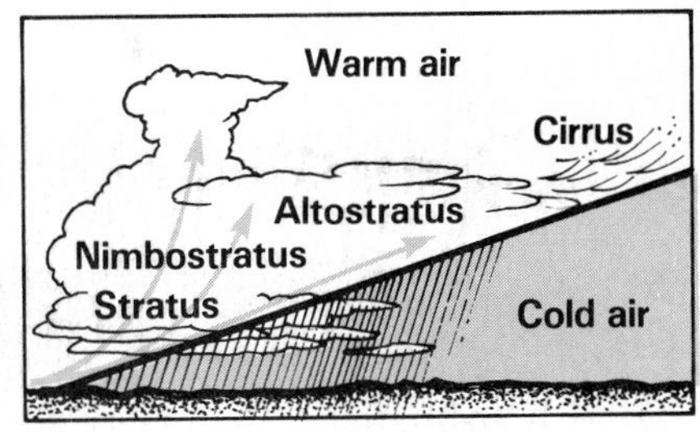

An occluded front forms when a cold front pushes a warm air mass up into the atmosphere.

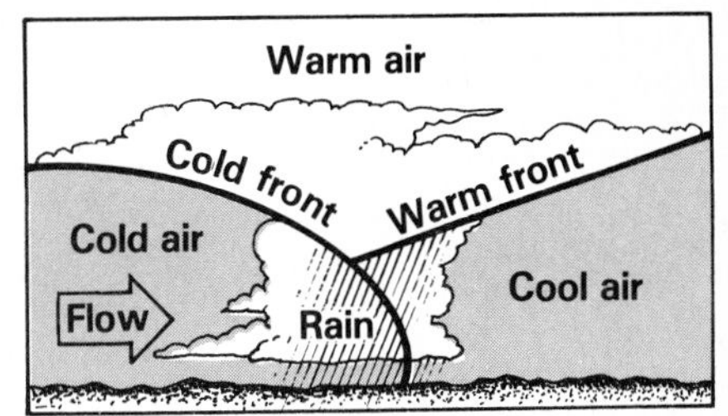

DIFFERENT TYPES OF FRONTS

STATIONARY FRONT: the boundary between two different air masses

COLD FRONT: forms where cooler air moves into warmer air

WARM FRONT: forms where warmer air moves up and over cooler air

OCCLUDED FRONT: forms when cooler air pushes under an entire warm air mass

These drawings show the life cycle of a cyclonic storm.

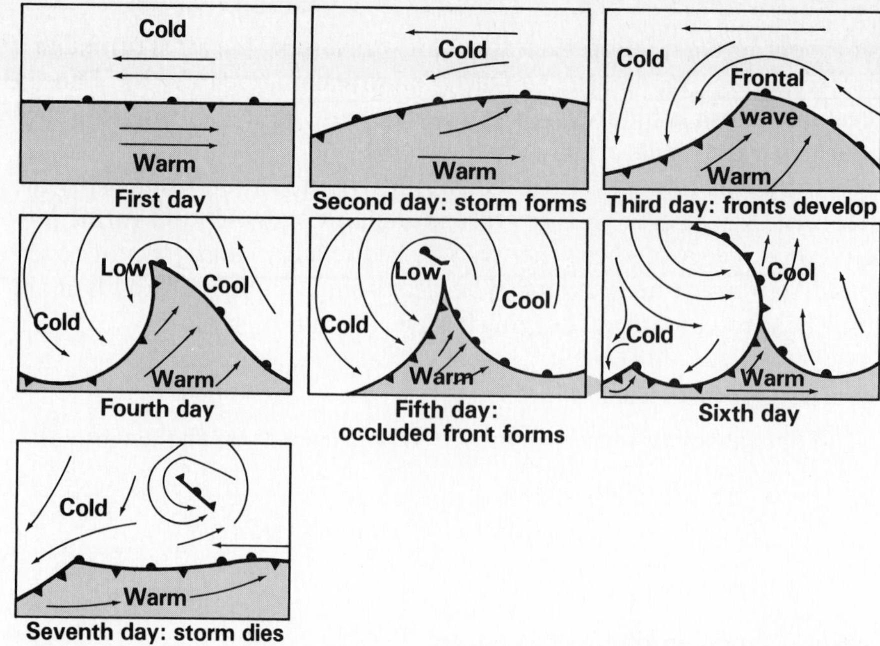

When an occluded front forms, the cold air mass pushes the entire warm air mass off the ground. As the great mass of warm, moist air is lifted and cooled, the water in the air condenses. Occluded fronts often produce heavy rains. As the warm air cools, the storm runs out of energy. **Finally, all that remains of the cyclonic storm is a churned mass of air.**

Cyclonic storms move across the United States about once every week. Their cold, warm, and occluded fronts produce wind, rain, and snow. The air masses that come with cyclonic storms change the air temperature as they move over an area. Meteorologists study cyclonic storms and prepare forecasts of their behavior. You can use weather forecasts to plan what to do or what to wear on a given day.

9. Describe the weather around a cold front, a warm front, and an occluded front.
10. How does a cyclonic storm move?
11. Describe and draw a picture of the life cycle of a cyclonic storm.

35D VIOLENT STORMS

Special conditions in the atmosphere cause violent weather to occur. HURRICANES, TORNADOES, and THUNDERSTORMS are three kinds of violent storms. When violent storms occur, they can destroy entire towns and kill many people. Meteorologists issue special forecasts and warnings about violent storms. You should learn how violent storms behave and how to protect yourself when they are predicted.

TYPES OF VIOLENT STORMS

HURRICANE: very large storms with high winds

TORNADO: small, very powerful, funnel-shaped clouds

THUNDERSTORM: short, violent storm that may produce lightning and hail

Hurricanes form over the warm waters of the South Atlantic between two wind belts. Under certain conditions, an area of low pressure may develop and grow into a gigantic storm. Hurricanes may measure up to 640 kilometers across and bring winds as high as 320 kilometers per hour blowing around a calm center. **This calm center is called the eye of the hurricane.**

Hurricanes produce heavy rains and high seas that flood large areas when the storms strike land. Hurricanes may cause tornadoes and violent thunderstorms as the wind belts move them slowly northward. The United States is hit by a hurricane about twice every year. Approximately every three years, a severe hurricane strikes, killing people and causing millions of dollars in property damage.

Tornadoes are small, but very violent, twisting storms. Tornadoes are funnel-shaped clouds produced by severe thunderstorms. Such storms form ahead of strong cold fronts. They travel over the land at speeds of thirty or sixty kilometers per hour. Winds inside the funnel may blow up to 470 kilometers per hour, whirling around a center of very low pressure. Tornadoes have caused houses and barns to explode as the normal air pressure inside the buildings tried to escape into the low pressure of the tornado. Meteorologists issue special warnings about tornadoes to help people get out of their way.

Tornadoes are funnel-shaped clouds with very strong winds.

Thunderstorms produce high winds, rain, hail, and lightning that can damage buildings and kill people. Thunderstorms form when warm, moist air is lifted rapidly into the atmosphere. The storms begin as cumulus clouds. The cumulus clouds grow into cumulonimbus clouds that can reach heights of 27,000 meters. In their final stage, the cumulonimbus clouds have flat tops as winds in the stratosphere blow the top parts of the clouds away.

Inside a thunderstorm, strong drafts of wind move up and down in the cloud. Friction in the rapidly moving air generates lightning, while rain falls in torrents from the growing cloud. When very strong updrafts form in a cloud, hail may fall. Hail does great damage, especially to crops.

LIGHTNING is the most dangerous aspect of a thunderstorm. A single lightning bolt may discharge up to 30 million volts at 100,000 ampheres. **Lightning strikes take place thousands of times every day.** The strikes kill hundreds of people every year. A few simple safety rules can help you protect yourself during a thunderstorm.

Lightning is caused by friction inside a thunderstorm.

LIGHTNING SAFETY RULES

1. Never stand in the open, near water, or under a tree during a thunderstorm.
2. Seek shelter in a car or building.
3. If you are caught outdoors, go to the lowest place you can find and lie flat on the ground.

Thunderstorms are the most common and smallest of the violent storms. Several hundred thunderstorms are occurring right now somewhere on the earth. The average thunderstorm releases as much energy as an atomic bomb. **Like cyclonic storms, hurricanes, tornadoes, and thunderstorms are nature's way of moving energy in the atmosphere.**

12. How are violent storms different from cyclonic storms?
13. Describe a thunderstorm. Explain the lightning safety rules.
14. Describe a tornado.
15. Describe a hurricane.

35E FORECASTING WEATHER

Meteorologists study the atmosphere to learn how it works and how to predict its behavior. They gather information about conditions in the atmosphere from weather stations all over the world. The information is used to make maps that show the atmosphere's condition. Air masses, low and high pressure areas, fronts, and violent weather are all shown with special symbols on weather maps. Meteorologists make new maps every six to twelve hours. **Using series of maps, they can watch the atmosphere change.**

In the 1970's, pictures from satellites in space became available as another way to watch the atmosphere. Satellite photographs are taken every thirty minutes and sent to earth for study. Series of the pictures can be used like a motion picture to show the atmosphere changing. Satellites also show weather activity over oceans and other areas where weather observers cannot easily go.

WEATHER FORECASTS are predictions about how the atmosphere will behave in the coming hours and days. Meteorologists use weather maps, satellite photos, balloons, radar, pilot and weather observer reports, and computers to make up forecasts. **A forecast includes information on the condition of the atmosphere, a description of how it has behaved, and a prediction of how it will behave.** Forecasts pay special attention to the possibility of violent storms. They

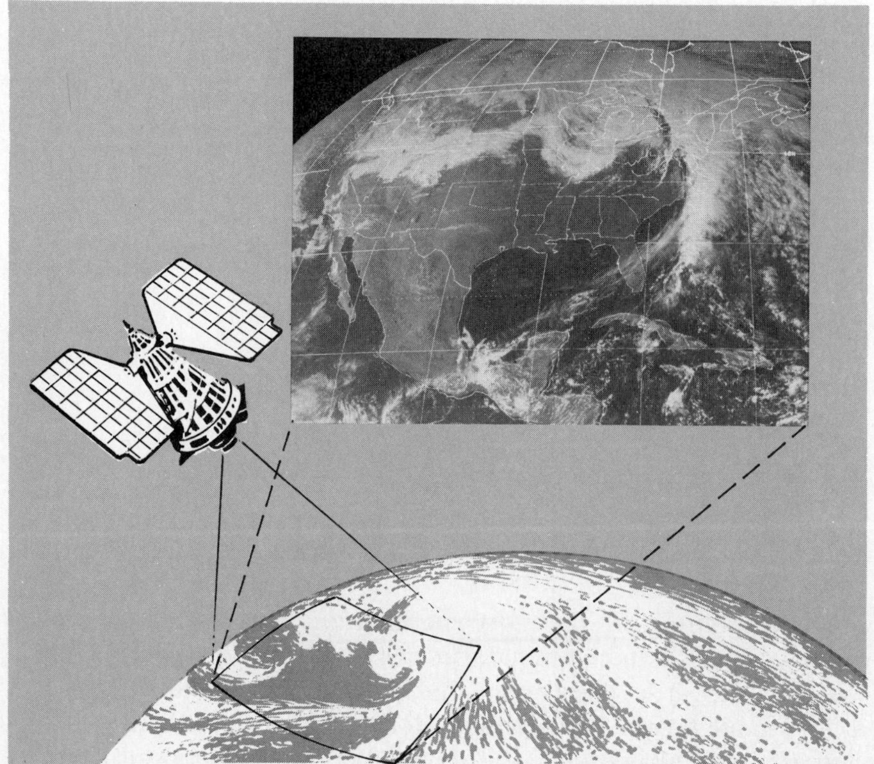

Weather satellites give meteorologists a way to watch the atmosphere change from space.

also provide information for special groups of people, such as pilots and farmers.

Forecasts can help you prepare for tomorrow's weather. Forecasts are printed in newspapers and broadcast on radio and television. They are also sent to airports and coastguard stations. A special network of weather radio stations around the United States broadcasts weather reports twenty-four hours a day.

When violent weather develops, meteorologists interrupt regular radio and television programs to broadcast warnings. They will tell you where the storms are and what to do to protect yourself. **You should listen carefully to their warnings and follow their directions. They could save your life!**

16. What major tools do meteorologists use to forecast the weather?
17. How do forecasts get to the public?
18. What kind of information does a forecast include?
19. What should you do when a violent storm warning is forecast?

ACTIVITY: Forecasting the Weather

MATERIALS: Newspapers, scissors, glue, markers, poster board

In this activity, you will see how the atmosphere changes. You will also learn how meteorologists prepare weather maps and write forecasts.

a. Collect newspapers for a period of several weeks.
b. Cut out the weather maps and forecasts. Glue them, in order, on the poster board. Also save any articles about violent storms.
c. Locate and mark the high and low pressure areas on your maps.
d. Mark the fronts and any violent weather.
e. Compare the forecasts for each day's weather with the actual weather as reported on the following day.

20. Describe how the cyclonic storms on your maps changed from day to day.
21. Were the forecasts for your area accurate? How did the weather relate to the passage of warm or cold fronts?
22. Describe how weather forecasts might affect your plans from day to day.

SUMMARY

VOCABULARY

storm
air mass
stationary front
cold front
warm front
occluded front
hurricane
tornado
thunderstorm
lightning
weather forecast

KEY FACTS AND CONCEPTS

Storms are violent disturbances in the atmosphere.

Storms move heat energy in the atmosphere from one place to another.

Storms create most of the weather that affects you everyday.

An air mass is a large body of air with the same temperature and moisture throughout.

The boundary between two air masses with different temperatures and moistures is called a stationary front.

A cyclonic storm is an area of low pressure with winds blowing counterclockwise around its center.

A cold front is the boundary where cooler air moves under warmer air.

A warm front is the boundary where warmer air moves up and over a mass of cooler air.

Cyclonic storms normally last from seven to ten days.

An occluded front occurs when cool air pushes an entire warm air mass up in the atmosphere.

Hurricanes are very large, violent storms.

Tornadoes are small, very violent, funnel-shaped storms.

Thunderstorms produce high winds, rain, hail, and lightning that can damage buildings and kill people.

Meteorologists study the atmosphere to learn how it works and to predict its behavior.

Forecasts are predictions about how the atmosphere will behave in the coming hours and days.

Forecasts can help you prepare for tomorrow's weather.

CONCLUSION

Storms create most of the weather that affects you every day. Cyclonic storms create most weather by forming fronts that move over the earth's surface. Violent storms do great damage and often injure people. Meteorologists prepare forecasts to help you prepare for tomorrow's weather.

23. What is the KEY IDEA of this chapter?

CHAPTER

36 Planet Earth

The Earth as a Body in Space

36A INTRODUCTION

While you are reading this paragraph, the earth will travel about 725 kilometers in its orbit around the sun. The earth is one of nine PLANETS traveling around an average-size star called the sun. The sun provides heat, light, and the gravity that holds the planets in their paths, or ORBITS.

The word *planet* means "wandering star". The name was given to a group of bright objects in the sky that appeared to move among the stars. Each of the planets is different, but the earth is unique. Scientists believe that only the earth supports life. All the planets rotate on imaginary lines called AXES and orbit the sun. **The earth's motion around the sun creates the seasons, a way of measuring time, and a system of determining location.**

The earth is a unique, life-supporting planet.

THE EARTH

ROTATES: turns on its axis
REVOLVES: travels in an orbit about the sun

Because you live on the earth, its motions affect your life. In this chapter, you will learn how the planet behaves as it rotates on its axis and revolves around the sun. You will also learn how the earth's nearest neighbor, the moon, affects the earth.

1. What is a planet?
2. Name and describe the two major motions of the planet Earth.
3. Why is the earth unique among all the planets?

36B LOCATION AND TIME

As the earth revolves around the sun it rotates, or turns, on a slightly tilted axis. The North Pole and South Pole mark the points at which the axis would pass through the earth. The earth rotates about fifteen degrees every hour and makes one complete turn every twenty-four hours.

Meridians, or lines, of LONGITUDE are imaginary lines drawn vertically at fifteen-degree intervals around the earth. **The meridians of longitude divide the world into time zones.** The meridian of longitude passing through the Greenwich Observatory in England was chosen as the starting point for the world's time zones. Therefore, the Greenwich meridian is often called the PRIME MERIDIAN.

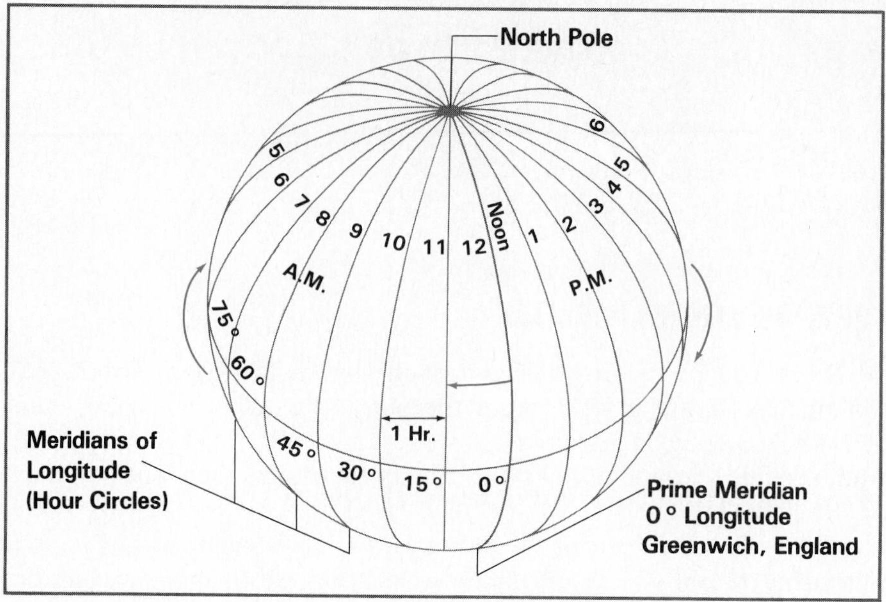

The earth rotates 15° on its axis every hour. Local time is measured by counting the hour circles east and west from Greenwich, England.

The time at any particular place in the world is called the LOCAL TIME of that place. The earth is divided into twenty-four TIME ZONES. Each zone is fifteen degrees wide. **The local time of the meridian that runs through the center of a time zone is the time used by all places within the zone.** The local time in each time zone differs from its neighboring zones by one hour. The meridians that divide time zones are called HOUR CIRCLES.

The earth's rotation also allows you to find your location on its surface. Because the earth turns on its axis, meridians help you find your east and west location. PARALLELS are a set of imaginary horizontal lines used to find north and south location.

Distances north and south, called LATITUDE, are measured from a line called the EQUATOR. **The equator is an imaginary line that cuts the earth in half horizontally.** The other parallels are drawn around the earth parallel to the equator. The parallels are numbered from 0° to 90°, beginning with the equator, which is 0°. All the other parallels are numbered at 10° intervals up to 90° at the North and South Poles.

Meridians of longitude (A) locate position east and west. Parallels of latitude (B) locate position north and south. When they are combined (C), you can locate any place on the earth.

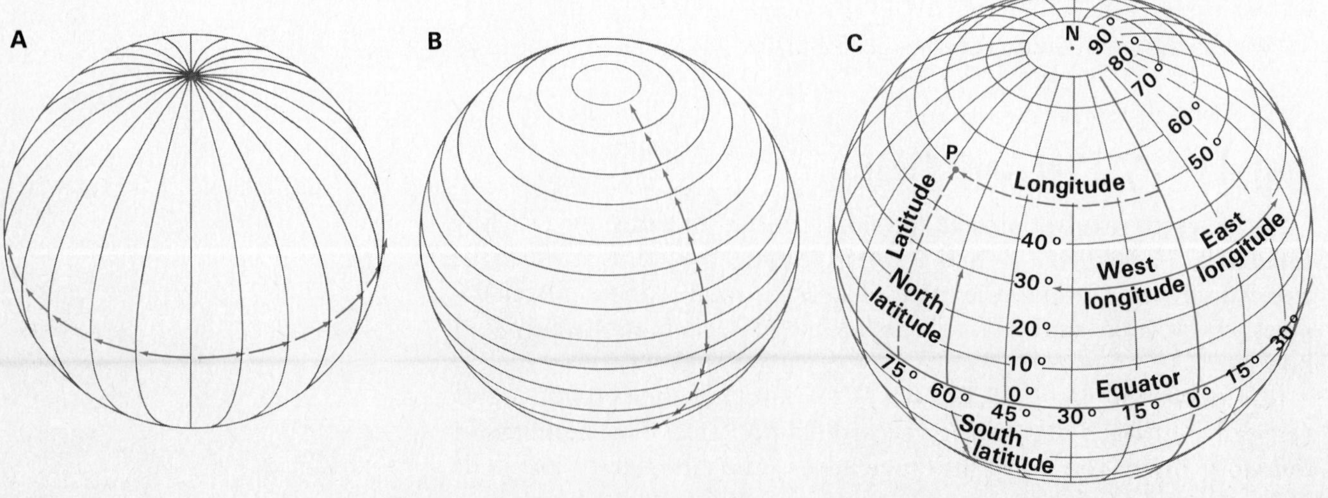

Together, meridians and parallels form an imaginary grid of lines that covers the earth. The grid helps you locate any point on the earth by knowing two positions. The first position is the distance east or west of Greenwich, England called longitude. The second position is the distance north or south of the equator called latitude.

Time and location are used every day to move ships and planes safely from place to place. Meridians of longitude are used to determine time. The same meridians that are used to determine time are used with parallels of latitude to pinpoint locations. Both time and location are a result of the earth's rotation.

4. What are meridians of longitude?
5. What is the prime meridian?
6. What are parallels of latitude?
7. What is local time? How is it determined?
8. What is a time zone?
9. How are longitude and latitude used to pinpoint a location?

36C SEASONS

As the earth revolves around the sun throughout the year, the length of day and night changes. The changes produce different periods of climate called SEASONS. The four seasons are, of course, summer, fall, winter, and spring. Each season has a unique climate. **The different weather conditions that characterize each season are caused by different amounts of heat energy that strike the earth's surface in one year.**

The earth's axis is not straight up and down. It is tilted 23½°. The tilt of the earth's axis causes the four seasons.

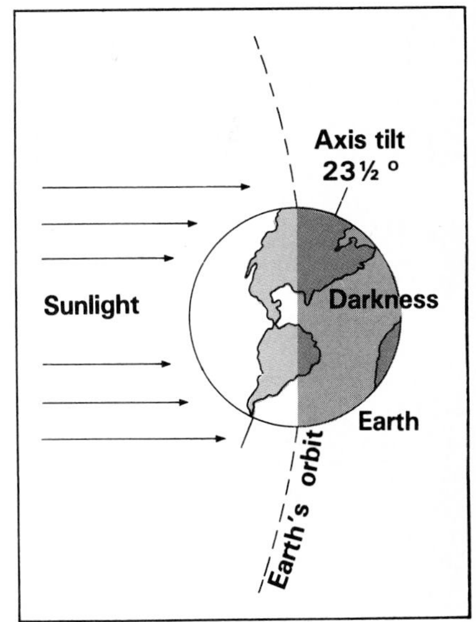

Throughout the year, the length of day and night changes. This happens because the earth's axis is not straight up and down. Instead, the axis is tilted at a 23½° angle. If the earth's axis were straight up and down, the earth would have twelve hours of daylight and twelve hours of darkness every day of the year. Because the earth is tilted, its relationship to the sun changes as it travels in its orbit.

You live on the northern half of the earth called the northern hemisphere. During the summer, the northern hemisphere is tilted toward the sun. Below the equator, the southern hemisphere is having winter because it is tilted away from the sun. **The hemisphere that is tilted toward the sun receives the sun's energy more directly. Also, the days are longer.** The combination causes the earth to receive more heat in that hemisphere, and the result is summer.

During the summer season in the northern hemisphere, the earth is tilted toward the sun. During the winter season, the earth is on the opposite side of the sun and the northern hemisphere is tilted away from the sun. June 21 is the SUMMER SOLSTICE, and December 21 is the WINTER SOLSTICE. On those days, the northern hemisphere is pointed directly toward or away from the sun. **The summer solstice is the longest day of the year and the first day of summer. The winter solstice is the shortest day of the year and the first day of winter.**

As the earth moves in its orbit around the sun, it passes two points at which the length of day and night are equal. On these two days the earth's axis is straight up and down in the direction of the sun. The

VERNAL EQUINOX, or first day of spring, occurs on March 20. The AUTUMNAL EQUINOX, or first day of fall, occurs on September 22 or 23.

SEASONS

SUMMER SOLSTICE: First day of summer, longest day of year (June 21)

AUTUMNAL EQUINOX: First day of fall, day and night equal (September 22 or 23)

WINTER SOLSTICE: First day of winter, shortest day of year (December 21)

VERNAL EQUINOX: First day of spring, day and night equal (March 20)

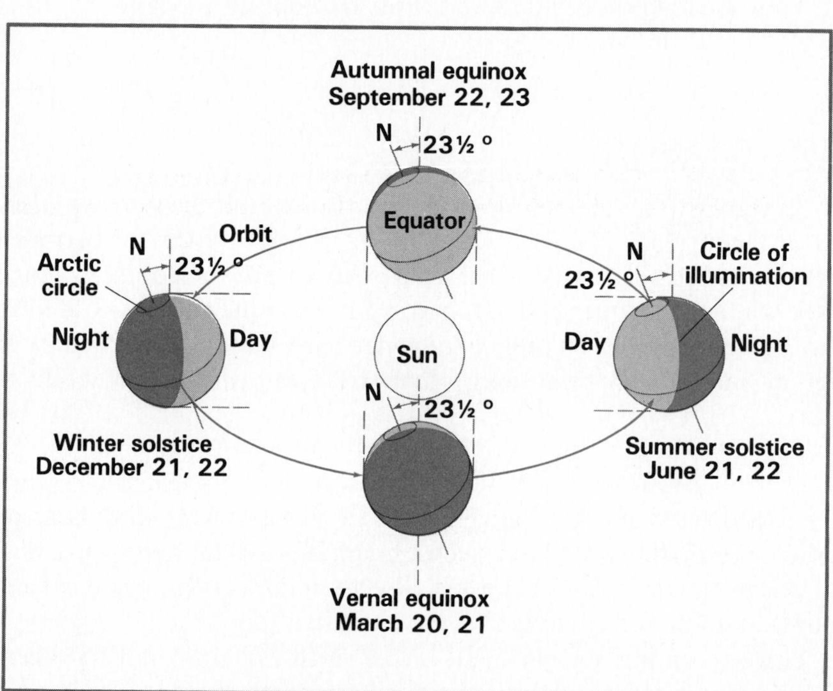

The earth's entire orbit around the sun takes just a few hours more than 365 days. The climatic changes known as seasons are caused by changes in the amount of the sun's energy striking the earth. The energy changes are caused by the earth being tilted on its axis as it spins its way around the sun.

10. What is a season?

11. What is the name for the first day of summer?

12. Why is summer warmer than winter in the northern hemisphere?

13. When it is winter in the northern hemisphere, what season is it in the southern hemisphere? Explain your answer.

14. Why are days and nights of equal length only on the autumnal and vernal equinoxes?

ACTIVITY: The Seasons

MATERIALS: Flashlight, globe, grid paper, poster board, markers

In this activity, you will simulate the earth's orbit about the sun and create a model of the seasons.

a. Five students will help set up the model.
b. Place one student in the center of a circle that is 3 m in diameter. This student will represent the sun and will use the flashlight.
c. One student will hold a globe tilted about 23½° and walk slowly counterclockwise around the sun. The circle represents the earth's orbit. The North Pole of the globe should always point in the same direction.
d. Watch what happens and record your observations.
e. Have the student stop with the North Pole pointing directly toward the sun. This position is June 21, summer solstice.
f. Make a sign and place it at that point on the circle.
g. Now move the earth one quarter of the way around its orbit. Place a sign at this point marking it September 22 or 23, autumnal equinox.
h. Move the earth to the point where the North Pole points directly away from the sun. Place a sign marking the point December 21, winter solstice.
i. Move the earth to the first day of spring, the vernal equinox, March 21, and place a fourth sign.
j. Move the earth to the summer solstice. Tape the grid paper on the globe over the United States. Use the flashlight to represent the sun's rays. Hold the light 2 decimeters from the grid and watch what happens. Repeat the process for the winter solstice. The summer solstice sun should shine more directly on the earth's surface than the winter solstice sun.

15. Describe the difference in the positions of the earth and the sun at winter and summer solstice.
16. If the light from the flashlight were sunlight striking the earth's northern hemisphere, would the earth be heated more in the summer or winter? Explain your answer.
17. Draw a diagram of the earth in its orbit about the sun and use it to explain why the seasons change throughout the year.

36D THE MOON—EARTH'S NEIGHBOR

The moon is the earth's nearest neighbor. The moon is about one quarter the size of the earth. The moon rotates on its axis and revolves around the earth once every 27½ days. Because the moon makes one turn on its axis in exactly the same time it takes to orbit the earth, the same side of the moon always faces the earth.

THE MOON

revolves around the earth.
shows phases by reflecting sunlight to the earth.
causes tides by pulling on the ocean waters.
has eclipses by passing through the earth's shadow.

One effect produced by the moon's revolution around the earth is PHASES. **The moon's phases are its different lighted shapes as seen from the earth.** The moon produces no light of its own, but reflects light from the sun to the earth.

If you watch the moon night after night, you will see that it appears to change shape. When the moon appears to be completely dark, the phase is called a NEW MOON. A new moon occurs when the moon is between the earth and the sun. Since the sunlight is coming from behind the moon, the moon does not reflect light toward the earth. When the moon is on the opposite side of the earth, the sun's rays are reflected back to the earth from half of the moon's surface. The familiar round, lighted sphere in the night sky is called a FULL MOON.

As the moon moves in its orbit between new moon and full moon, the shape of the lighted portion appears to change. **The changes occur because you are seeing the lighted portion from a different angle every night. As the angle changes, the moon appears to have different shapes.**

Every 29½ days, the moon moves through all eight of its phases. It changes from completely dark (new moon phase) to fully lighted (full moon phase) and back again. People in ancient times used lunar calendars to keep track of the passage of time. Today's months began as LUNAR MONTHS, or the time from one new moon to the next.

Tides. The moon's gravitational pull causes TIDES in the oceans. **Tides are the rise and fall of the oceans.** The pull of gravity causes a

The phases of the moon change as the moon revolves around the earth, reflecting the sun's rays back to the earth.

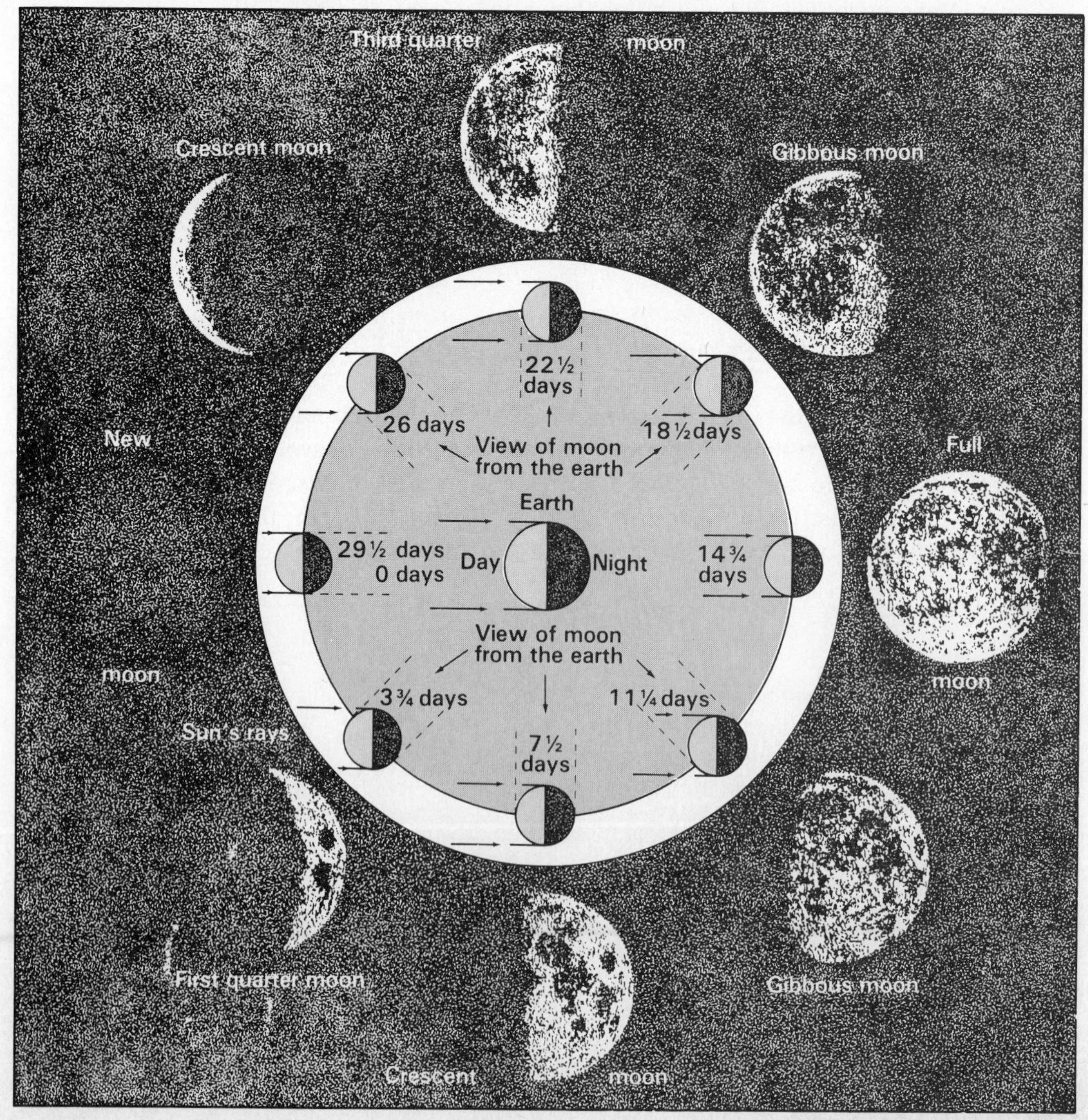

bulge on the side of the earth facing the moon. Another bulge forms on the opposite side of the earth because of centrifugal force. The bulges follow the moon as the earth revolves, so the bulges move around the earth about once every day. Both of these bulges are known as high tides. At the same time as high tides are occurring, low tides are occurring between the two bulges.

Most places on the earth have two low and two high tides every day. Because of the earth's rotation, the moon rises fifty minutes later every day. As a result, the tides are also fifty minutes later each day.

These photos show the difference between high and low tide in the Bay of Fundy in Nova Scotia.

Tides change in size during every lunar month. Every two weeks, during new and full moons, the earth, moon, and sun line up. When they do, their gravitational fields combine and cause very high tides. These high tides are called SPRING TIDES. One week after a spring tide, the earth, moon, and sun form a right angle. The reduced pull of gravity causes lower tides called NEAP TIDES.

A special kind of event, called a LUNAR ECLIPSE, occurs when the moon passes through the earth's shadow. **For the moon to pass through the earth's shadow and be eclipsed, the earth, moon, and sun must be exactly in line with one another.** The moon revolves around the earth in an orbit that is tilted in relation to the earth's orbit around the sun. So the earth, moon, and sun only line up when the orbits cross. **Because the earth's shadow is very large, lunar eclipses occur several times during most years.**

A less common kind of eclipse, called a SOLAR ECLIPSE, occurs when the moon passes exactly between the sun and the earth. **During a solar eclipse, the moon blocks out the sun and casts its shadow onto part of the earth.** Because the moon is small and close to the earth, it casts a very small, round shadow. In order to see a solar eclipse, you must be directly beneath the moon's shadow. Most people never see an eclipse of the sun.

18. Why does the moon have phases?
19. Explain how tides are formed.
20. What are spring and neap tides? Why do they occur?
21. What is an eclipse?

Spring tides occur when the earth, moon, and sun line up in their orbits. Neap tides occur two weeks later when the earth, moon, and sun form a right angle.

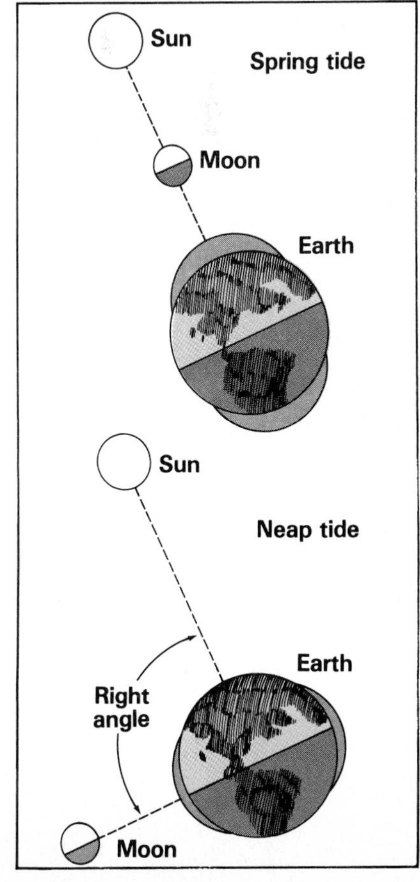

SUMMARY

VOCABULARY

planet
orbit
axis
longitude
prime meridian
local time
time zone
hour circle
parallels
latitude
equator
season
summer solstice
winter solstice
vernal equinox
autumnal equinox
phase
new moon
full moon
lunar month
tide
spring tides
neap tides
lunar eclipse
solar eclipse

KEY FACTS AND CONCEPTS

The earth is one of nine planets traveling around an average-size star called the sun.

The earth is a unique planet because it supports life.

The earth's motion about the sun creates the seasons, time, and a system of location.

Because you live on the earth, you have a special interest in the way it behaves.

The earth rotates about 15° every hour and makes one complete turn every 24 hours.

Meridians of longitude are imaginary lines drawn vertically around the earth.

The earth's rotation allows you to keep time and to find your location on its surface.

Meridians determine east and west location.

The equator is an imaginary line that cuts the earth in half horizontally.

Parallels are imaginary lines drawn around the earth parallel to the equator.

Parallels are used to find location north and south of the equator.

Meridians and parallels together form a grid that allows you to locate any point on the earth by knowing two positions.

Changes in the length of day and night and the angle of the sun's rays striking the earth cause the seasons.

The earth's axis is tilted at a 23½° angle.

Summer solstice is the longest day of the year and the first day of summer.

Winter solstice is the shortest day of the year and the first day of winter.

On the vernal and autumnal equinoxes, the length of day and night are equal.

As the earth moves around the sun, the changing energy causes the four seasons—summer, fall, winter, and spring.

The moon is the earth's nearest neighbor.

During a lunar month, the moon changes from completely dark (new moon phase) to fully lighted (full moon phase) and back again.

The pull of the moon's gravity causes bulges in the oceans called tides.

Most oceans have two high and two low tides.

Spring tides occur when the moon lines up with the earth and the sun.

Neap tides occur when the earth, moon, and sun form a right angle.

A lunar eclipse occurs when the moon passes through the earth's shadow.

A solar eclipse occurs when the moon passes exactly between the sun and the earth.

CONCLUSION

The earth's motion is important in your life. Its rotation and revolution determine the length of your day and year. They also allow you to tell time and locate your position on the earth's surface. The moon also affects your life. Its phases light the evening sky, and its gravitational pull on the oceans creates the tides.

22. What is the KEY IDEA of this chapter?

CHAPTER

37 The Solar System

Earth's Neighbors in Space

37A INTRODUCTION

The earth is one member of a large system of planets revolving about a star called the sun. In addition to planets, the system contains MOONS, ASTEROIDS, COMETS, and METEOROIDS. Together, they form the SOLAR SYSTEM.

MEMBERS OF THE SOLAR SYSTEM

SUN: the earth's star

PLANETS: large, solid bodies orbiting the sun

MOONS: smaller bodies orbiting the planets

COMETS: balls of frozen gas that orbit the sun far out in space

METEOROIDS: small rocks and dust that float in space

The solar system is the earth's family in space. It is made up of the sun, planets, moons, asteroids, meteoroids, and comets.

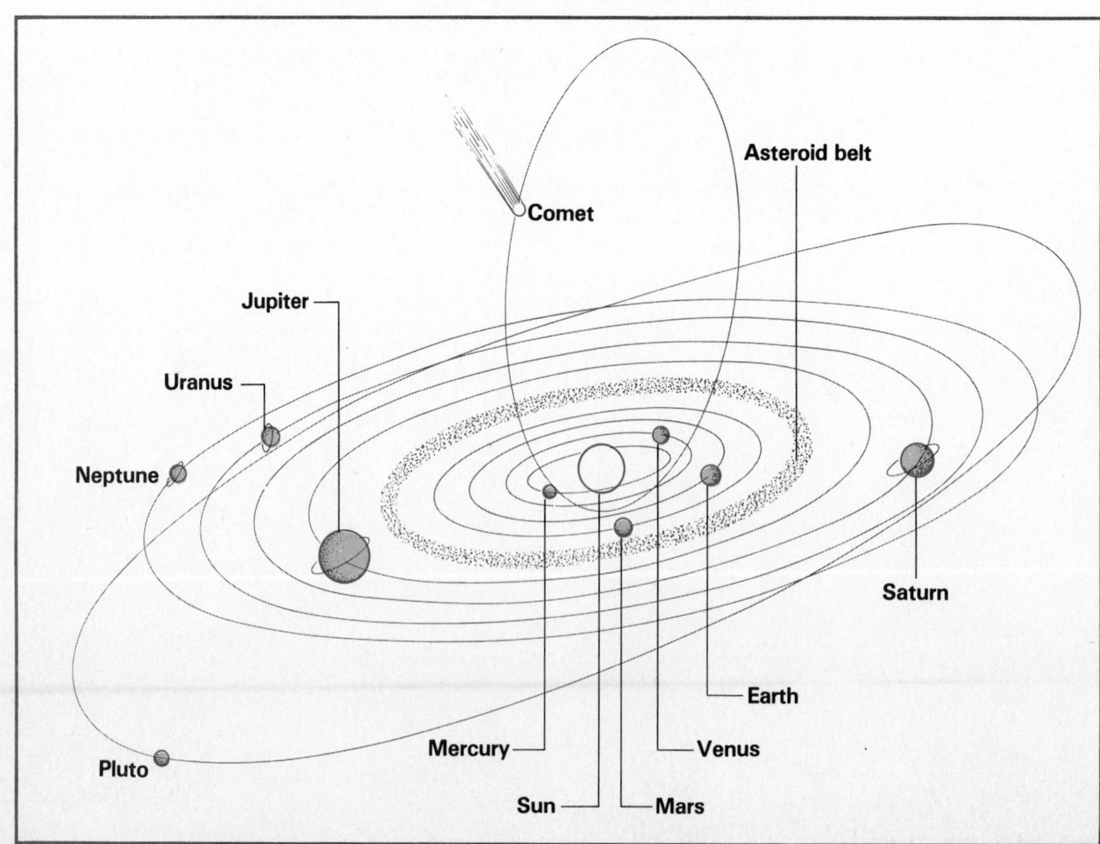

The solar system is the earth's family in space. Each member is different from all the others. As far as scientists know, only the earth supports life.

In this chapter, you will study each of the major members of the solar system. You will learn how they behave and what makes each different from all the others.

1. What is the solar system?
2. Name the major kinds of bodies in the solar system.

37B THE SUN

The sun is an average-size star, one of millions of stars in the universe. Yet the sun is so large that more than one million earths could be placed inside it with room to spare. The sun is a great ball of hydrogen and helium gas. It makes one complete turn on its axis about once every twenty-five days. The sun's field of gravity holds the planets and other bodies in their orbits.

The sun provides light and heat to the entire solar system. The light and heat are produced inside the star by a process called FUSION. Fusion takes place at very high temperatures and pressures. **During fusion, two hydrogen atoms combine to form one helium atom, and tremendous amounts of energy are released.** Every second, about four million tons of hydrogen are fused in the sun. This process results in temperatures of 6,000° Celsius at the surface of the sun and 15,000,000° Celsius at the core of the sun. The fusion process produces the heat and light that make life possible on the earth.

The photo on the top shows sunspots on the sun's surface. The photo on the bottom shows a solar prominence.

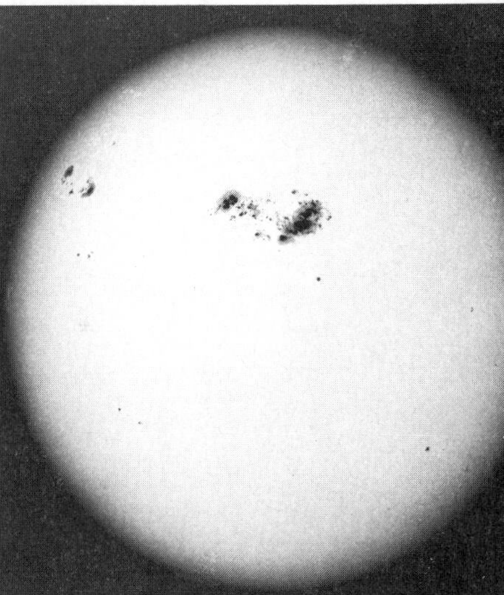

FUSION IN THE SUN PRODUCES HEAT AND LIGHT

1 hydrogen atom + 1 hydrogen atom = 1 helium atom + energy

The surface of the sun is constantly changing. Scientists have observed areas on the sun that appear darker than the rest of its surface. These areas are called SUNSPOTS. **Sunspots are places on the sun's surface that are cooler than the rest of its surface.** The number of sunspots that appear on the sun's surface is constantly changing.

Scientists have also observed streams of gas that shoot out into space from the sun's surface. These arching streams of gas are called SOLAR PROMINENCES. Energy released by solar prominences can disrupt radio and television reception on the earth.

You should never look directly at the sun. When you do, the light is focused on the back of your eye and can burn your retina. Retina burns do not heal. Looking directly at the sun can cause permanent damage to your eyes.

3. What is the sun made of?
4. Describe the process that produces energy in the sun. What is it called?
5. What are sunspots and solar prominences?
6. Why should you never look directly at the sun?

37C THE PLANETS

There are nine planets in the solar system. **Astronomers in ancient times called them planets, which means "wandering star," because they seemed to wander along a path in the night sky.** The four planets nearest the sun are called the INNER PLANETS. The remaining five are known as the OUTER PLANETS.

THE SOLAR SYSTEM

Inner Planets	Outer planets
Mercury	Jupiter
Venus	Saturn
Earth	Uranus
Mars	Neptune
	Pluto

Between the inner and outer planets there is a belt of rock fragments called ASTEROIDS. Scientists believe that asteroids may be the remains of a tenth planet that broke apart millions of years ago. **There are tens of thousands of asteroids in the belt that circles the sun.** Only about 10 are more than 160 kilometers in diameter. The smallest known asteroid is about 150 meters in diameter. Not all asteroids in the solar system are found within the asteroid belt. A few orbit the sun in other places in the solar system as well. One asteroid, called Eros, comes relatively close (within twenty-three million kilometers) to the earth from time to time.

The four inner planets are MERCURY, VENUS, EARTH, and MARS. **Mercury is the planet closest to the sun.** It has no atmosphere and its temperature during the day reaches about 430° Celsius.

Venus is about the same size and mass as Earth. But Venus has a very thick atmosphere made up mostly of carbon dioxide. The atmospheric pressure at the surface of Venus is 100 times the pressure on Earth. This thick atmosphere causes daytime temperatures of more than 500° Celsius. High temperatures, large amounts of carbon dioxide, and only small traces of water vapor make the possibility of life on Venus very unlikely.

Earth is the third planet from the sun. With an atmosphere of nitrogen and oxygen, mild temperatures, and plenty of water, Earth is the only proven home for life in the solar system.

Mars is the fourth of the inner planets. It takes 687 Earth days for Mars to travel around the sun. Because Mars takes twice as long as Earth to orbit the sun, Mars' seasons are twice as long as Earth's.

Mars is a barren, red-colored planet. Yet when the space probe *Mariner 9* photographed Mars' surface in 1971, old stream beds and signs of water erosion were seen. This seems to indicate that water was once plentiful on the planet. *Mariner 9* also photographed large volcanoes and a huge canyon. This canyon is 240 kilometers wide at one point and 6.5 kilometers deep. On Earth, it would stretch from New York to California.

In 1976, two *Viking* spacecraft landed on Mars. Their instruments indicated that Mars' atmosphere may once have been like Earth's.

Now, however, Mars' surface is cold, with an average temperature of −50° Celsius and polar ice caps made of frozen carbon dioxide, or dry ice. With no liquid water and below-freezing temperatures, Mars cannot support life.

The *Viking* spacecraft that took this photo of the surface of Mars also sent back a low temperature reading of −86° Celsius and a high reading of −31° Celsius.

The four giant outer planets—JUPITER, SATURN, URANUS, and NEPTUNE—contain about ninety-nine percent of all the material in the solar system with the exception of the sun. With the exception of Pluto, the outer planets have atmospheres composed mainly of hydrogen, helium, methane, and ammonia. The largest planets, Jupiter, Saturn, and Uranus, all have a number of moons orbiting them the way the moon orbits the earth.

Jupiter, Saturn, and Uranus are circled by large, flat rings. The rings are made of millions of chunks of ice, rock, and dust that orbit the planets. The seven rings of Saturn have been observed for hundreds of years. They can be seen through even a small telescope. The rings around Jupiter and Uranus were seen for the first time in 1977 when an unmanned space probe photographed them.

Saturn is one of the three very large outer planets that have flat rings of rock and ice orbiting them.

Uranus, Neptune, and Pluto are very cold planets because they are far from the sun. Uranus and Neptune are each about three-and-one-half times the size of the earth. They are green in color because of the methane in their atmospheres. Both planets are believed to have solid cores surrounded by thick layers of ice.

Pluto is the farthest planet from the sun. Its orbit is 5,900,000,000 kilometers away from the sun, and it takes 248 Earth years to make one revolution. Pluto receives very little energy from the sun and, as a result, its surface temperature is about −230° Celsius.

Some scientists believe that Pluto may not be a planet at all. Pluto may be a moon that escaped Neptune's gravitational force. Whether Pluto is a planet or an "escaped" moon, its atmosphere and orbit are different from the other planets'. Pluto has little or no atmosphere unlike the other outer planets. Its orbit around the sun is also unusual. For a twenty-year period during each revolution, Pluto is closer to the sun than Neptune.

7. What are asteroids? Where is the asteroid belt located?
8. Name and describe the four inner planets.
9. Why is the possibility of life on Venus unlikely?
10. What did the photographs of *Mariner 9* reveal about the surface of Mars?
11. Name and describe the five outer planets.
12. What makes Pluto different from the other outer planets?

ACTIVITY: A Model of the Solar System

MATERIALS: Meter sticks, masking tape, poster board, markers

In this activity, you will learn about the size of the solar system. You will also learn some of the characteristics of the planets.

a. Your teacher will divide your class into groups of five students each.
b. Each student in your group should gather information from the media center or library about two planets. One student will need to study one planet and the asteroid belt.
c. Construct a model of the solar system using the following information.

Planet	Actual distance	Model distance
Sun	----0----	----0----
Mercury	57,900,000km	0.4 m
Venus	108,200,000 km	0.7 m
Earth	149,600,000 km	1.0 m
Mars	227,900,000 km	1.5 m
Asteroids	418,880,000 km	2.8 m
Jupiter	778,300,000 km	5.2 m
Saturn	1,427,000,000 km	9.5 m
Uranus	2,870,000,000 km	19.1 m
Neptune	4,497,000,000 km	30.1 m
Pluto	5,900,000,000 km	39.5 m

d. Label each planet's location and that of the asteroid belt. Include the planet's size and the time it takes to orbit the sun. Also write a short description of the planet. Attach a photograph or drawing, if you can copy one.
e. Conduct a tour of the solar system for your teacher and classmates.
f. Toliman Centaurus is the closest star to the solar system. It is about 41,000,000,000,000 kilometers from the earth. See if you can figure out how far away it would be on your model. Put an arrow beyond Pluto pointing the way to the star and giving its distance from the sun.

13. How big is your model of the solar system?
14. On your model, the sun would be about 3.0 cm in diameter. How small would that make the planets?
15. How does the size of a person compare to the size of the solar system?

37D METEOROIDS AND COMETS

As the earth moves through space, it collides with more than 100 million meteoroids every day. **Meteoroids are rocks, dust, and other debris floating in space.** Meteoroids have an average mass of less than one hundredth of a gram. Most burn up quickly in the atmosphere.

When a meteoroid enters the earth's atmosphere, friction between the meteoroid and the atmosphere causes it to burn and glow. **Meteoroids burn where the atmosphere is thick enough to heat them and slow them down.** The meteoroid's trail or streak of light in the night sky is called a METEOR, or "shooting star." If you watch the night sky, you may see a meteor. Meteors are about 87 kilometers long and occur about 120 kilometers up in the atmosphere.

A meteorite is a piece of metallic or stony matter that enters the earth's atmosphere from space. This meteorite looks like an ordinary rock.

When a meteoroid strikes the earth, it is called a METEORITE. Most meteorites are small, but many collide with the earth. Scientists estimate that meteorites add more than 1,000 metric tons to the earth's mass each day.

Occasionally, a very large meteorite strikes the earth. Such meteorites crash into the earth at high speeds and blast out large craters. One such meteorite hit Siberia in 1908. The blast was felt eighty kilometers away, and the impact destroyed everything in an area more than sixty kilometers across.

Another meteorite struck what is now Arizona many years before people came to North America. That meteorite blasted out a giant hole called Barringer Crater, which is 1,265 meters across and 174 meters deep. Scientists studying the earth from space have discovered other meteorite impact features around the world.

A very large meteor struck the earth, blasting out this giant crater in Arizona named Barringer Crater.

Comets are another special group of visitors from space. Comets are thought to be made up of frozen gases such as ammonia, methane, and carbon dioxide. Dust and rock fragments are trapped in the frozen gases, forming something like a dirty snowball.

As a comet approaches the solar system, energy from the sun causes some of its gases to vaporize. The energy pushes the gases away from the comet, causing them to stream out away from the sun and to form a tail.

Comets are actually members of the solar system. Most comets have orbits that take them far from the sun. Some travel many millions of kilometers from the solar system. Their orbits eventually bring them back to loop around the sun and then plunge back into space.

Scientists have identified many comets. Some comets, like one called Encke, take only 3.3 years to complete an orbit. Others, like Kohoutek, which passed around the sun in 1973, will not return for 75,000 years. A few comets are well-known. Halley's Comet, for example, takes seventy-six years to complete an orbit. Scientists have watched Halley's Comet for more than 2,000 years. They are looking forward to the comet's next visit, which is expected in 1985-86.

This photograph of the head of Halley's Comet was taken on May 8, 1910 during its last return to the solar system.

16. What are meteoroids? Why do they form trails of light in the night sky?

17. What kind of feature is produced when a large meteoroid strikes the earth? Describe one that is located in the United States.

18. What is the difference between a meteroid, a meteor, and a meteorite?

19. What is a comet?

20. Why do comets have tails?

SUMMARY

VOCABULARY

moon
asteroid
comet
meteoroid
solar system
fusion
sunspots
solar prominences
inner planets
outer planets
Mercury
Venus
Earth
Mars
Jupiter
Saturn
Uranus
Neptune
meteor
meteorite

KEY FACTS AND CONCEPTS

The earth is one member of a large system of planets revolving about the sun.

The solar system is the earth's family in space.

The sun is an average-size star.

The sun's field of gravity holds the planets in their orbits to form the solar system.

The sun provides light and heat to the entire solar system.

Energy produced by sunspots and solar prominences often disrupts radio and television reception on the earth.

The four inner planets are Mercury, Venus, Earth, and Mars.

Between the inner and outer planets there is a belt of rock fragments called asteroids.

The five outer planets are Jupiter, Saturn, Uranus, Neptune, and Pluto.

Meteroids are rocks, dust, and debris floating in space.

Most meteoroids burn up when they enter the atmosphere, leaving fiery trails, called meteors, in the night sky.

Meteoroids that strike the earth are called meteorites.

When meteorites strike the earth, they form craters.

Comets are frozen balls of gas, dust, and rock that orbit the sun far out in space.

Comets form tails as they approach the sun.

CONCLUSION

The solar system is the earth's family in space. The earth's neighboring planets move about an average-size star called the sun. The sun produces the energy that makes life possible on the earth, while its gravity keeps the earth in orbit. Meteors, comets, moons, and asteroids are also parts of the solar system.

21. What is the KEY IDEA of this chapter?

CHAPTER

38 Beyond the Solar System

Bodies Far Out in Space

This modern telescope allows astronomers to see objects deep in space.

38A INTRODUCTION

People have always wondered what lies beyond the earth. Astronomers in ancient times had only their eyes to look at the stars, but as civilization progressed, scientists invented the TELESCOPE to help them study bodies in space. Telescopes gather and concentrate the faint light of distant stars so that stars and other bodies in space become clearer.

Using telescopes, modern astronomers can see objects in space that people hundreds of years ago never dreamed existed. Modern astronomers can investigate the universe, which includes everything in space. They use their knowledge about the stars to explore the origin of the earth and the solar system.

In this chapter, you will learn about the same stars that ancient astronomers watched. You will also learn about some of the new bodies that have been discovered by modern astronomers. Most important, you will learn that the earth is only one of many bodies in space and that it is very small in relation to the size of the universe.

1. How do modern astronomers differ from ancient astronomers in the way they study the stars?
2. How do modern astronomers use their knowledge about the stars?

38B STARS

Stars are so far away from the earth that the distance must be measured in LIGHT-YEARS. **A light-year is the distance that light travels in 365 days, which is 9 trillion kilometers.** The stars closest to the earth are in the constellation Centauri. They are about 4.3 light-years, or about 30 trillion kilometers, away. Light from this constellation travels 4.3 years to reach the earth. Some other stars are so far away that their light takes 15,000 million light-years to reach the earth.

Astronomers study starlight because it can reveal a great deal about stars. Starlight's colors, as seen through special instruments, can reveal a star's chemical composition, temperature, speed, and direction of travel.

Astronomers use different kinds of telescopes to study the stars. Giant optical telescopes gather visible light for study. Radio telescopes are able to pick up radio signals emitted by stars. High-altitude balloons, rockets, and satellites are used to pick up X-rays and gamma

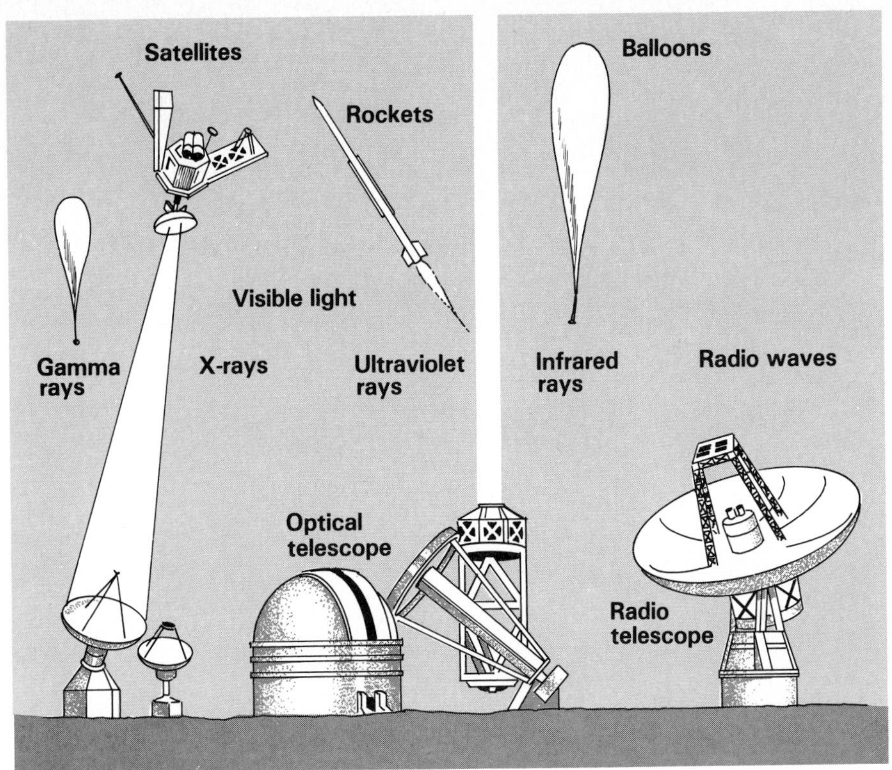

Astronomers use telescopes, balloons, rockets, and satellites to gather information about the stars.

rays from the stars. The information gathered from all these different sources forms a picture of the stars.

Like the sun, stars are gigantic balls of hydrogen and helium gas. The light that stars produce comes from the fusion of hydrogen atoms. This nuclear reaction produces helium and a great amount of energy.

Most stars have a life cycle. A star often begins as a giant cloud of contracting gas. When the temperature and pressure become high enough inside the cloud, fusion begins and energy is released in the form of light and heat.

Over millions of years, the star becomes first a small, red star. It grows slowly hotter, changing to a yellow star. As its fuel runs out in the later stages of it life cycle, the star becomes very large and is known as a RED GIANT. Many red giants are large enough to contain the sun and the inner planets. Finally, when fusion stops, the star collapses into a small, very dense WHITE DWARF. What was once a red giant has become smaller but 100,000 times denser than the earth.

Not all stars follow this pattern, however. Some stars periodically vary in brightness. One group of stars, called VARIABLES, flash on and off very precisely. The time typical variable stars take to increase in brightness and dim again ranges from one to fifty earth days.

NOVAS are stars that increase in brilliance 100,000 times or more within a few hours or days. **A nova is caused by an explosion inside a star.** A nova will seem to appear in the sky and then disappear. The star usually returns to normal brightness in a few days.

If an explosion is so great that it blows the star apart, it is called a SUPERNOVA. **Supernovas are very rare.** Most astronomers think a supernova can be seen from the earth only about once every 300 years. Supernovas blow stars apart and create expanding clouds of gas. Many of these clouds of gas can be seen through telescopes. They are believed to mark places where explosions took place long ago.

This drawing illustrates the life cycle of a typical star.

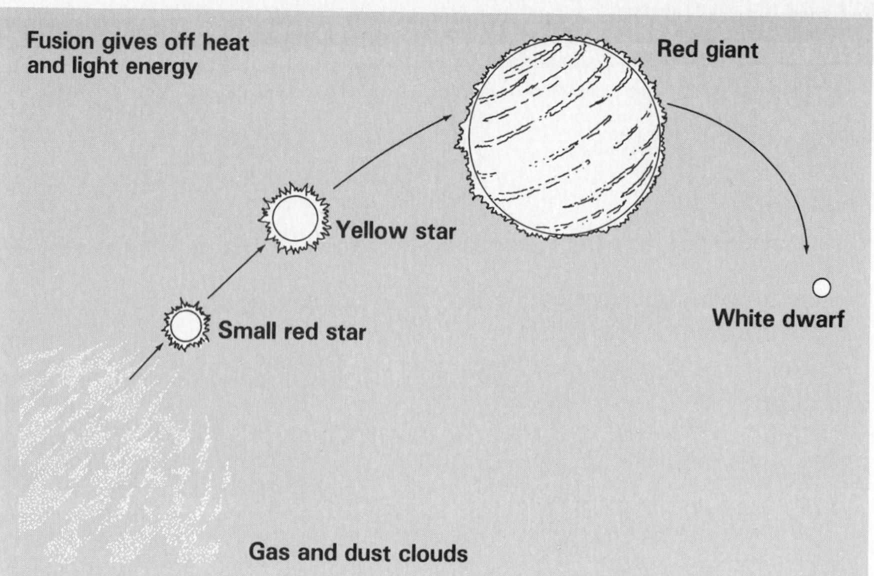

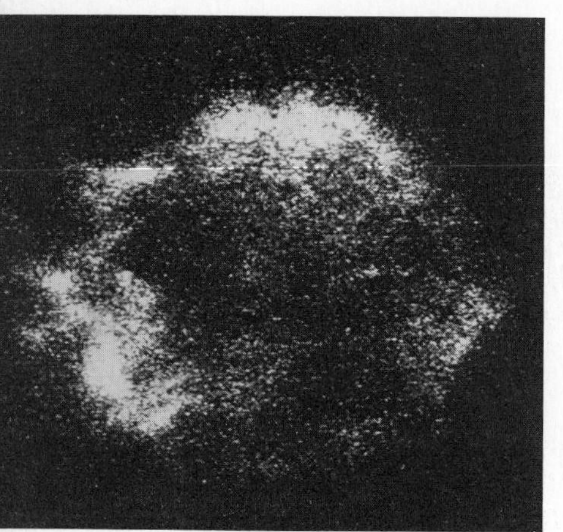

The expanding shell of gas shown in this photo was probably formed by a supernova.

TYPES OF STARS

RED GIANTS: stars that are very large, bright, and red

WHITE DWARFS: stars that are very small, dense, and white

VARIABLE STARS: stars whose brightness keep changing

NOVAS: stars that get suddenly brighter because of internal explosions

SUPERNOVAS: stars that get hundreds of millions of times brighter because of violent internal explosions that blow them apart

3. What are stars?

4. Describe the typical life cycle of a star.

5. What is a light-year? Why do astronomers use light-years to measure the distance from the earth to stars?

6. What can astronomers learn from starlight?

7. What are novas and supernovas? How are they different from each other?

38C CONSTELLATIONS

Because stars are so far away, they must move a great distance for astronomers to detect any change in their positions in the sky. The stars appear to occupy the same positions year after year and century after century. Because the earth revolves around the sun and rotates on its axis, the stars appear to revolve in the sky.

In the Northern Hemisphere, the stars appear to revolve about a single point in the sky. That point is marked by a star named Polaris, or the North Star. The height of Polaris above the horizon is determined by your latitude. That is, the closer you are to the North Pole, the higher Polaris appears to be in the northern sky.

You can see about 6,000 stars with the unaided eye. Many of the brighter stars form recognizable patterns called CONSTELLATIONS. **Ancient astronomers saw the patterns, named them, and told stories about them. These stories became part of their folklore.** Ptolemy, the last of the great ancient astronomers, listed forty-eight constellations. Since then, another forty have been named.

Because the earth orbits the sun, different constellations appear in the night sky during different seasons. The stars also rise at different times during the night depending on the season. Some constellations nearer Polaris stay above the horizon all night long throughout the year.

Among the best known of the constellations are Ursa Major and Ursa Minor. The words *Ursa Major* mean "Big Bear." The seven stars in the tail of the Big Bear form the Big Dipper. You can use the Big Dipper to find other constellations. For example, two bright stars in the cup of the Big Dipper point to Polaris. For this reason, they are called pointers. Polaris is the last star in the handle of the Little Dipper. The Little Dipper is part of the Little Bear, or Ursa Minor.

Other stars in the Big Dipper point to constellations like Gemini, the Twins; Leo, the Lion; and Boötes, the Herdsman.

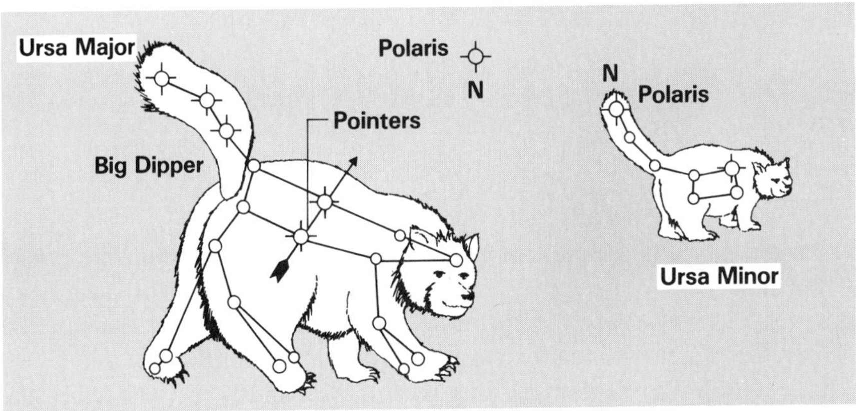

Constellations provide an easy way to find other features in the night sky. Variable stars and other features are located in particular constellations. If you learn to recognize the constellations, you can quickly find the star you are looking for.

8. What are constellations?
9. What use do constellations serve?

The earth is a very small part of one spiral galaxy called the Milky Way.

38D GROUPS OF STARS

If you look at the sky on a clear night, you will see a thick, "milky" band of light. Through a telescope, you can see that the "milky" band is actually thousands of stars. This band of stars is just one of the gigantic, flat, spiral arms of the MILKY WAY GALAXY.

The earth is part of the Milky Way Galaxy. Astronomers have studied the Milky Way Galaxy. It contains about 100 to 200 billion stars. The galaxy is about 100,000 light-years in diameter and about 20,000 light-years thick at its center.

ACTIVITY: The Constellations

MATERIALS: posterboard, markers

In this activity, you will learn about some of the more famous constellations. When you have completed this activity, you should know the stories of several constellations and what they look like in the night sky.

a. Use the resources in your school's library or media center to locate a picture and the story of three of the following constellations:
   Ursa Major—the Great Bear
   Ursa Minor—the Little Bear
   Draco—the Dragon
   Gemini—the Twins
   Pegasus—the Winged Horse
   Orion—the Hunter
   Taurus—the Bull
   Lyra—the Lyre
   Scorpio—the Scorpion
   Sagittarius—the Archer
   Cygnus—the Swan
   Leo—the Lion
   Boötes—the Herdsman

b. Draw a picture of each constellation showing the figure's outline and the position of the stars within the outline like the drawings on page 269.

c. Write a description of each constellation. Include in your descriptions the stories or myths told about each constellation, the stars or other special features each constellation contains, and where to look for each constellation in the night sky.

d. Tell your class about one of the three constellations you studied.

e. Combine the best drawings and descriptions and make a class bulletin board.

10. How did constellations come to be named?

11. Can you think of reasons why ancient astronomers named constellations?

The earth's star, the sun, is about 32,000 light-years from the center of the galaxy. The sun moves in an orbit about the center of the galaxy at 250 kilometers every second. Even at this speed, it takes the sun 225 million Earth years to make one orbit around the galaxy.

The Milky Way Galaxy is only one of thousands of galaxies in the universe. Galaxies seem to take several different shapes so they are divided into three major groups. IRREGULAR GALAXIES seem to have no definite shape. ELLIPTICAL GALAXIES have a definite elliptical, or oval, form. SPIRAL GALAXIES have flat arms that spiral around a thick center. The Milky Way Galaxy is a spiral.

These photos show the three types of galaxies: irregular, elliptical, and spiral.

Galaxies seem to occur in groups. Average groups contain about 150 galaxies about 15 million light-years in diameter. Very large groups may contain thousands of galaxies.

Galaxies are just one way in which stars may be grouped. Another way stars are grouped is in STAR CLUSTERS. Clusters contain widely varied numbers of stars. **There are two types of star clusters in the Milky Way Galaxy.** Open clusters contain only a few hundred stars in loosely organized groups. Globular clusters are tightly concentrated groups of 100,000 to 10 million stars. To the unaided eye, star clusters appear to be one star or a faint, white cloud.

12. Describe the Milky Way Galaxy.
13. What are the three major types of galaxies?
14. What is a star cluster?
15. Describe two kinds of star clusters.

A globular cluster contains tens of thousands of stars in a relatively small area.

38E STRANGE BODIES IN SPACE

Nebulae. Astronomers have discovered many unusual features in the depths of space. One of the most common features is a NEBULA (plural: nebulae). **A nebula is a cloud of gas and dust floating in space.** Some nebulae are dark and block out the light of the stars behind them. These nebulae hide many of the stars in the Milky Way Galaxy. Other nebulae give off light because the stars imbedded in them cause them to glow. Another type of nebula is formed by supernovas. Supernovas form rapidly expanding shells of gas that give off light.

Quasars. In the years following the invention of the radio telescope, many new and mysterious bodies were found in the universe. It was not until 1960 that the first of the strange sources of radio noise was identified and named.

QUASARS were discovered because they give off a "roar" of radio energy. They appear as faint, bluish objects very deep in space. All the known quasars are more than 2,000 million light-years away and 200 times brighter than a typical galaxy would be at that distance. Quasars are only about ten light-years in diameter, or about one ten-thousanth the size of an average galaxy.

Pulsars. In 1967, a research worker named Jocelyn Bell discovered radio sources that were pulsing very precisely every 1.337 seconds for exactly one thirtieth of a second. These sources are called PULSARS. Further study has revealed that pulsars may be very small but tightly packed masses of neutrons. The masses are thought to be the only remains of supernovas. **Pulsars are only about fifteen to thirty kilometers in diameter, but they send out enormous amounts of energy.**

Black Holes. Probably the strangest phenomenon in the universe is the BLACK HOLE. **Some astronomers believe that black holes may be the final stage in the life cycle of very large stars.** They believe that a star collapses, creating a gravity field so great that even light energy cannot escape. As a result, nothing can be seen in the area of a black hole. The only evidence to support the existence of black holes is that all the material around them in space moves toward the "holes" and disappears. Some astronomers believe that black holes could pull in all the matter in a galaxy and perhaps even the universe.

The Crab Nebula shown in this photo is located in the constellation of Taurus, the Bull. It contains a pulsar, which gives off pulses of radio energy.

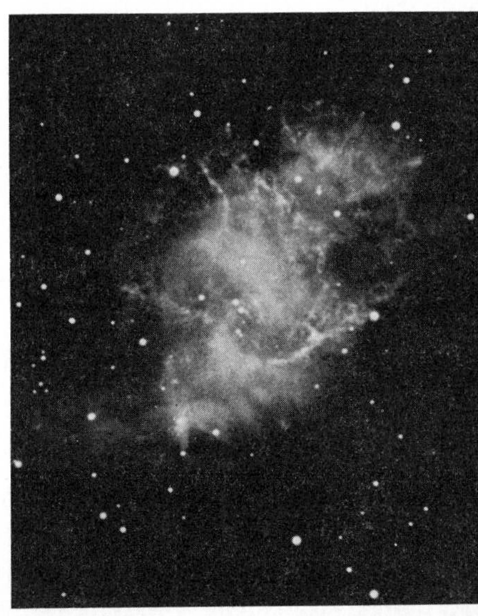

NEBULA: a bright or dark cloud of gas and dust floating in space
QUASAR: a small object giving off a "roar" of radio energy
PULSAR: a small object giving off pulses of radio energy
BLACK HOLE: an area where the force of gravity is so great that not even light can escape

16. What is a nebula?
17. What are quasars?
18. What are pulsars?
19. What are black holes?

SUMMARY

VOCABULARY

telescope
light-year
red giant
white dwarf
variables
nova
supernova
constellation
Milky Way Galaxy
irregular galaxy
elliptical galaxy
spiral galaxy
star cluster
nebula
quasar
pulsar
black hole

KEY FACTS AND CONCEPTS

The earth is only one very small object in space.

Stars are so far away from the earth that the distance must be measured in light-years.

The light from a star can reveal its composition, temperature, speed, and direction of travel.

Most stars begin as large clouds of contracting gas and end as white dwarfs.

Novas are stars that briefly give off a great deal of light because of an internal explosion.

Supernovas are stars that get hundreds of millions of times brighter because of violent internal explosions that blow them apart.

Constellations are patterns of stars in the night sky.

Constellations can be used to quickly find objects or places in the sky.

Galaxies are rotating disks of stars.

There are three major types of galaxies—irregular, elliptical, and spiral.

The earth is part of the Milky Way Galaxy.

Star clusters are irregular groupings of stars that may contain as few as 100 stars or as many as 10 million stars.

Nebulae are clouds of gas and dust in space.

Quasars are small objects deep in space that give off a "roar" of radio energy.

Pulsars are small objects deep in space that give off strong, precisely spaced pulses of radio energy.

Black holes are thought to be the final stage in the life cycle of large stars.

The gravity field around a black hole is so great that even light cannot escape.

CONCLUSION

The universe is made up of a variety of objects. They vary in size from very small to so large that they are hard to imagine. The earth is only one very small planet orbiting an average-size star inside one galaxy in a very large universe.

20. What is the KEY IDEA of this chapter?

UNIT **FIVE**

Technology

SCIENCE COMPETENCIES

Unit 5 will help you to master one LIFE SKILL:

APPLYING TECHNOLOGY—How to Be a Functionally Literate Citizen

CHAPTER

39 Technology

Using the Knowledge of Science

39A INTRODUCTION

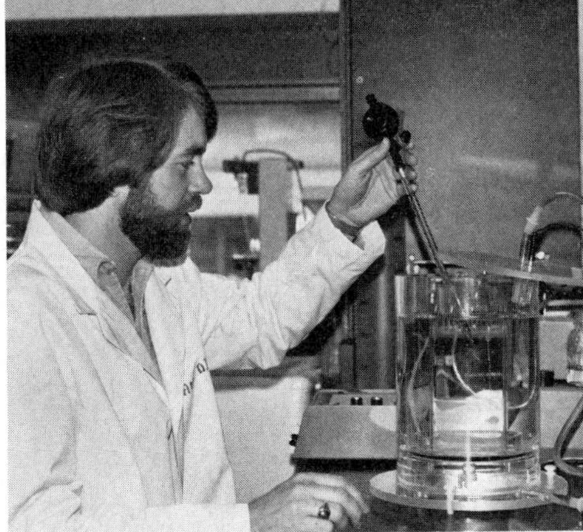

The man in this photo is an applied scientist. He works for a company that uses knowledge about genes to make medical products.

Science is the process of pursuing knowledge. To pursue knowledge, scientists use the scientific method. Using the scientific method, scientists are able to make new discoveries. The discoveries result in the shaping of the facts, laws, and theories of science.

The facts, laws, and theories that are shaped by scientific discoveries form the groundwork, or basic foundation, of science. This is why the research done by scientists is called BASIC SCIENCE.

When basic science is put to use, it is called APPLIED SCIENCE. Another word for applied science is TECHNOLOGY. The subject of this chapter is technology.

THE TWO KINDS OF SCIENCE

Kind	Definition	Examples
BASIC SCIENCE	Pursuing knowledge	Gathering weather data Measuring electronic circuits
APPLIED SCIENCE	Using knowledge	Building rockets Designing computers

1. What is science
2. What is basic science? Give an example.
3. What is applied science? Give an example.
4. What is technology? Give an example.

39B TECHNOLOGY AND ITS IMPORTANCE

Technology is the process of using the knowledge of science to produce useful products. Airplanes, medicines, and can openers are examples of technology. Most of the manufactured products you see around you are the result of technology.

There can be no applied science, or technology, until there has been basic science. In the first four units of this book, you studied basic science. In this unit, you will study technology. You will see how basic science has been used to create products that enhance the quality of your life.

SCIENTIFIC KNOWLEDGE	PRODUCT OF TECHNOLOGY
Air is a poor conductor of heat.	Insulated ice chest
Bacteria grow best at body temperature.	Refrigerator
Electricity makes an iron wire heat up.	Toaster, hair dryer, electric heater
Good tasting chemicals can dissolve in fats.	Margarine

People often confuse science with technology. **Science and technology are related, but they use different processes to achieve different results.** The result of science is information; the result of technology is a product.

The first raw materials discovered by people in ancient times were stone, wood, and fire. They used stones to make tools and weapons, wood to build shelter, and fire to cook their food and keep warm. Thus, early people used the raw materials available to make products of technology.

Technology has come a long way since people had only stone, wood, and fire to work with. But it has advanced slowly. People existed on the earth for over 700 life spans before the printing press was invented. The electric motor, which replaced muscle and animal power, has been in existence for only the past two life spans. **Most of the things that have been produced to improve the quality of life have been invented within your or your parents' life span.**

Technology is important because it helps people to do work faster and easier. Technological inventions enable people to work more with their minds and less with their bodies.

One recent technological invention is the electronic computer. An example of how an electronic computer can speed up the mental process while reducing the physical process is the calculation of pi.

Pi equals 3.1416. It is the ratio of the circumference of a circle to its diameter. In 1850, a mathematician calculated pi to 707 decimal places. In 1960, an electronic computer calculated it to 100,000 places. Without a computer, it would take a person, working eight hours a day on a desk calculator, 30,000 years to make this calculation. How long do you think it would take someone to calculate pi to 100,000 decimal places using only pencil and paper?

People have been performing tasks unassisted by machines and computers for most of history. People built the pyramids, plowed their farms, and moved their products with mind and muscle power alone. **Technology is now changing the way people live.**

5. What is technology?
6. Why can there be no technology without basic science first?
7. How are science and technology related?
8. How are science and technology different?
9. Why is technology important?

39C THE PEOPLE WHO CREATE TECHNOLOGY

People have created technology to make more efficient use of their mental and physical energy. People who specialize in designing, testing, and building the products of technology are ENGINEERS. Scientists and engineers differ in their work.

SCIENCE AND TECHNOLOGY

Scientist	Engineer
Scientists use the scientific method to make new discoveries.	Engineers use the discoveries of science to make new products.
Knowledge: data and information	Products: highways, computers, drugs

There are different types of engineers.

Type of Engineer	Uses Knowledge Mostly From
Chemical	Chemistry
Mechanical	Physics
Electrical	Physics
Civil	Physics
Environmental	Biology
Petroleum	Geology
Genetic	Biochemistry

You do not have to be an engineer to use the knowledge of science to create and build things. In your daily life, you often use the methods of science and technology. When you push down on a bicycle pedal, you apply the knowledge of forward force. This is applied to a product, a wheel, which moves you forward. You have often acted like a scientist, who discovers knowledge, and an engineer, who puts knowledge to work.

The copy machine is an example of technology. Its inventor, Chester Carlson, practiced the art of engineering. Carlson started the copy machine industry with experiments he carried on in his kitchen in his spare time. In 1937, Carlson filed his first patent application for his process called xerography. Later, he applied his basic knowledge of xerography to produce the first xerographic copier.

In 1947, a small company that produced photographic paper agreed to help finance Carlson's work. Nine years later, in 1956, an Englishman named Joseph Rank provided more funds for the machine to go into full-scale production. The first *Xerox* machine appeared in 1959, some thirty years after Chester Carlson started his research and technology.

This photo shows Chester Carlson with the copy machine he invented.

Steve Wozniak is half of the team that started the Apple Computer Company.

The personal computer, like the copy machine, is an example of technology. In 1975, nineteen-year-old Steve Jobs was a technician at an electronics company. His friend, Steve Wozniak, worked for another electronics company. They built a computer in Jobs' parents' living room and called it *Apple I*.

They took their computer to a computer store and the owner ordered fifty. They were in business. Jobs then sold his car, and Wozniak sold his calculator. With $2500, they started the Apple Computer Company. Today, the Apple Company is a highly successful business.

Technology is created by people to be used by people. Engineers, inventors, students—anyone can create, design, and build. Just as solving difficult problems makes science challenging and exciting, creating useful products makes technology fascinating to many people.

10. Why do people create technology?
11. How do scientists and engineers differ from one another?
12. Name some kinds of engineers.
13. Name some ways you have acted like a scientist or an engineer.
14. Who was Chester Carlson?
15. Who creates technology?

39D EXAMPLES OF TECHNOLOGY

The following inventions are further examples of the products of technology.

The Internal-Combustion Engine. In the internal-combustion engine, a gasoline-air mixture is exploded inside a cylinder to push a piston. The piston drives a shaft which, through a set of gears, turns the tires of a vehicle.

The Robot. A robot is a machine that can perform complex tasks formerly done by humans. Large robots can drill holes in metal plates.

The industrial robots shown in this photo are assembling automobiles in a Detroit plant.

Smaller robots can spray liquid cosmetics, such as eye shadow and face blush, into small metal pans which are then inserted into compact cases. The robot can save a company money and can free people to do more rewarding work.

ACTIVITY: Working More Efficiently

MATERIALS: Heavy string, one long pencil, several pencils of different lengths or objects of similar shape, several books, two tables or desks for support

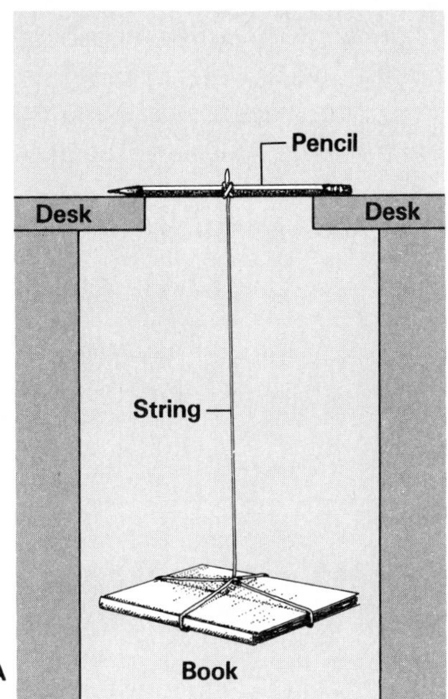

A

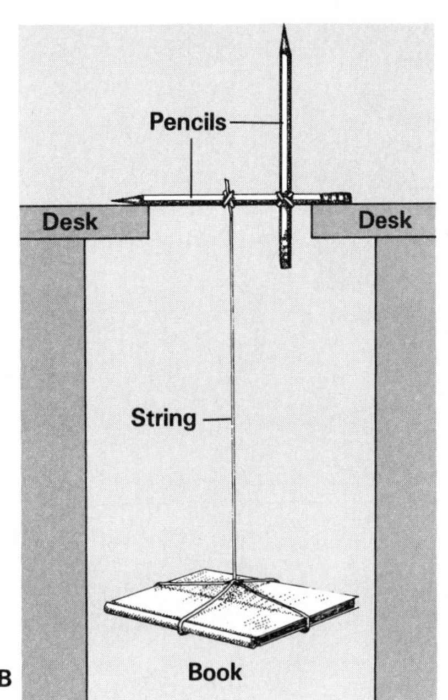

B

You learned in Unit 3 that work is applying a force to an object to move it over a distance. If you pick up a book, you are working. You have applied a force to move an object. However, you can apply the concept of mechanical advantage to move an object. The concept of mechanical advantage states that you can apply a small force to move a heavy mass.

---

a. Place two desks or tables close enough together so that your long pencil can rest on both.

b. Tie one end of the string to your book. Tie the other end to the pencil.

c. Rotate the pencil so that the string starts to wrap around it. Continue rotating until you have lifted the book as far as it can go.

d. Lower the book to the floor. Tie a short pencil to the first pencil so that they are at right angles to each other.

e. Using the short pencil as a handle, rotate it so that your book is lifted as before. Answer question 16.

f. Repeat steps d and e using a medium-length pencil. Answer question 17.

g. Repeat steps d and e using a long pencil. Answer question 18.

h. Repeat the experiment using two books. Answer question 19.

---

16. Compare the amount of time and effort used to lift the book in steps c and e.
17. Compare the amount of time and effort used to lift the book in step f.
18. Compare the amount of time and effort used to lift the book in step g.
19. Compare the amount of time and effort used to lift the two books in step h.
20. To lift the book, you used a simple machine called the wheel and axle. Which pencil was the wheel, and which was the axle? Explain your answer.
21. Find a definition of mechanical advantage and explain how it applies to this activity.
22. List all of the things you did in this activity that illustrated the use of technology.
23. How did this activity illustrate the concept of technology?

In this photo, Robert Harvey holds the artificial heart he invented.

The Artificial Heart. Still in its early development, the artificial heart has been developed by Robert Harvey. The heart is made of a light metal and a special plastic, each a technological wonder in itself. The heart would be powered by battery packs worn on a person's belt. Ultimately, Harvey wants to place the battery inside the person's rib-cage.

The Telephone Switchboard. There is no longer any need for a group of operators to sit at giant switchboards plugging cords into holes. The modern switchboard for a small business can be slightly larger than a desk phone and can be operated by one person.

The Disc Brake. In a disc brake, a revolving disc is gripped between two brake pads to stop a turning tire. The disc is open to the air to release the heat produced when the brake pads rub against the disc.

24. Name some common technological inventions.

SUMMARY

VOCABULARY

basic science
applied science
technology
engineer

KEY FACTS AND CONCEPTS

Science is the process of pursuing knowledge.

The basic foundation of science is its facts, laws, and theories.

Basic science is the process of pursuing knowledge.

Applied science is the process of using knowledge.

Technology is the process of using the knowledge of science to produce useful products.

Basic science must precede applied science.

Engineers specialize in creating the products of technology.

Most technological inventions have appeared within the past two life spans.

Technology enables people to work more with their minds and less with their bodies.

Technology is created by people to be used by people.

Anyone can be an engineer or an inventor.

CONCLUSION

Technology is the process of using the basic knowledge of science to produce useful products. The purpose of technology is to create devices that will enable people to do work faster and easier. Engineers specialize in producing the products of technology. However, anyone can practice the art of engineering. Every inventor who designs and builds useful objects is an engineer.

25. What is the KEY IDEA of this chapter?

CHAPTER

40 Technology and Design

The Method of Technology

40A INTRODUCTION

The paper clip is a technological invention that rivals any complex piece of machinery. The paper clip is not only useful, it represents a design that is beautiful because of its simplicity. **The person who invented the paper clip used the same mental process as the person who invented the personal computer.**

In Unit 1, you learned that scientists use the scientific method to discover basic knowledge. In this chapter, you will learn how engineers and inventors use the TECHNOLOGICAL METHOD. **The products of technology have resulted from people using a method of technology.**

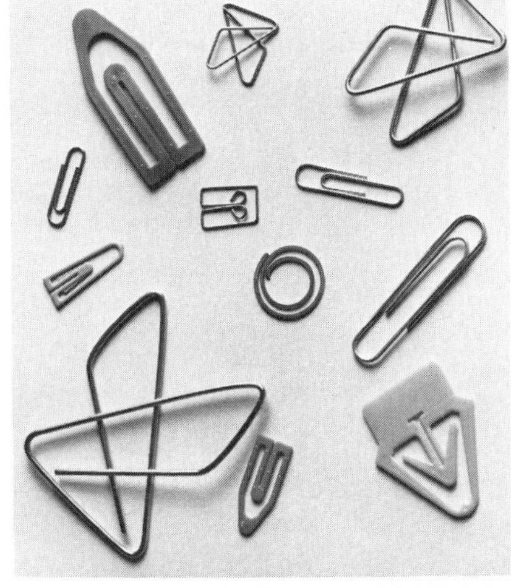

The paper clip is a marvelous technological invention. Can you think of another design for a paper clip?

THE METHOD OF TECHNOLOGY

1. Recognize a NEED.
2. Get an IDEA.
3. Find the FACTS.
4. Make a detailed DESIGN.
5. BUILD the product.
6. TEST the product.
7. MODIFY the design, if necessary.
8. USE or sell the product.

The steps of the technological method can be used at any time and in any order. Like the scientific method, there is no one way to use the technological method. The eight steps of the technological method can be used to describe how a product may have been made.

The technological method can be used by anyone who wants to invent a product. If you like to create, design, and build things, you will find it valuable to know the steps of the technological method. The steps of the technological method will be explained in this chapter.

1. What is the scientific method?
2. What is the technological method?
3. What has resulted from people using a method of technology?

There is a technological need to find a solution to the energy crisis. How would a gasoline shortage affect your life?

40B THE METHOD OF TECHNOLOGY: NEED AND IDEA

Recognize a Need. **A need is something people want, crave, require, desire, or find essential.** For example, there is a need for solutions to the energy, water, and food crises. Whoever fills these needs will make a major contribution to society.

The recognition of a need is not always the first step in the technological method. Sometimes, a product is developed first and then the public is persuaded to see a need for it. Advertising persuades you to think that you have bad breath, body odor, and dry skin. Therefore, you see a need to buy the newest mouthwash, deodorant, and skin cream.

Get an Idea. How many times have you seen a new business or a new product and said, "Why didn't I think of that?" You could have thought of the Hula-Hoop, Rubik's Cube, Apple computer, or Frisbee.

> In 1967, Ron Rice was a twenty-seven-year-old high school chemistry teacher who worked part time as a lifeguard in Daytona Beach, Florida. He had an idea, so he borrowed $500 and bought a large trash can, chemicals, oils, and bottles.
>
> After a few hours of mixing his product in his basement, Rice was offering his suntan lotion to his fellow lifeguards. Today, Rice's *Hawaiian Tropic* is the second best-selling brand in the United States. It has twenty percent of the market and is surpassed only by *Coppertone.*
>
> Ron Rice saw a need, and he had an idea to fill that need.

Thinking of an idea involves a mysterious combination of daydreaming, creative thinking, and positive attitude. The foundation for ideas is education. The more you read, listen, pay attention, and study, the more you will know. The more you know, the greater will be your fund of knowledge from which ideas spring.

4. Name two steps that often begin the technological method.
5. What is the importance of recognizing a need?
6. What does it mean to think of an idea?
7. What helps people think of ideas?

40C THE METHOD OF TECHNOLOGY: FACTS AND DESIGN

Find the Facts. Coming up with an idea is much like hypothesizing. **Before an idea can be applied and tested, the facts must be gathered.** An idea is only an educated guess as to how a need could be filled. To find the facts, a person must read scientific research and study how other people have attempted to fill the need. Such information can be found in the library.

For instance, there is currently a need for more fresh water. Farm crops now consume eighty percent of the water in the United States. Much of this water is pumped to the surface from underground. Presently, for every hundred liters of water pumped out of the earth, only seventy-four liters are returned. So much water is pumped out of the ground that it is estimated that some now-productive farmland stretching from northern Nebraska to northern Texas will go dry in forty years.

Several ideas for obtaining fresh water are being tried or tested. Most of these ideas involve a process called DESALINIZATION. **The process removes the salt from sea water to produce fresh water.**

You could solve the water crisis. All you need to do is to find a way to remove the salt from sea water. You could begin your research by finding the definitions for such words as *distillation, deionization,* and *electrodialysis.* After you learn what these words mean, you can proceed to design your own system to produce fresh water.

Finding the facts is important. The facts tell you what has been done, what is being done, and what could be done to solve a problem.

Draw the Design. You need a design before you can build anything. That is, the idea for a product and the facts must be worked out on paper before the product appears. A design is a detailed drawing of how the product should look.

Before you build anything, you must have a set of plans.

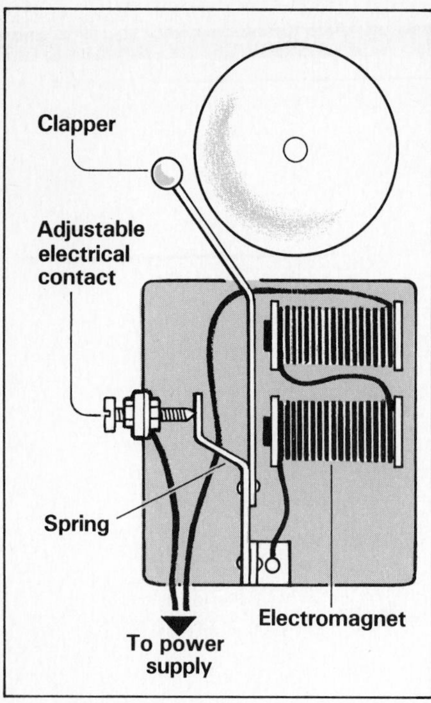

A drawing of the inside of an electric bell helps you to see how it works.

A design is like a graph in that it helps you to see a product in picture form. For instance, it is much easier to understand how an electric bell works if you can see a drawing of the inside of one.

8. How are an idea and a hypothesis alike?
9. What must be done before an idea can be applied and tested? Explain your answer.
10. Where does a person go to find the facts?
11. How are a design and a graph alike?
12. Why is a detailed design important?

40D THE METHOD OF TECHNOLOGY: BUILD AND TEST

Build the Product. The design is used to build a product. Based on the design, duplicate copies of a product can be made.

Building a product is similar to conducting an experiment. The purpose of conducting an experiment is to test a hypothesis. **The purpose of building a product is to apply, or test, an idea.**

The first example of an idea that is built is called the PROTOTYPE. **A prototype is the original model from which the final product may be built.**

Test the Product. After the prototype of a product is built, it is tested. Professional testing is done by QUALITY ENGINEERS.

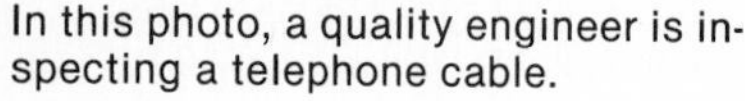

In this photo, a quality engineer is inspecting a telephone cable.

Testing a product involves putting the product through tests that have been devised by the person or company wanting information about the product's quality. Tests are not devised by the quality engineer.

As a product is tested, data are gathered. The engineer doing the testing neither accepts nor rejects the product. The engineer turns over the data to the person who wanted the facts gathered. **The data then help the person or company determine whether a product should be modified or if it can go into production.**

13. What is the design used for?

14. How is building a product similar to conducting an experiment?

15. What is a prototype?

16. What is a quality engineer?

17. What happens to the data that a quality engineer collects?

18. Imagine that you are given a new toothpaste to test. What factors would you test for?

40E THE METHOD OF TECHNOLOGY: MODIFY AND USE

Modify the Design. Modifying the design is similar to drawing a conclusion in the scientific method. When the test data of a product are examined, a conclusion must be reached about the product's future. The data can indicate that the product should be modified and the entire method of technology repeated. Or, the data can indicate that the product is acceptable and that production could proceed. Companies make decisions about new products based on test data.

Whether to modify a product or send it into production is a critical decision. Great amounts of money can be made or lost with this decision. Change or improvement do not necessarily mean public acceptance. People will often choose to continue using a product that they are comfortable with. Also, people are usually unwilling to pay more for an improved version of a familiar product. For example, the image on a television screen could be made sharper, but studies show that the public is not willing to pay for this improvement.

Calculators have been modified over the years. From top to bottom is an abacus, adding machine, and electronic calculator.

Use or Sell the Product. The result of the technological method is a product. The product is either used by the inventor or marketed. The product is never really final because the inventor or the company that owns the product continues to look for ways to improve it. Companies also continually modify products to prevent them from becoming obsolete.

There are many products on the market today that have withstood the test of time and continue to be popular. Some products that have been used for many years include the pencil sharpener, light bulb, and stapler. Other products continue to be sold because they have been greatly improved over the years. Such products include the watch, automobile, and laundry detergent. Other products are not used by people any more and have become obsolete. Some obsolete products are the ink well, washboard, and icebox.

> Just as the purpose of science is to continually seek new knowledge, the purpose of technology is to continually improve upon or make products.

In the next four chapters, you will learn about many of the products of technology and how they have been developed. **Many people enjoy the challenge of technology, that is, producing something successful from an idea.**

19. How is modifying a design similar to drawing a conclusion?

20. Why is modifying the design a critical step?

21. What is the result of technology? Why is the product never really final?

22. Why is technology exciting?

23. What do the products of technology result from?

ACTIVITY: Building a Rubber Band-Powered Car

MATERIALS: Coat hangers, rubber band, cardboard

You will be given three items. Using the technological method, you will build a car powered by one rubber band. Then, you will enter this car in class competition to see whose car will travel the farthest.

a. You can use as many as two coat hangers. You will also be given rubber bands of the same size and a piece of cardboard.

b. Other than any hand tools needed to cut and bend the wire, rubber band, and cardboard, you may not use any other tools or materials.

c. Your task is to build a car that will travel forward by means of a rubber band. A possible design is shown at the right.

d. Write a report on your technological effort. In your report, explain how you used the eight steps of the technological method.

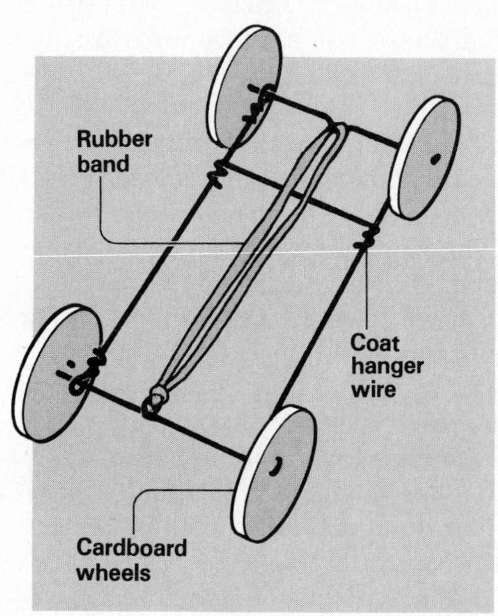

SUMMARY

VOCABULARY

technological method
desalinization
prototype
quality engineer

KEY FACTS AND CONCEPTS

The products of technology have resulted from people using the technological method.

The eight steps of the technological method are: (1) recognize a need, (2) get an idea, (3) find the facts, (4) make a detailed design, (5) build the product, (6) test the product, (7) modify the design, and (8) use or sell the product.

The technological method can be used by anyone who wants to invent a product.

A need is something people want, crave, require, desire, or find essential.

The foundation for ideas is education.

Before an idea can be applied and tested, the facts must be gathered.

Like a graph, a design helps you to see a product in picture form.

The purpose of building a product is to apply an idea.

The first example of an idea that is built is called a prototype.

After the prototype of a product is built, it is tested.

The data collected from the testing process are used by a person or a company to determine whether a product should be modified or should go into production.

The decision to modify a product or send it into production can result in the gain or loss of great sums of money.

The result of people using the technological method is a product.

The challenge and excitement of technology is creating something from an idea.

CONCLUSION

Technology is the process of producing a product. The process used to produce a product is called the technological method. The technological method consists of eight steps that guide a person from recognizing a need to building a product that fills the need. All the products you see around you are the result of the technological method.

24. What is the KEY IDEA of this chapter?

CHAPTER

41 Technology and Materials

Building for Tomorrow

41A INTRODUCTION

During the last century, new materials have changed almost every aspect of life. **Materials discovered by scientists have been applied by engineers to build a different world.** Today, roads are hard and smooth, buildings are built of steel and glass, and clothes are made from chemicals. Both new materials and old materials used in new ways are changing people's lives.

A material is any substance from which something is made. In this chapter, you will study several different kinds of materials. You will learn about some of the products made from these materials and how they affect your life.

Although new materials are shaped into products by engineers, they often begin as discoveries made by scientists working in basic research. Because engineers have applied scientific discoveries to make new products, society now enjoys more conveniences than ever before.

1. What is a material?
2. How does the work of engineers affect your life?

41B CONCRETE

In 1824, Joseph Aspdin, an English bricklayer, invented an improved CEMENT. Aspdin called the material *portland cement*. **Cement is a fine, gray powder that forms a binding paste when combined with water.** Over the years, different kinds of cement have been developed for many different uses.

Portland cement is used mainly to make CONCRETE. **Concrete is made by mixing cement with water, sand, and gravel. The mixture hardens into a very strong material that lasts a long time and requires little care.**

Before concrete becomes solid, or sets, it can be poured, molded, and shaped into many forms. In the building of large structures, wet concrete is poured into wood, plywood, or steel forms. The forms give the concrete its shape. Once the concrete hardens, the forms are removed.

To make concrete even stronger, engineers can mold it around steel beams or rods. This is called reinforced concrete. Most large structures, such as skyscrapers and bridges, are constructed with reinforced concrete.

One of the more unusual uses for concrete is as a ship-building material. A special type of concrete is sprayed onto a wire form and allowed to harden very slowly. The result is a hull that is very hard and strong. Many boats are built from concrete because it is stronger and cheaper than many other materials.

Concrete is the most common building material in the modern world. Its strength, availability, and low cost have made it an ideal choice for the construction of highways, skyscrapers, bridges, and other large structures. New uses for concrete are continually being developed.

Concrete is mixed and spread by machines and then smoothed out by hand. This photo shows work being done on reinforced concrete.

ACTIVITY: Making Your Own Concrete

MATERIALS: Portland cement, small gravel, sand, water, measuring spoon, paper cups, nail, hammer

Sample No.	Cement (spoons)	Sand (spoons)	Gravel (spoons)	Hardness Test Results
1	1	2	1	
2	2	2	1	
3	3	2	1	
4	4	2	1	
5	5	2	1	

Hardness Scale

5 Hardest
4
3
2
1 Softest

Concrete is a mixture of *portland cement,* gravel, sand, and water. In this activity, you will find out what happens to concrete when different amounts of cement are used in the mixture.

a. Label five cups with numbers 1 through 5.
- b. Make a chart like the one shown above.

c. Measure the amounts of materials shown in the chart into the correct cups.
d. Add small amounts of water to the cups and stir until each mixture is completely wet.
e. Let the cups stand overnight.
f. Remove each concrete sample from its cup and break it with the hammer and nail.
g. Mark the hardness of the concrete on the chart using a scale of 1 for the softest and 5 for the hardest.

3. Describe what happened to the concrete mixture overnight.
4. How did different amounts of cement affect the hardness of the concrete?
5. Describe one way the strength of concrete might be controlled.

SOME USES FOR CONCRETE	
highways	bridges
sidewalks	walls
beams	ship hulls
floors	fountains
dams	monuments

6. What is cement?
7. What is concrete?
8. Describe the advantages of concrete as a building material.

41C GLASS

GLASS is one of the oldest materials used by people. In about 1500 B.C., Egyptians were making glass vessels. During the Middle Ages, people began making glass containers and other small glass objects. About one hundred years ago, scientists and engineers began to study glass. Today, the technology that has grown from that research has produced many different kinds of glass with thousands of uses.

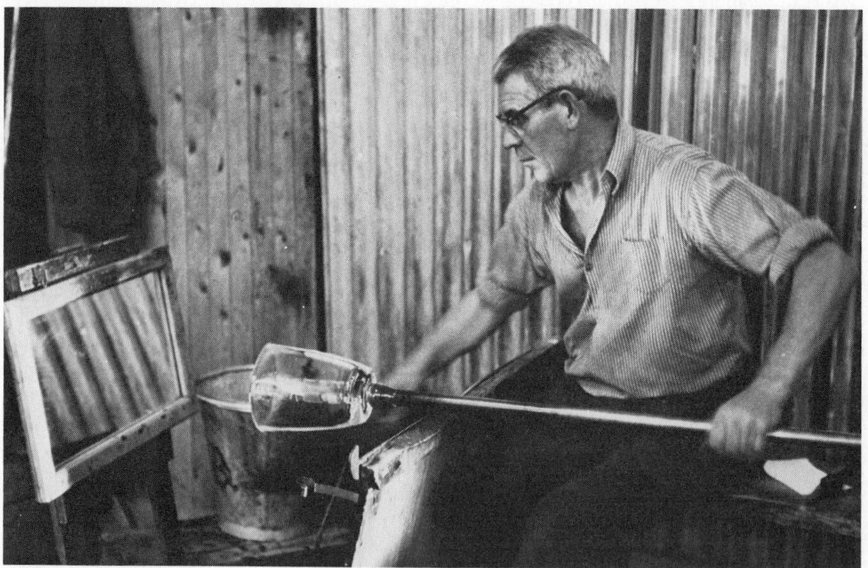

The man in this photo is making glass the same way it has been made for thousands of years.

Glass is made mainly from sand, soda, and lime. A glassmaker mixes together various amounts of sand, lime, soda, and other ingredients to make different types of glass. The mixture is heated until it is syrupy. When the syrup cools, it is glass. The ingredients used in glassmaking vary, depending on the type of glass being made.

Different manufacturing processes are used to produce different kinds of glass. Each process produces a special glass for a particular use. The first step in all glass manufacturing processes is to melt the basic ingredients together. If optical glass is being made, the raw materials must be especially pure so that the glass is flawless. The molten glass may then be poured into forms for optical lenses for eyeglasses, microscopes, telescopes, and cameras.

SOME USES FOR GLASS	
KINDS OF GLASS	**USES**
optical glass	camera and telescope lenses
glass blocks	building materials
plate glass	windows
molded glass	bottles
heat-resistant glass	oven windows
ceramic glass	baking dishes
glass fiber wool	insulation
glass fiber cord	tires, boats, cars
acid-resistant glass	chemical plant pipes, tanks
shatter-proof glass	car windows

If plate glass is being made, the molten glass is floated on an even surface of molten tin. Bottles are made when molten glass is pushed into a mold by a stream of compressed air. Fiberglass is made when molten glass is drawn through tiny holes in the bottom of a glass furnace. Fiberglass has many uses. It is used for electrical insulation, automobile parts, clothing, and drapery.

Many new types of glass are invented every year. Photochromic glass automatically darkens when the sun is out and lightens when the sun goes down. It is used to make sunglasses and windows. Ceramic glass can withstand extreme heat and cold, chemicals, and sudden temperature changes without breaking. Because of its great strength, ceramic glass is used for a wide variety of products, including cookware, turbine engines, and electronic equipment. Bundles of thin glass fibers, called fiber optics, can carry television signals and telephone conversations over long distances.

Each year, more uses for glass are discovered, making it one of the most useful modern materials.

Glass fiber cables like these are made of many fibers. Each fiber can carry thousands of messages at one time.

9. How is glass made?
10. Name some special kinds of glass and what they are used for.
11. Describe three uses of glass that affect your life.

41D PLASTIC

Your alarm clock, your desk at school, and your clothing may all be made of PLASTICS. **Plastics are synthetic materials that can be shaped into almost any form.** The substances used to make plastics are called SYNTHETIC RESINS. Synthetic resins are made from chemicals that come from such raw materials as wood, coal, and oil. **All plastics are made the same way. A synthetic resin undergoes a chemical reaction and is changed into a new substance with different properties.**

Chemical manufacturers make synthetic resins and sell them to plastics companies. Plastics companies make the plastic products you are familiar with. **Chemists explain a molecule of synthetic resin as a long chain of carbon atoms.** Each link in the chain is called a MONOMER.

This photomicrograph shows fine molecular threads linking polymers to form a network of plastic molecules. A photomicrograph is a photograph taken through a microscope.

The entire chain is called a POLYMER. Making synthetic resins involves "building" polymers by combining chemical compounds. When the compounds are combined, chemical reactions occur. It is during these chemical reactions that polymers are formed.

Plastics manufacturers use synthetic resins to make many different kinds of plastic products. The resins are usually combined with coloring agents, fillers, and other compounds to make thousands of different plastics. Each type is best suited for particular kinds of uses. Chemical engineers study the properties of plastics and select the best one for each application.

The plastic film that makes up this communications satellite had to be strong enough to support many times its own weight. The person suspended from the parachute in front of the satellite is inspecting the film for tiny flaws.

SOME TYPES OF PLASTICS

KINDS OF PLASTIC	USES
molded rigid plastic	containers and windows
rolled flexible plastic	flat sheets and tubes
synthetic fibers	clothing

All plastics are classified as either (1) THERMOSETTING or (2) THERMOPLASTIC, depending on the way they act when heated. **Thermosetting materials can be heated only once.** After melting, they harden as more heat is applied. Polyester and silicone are two widely used examples of thermoset plastics. Some thermoset plastics are used as casings for clocks and radios. Other thermoset plastics are used with glass fibers to make fishing rods and boats.

Thermoplastic materials can be melted again and again like candle wax. They melt when heated to a certain temperature, and they harden again when they cool. Two widely used thermoplastics are polyvinyl chloride and polyethelene. Polyvinyl chloride (PVC) is used to make plastic pipe, raincoats, upholstery, garden hose, and electrical insulation for house wiring. Polyethelene is also used for many different products. In one form, it is used to make thin, transparent film for packaging food. In another, it is molded into flexible squeeze bottles.

One very common use of plastic is as fiber for clothing. Nylon, rayon, and polyester are all plastic fibers. These fibers are called SYNTHETIC FIBERS because they are made from chemicals rather than from natural materials. Synthetic fibers are used because they hold their shape and are dirt and wear resistant.

Plastics are a product of basic chemical research. Engineers have taken new chemicals and have used them to make thousands of products that you use every day. New plastics are also being developed to meet needs in space exploration, computer science, and medicine.

12. What are plastics?
13. What are synthetic resins?
14. What is the difference between thermosetting material and thermoplastic material?
15. Make a list of at least ten plastic items you have used today. Explain how each is different from the others.

The synthetic fibers being woven here will be made into automobile tires.

41E METALS

Metals are elements like iron, copper, aluminum, and tin. People living thousands of years ago used metals for making weapons, tools, and jewelry. As they learned to use metals, people developed technology.

Only in recent years have scientists been able to study metals in the laboratory. Much of what is known about metals has been learned through trial and error. Using the new science of METALLURGY, scientists are studying ways to make more metals available for use. **Metallurgy is the science of purifying metals and preparing them to be used.**

Pure metals are chemical elements that have unique kinds of properties. The strength of metals makes them useful as building materials. Metals are also malleable, which means they can be beaten into different shapes. Some metals are ductile, which means they can be made into long, thin wires. Because they conduct electricity, copper, silver, gold, and aluminum are used to make electrical wire and switches. Some metals, like iron, can be magnetized and used to make electricity in generators. Because other metals, like aluminum, are lightweight they are used for airplane bodies, rocket parts, and food packaging.

Metals are mined from the earth where they have been concentrated by natural processes. Most metals, except gold, combine with oxygen, sulfur, and other elements in the environment to form ORES. As a result, these metals must be refined to remove their impurities. **Metallic ores are usually refined by heating.** This results in pure metals. A pure metal can then be shaped into various products.

Special mixtures of metals are called ALLOYS. **Alloys are made by melting two or more metals together.** The alloy has properties different from the original metals. Alloys are generally stronger than pure metals. The desired properties of an alloy are obtained by mixing the metals in different proportions.

Brass is an alloy. It is made by melting different amounts of copper and zinc together. The resulting alloy is stronger and less subject to corrosion than either copper or zinc. By varying the amounts of

Because of their great strength, metals are used to build large bridges and tall buildings.

copper and zinc or by adding small amounts of other elements, metallurgists have made many different brass alloys. Each alloy has special uses.

Modern industry depends on metals and alloys to produce many of the products you use every day. Without metals for tools, other products could not be made. Engineers are making metals perform new tasks. The discovery of special alloys, treatments, coatings, and hardening processes will make metals even more useful in the future than they are today.

16. What is a metal?
17. Explain how an alloy is different from a pure metal.
18. List five properties of metals and explain how they are used in technology.

SUMMARY

VOCABULARY

cement
concrete
glass
plastic
synthetic resin
monomer
polymer
thermosetting
thermoplastic
synthetic fibers
metallurgy
ore
alloy

KEY FACTS AND CONCEPTS

During the last century, new materials have changed almost every aspect of life.

A material is any substance from which something is made.

New materials are shaped into products by engineers. New materials often begin as discoveries made by scientists working in basic research.

Cement is a fine, gray powder that forms a binding paste when combined with water.

Concrete is made by mixing together cement, sand, gravel, and water.

Concrete is the most common building material in the modern world.

Glass is one of the oldest materials used by people.

Glass is made mainly from sand, soda, and lime melted together.

Different manufacturing processes are used to produce different kinds of glass.

Many new types of glass are invented every year.

Plastics are synthetic materials that can be shaped into almost any form.

Plastics are made when a synthetic resin undergoes a chemical reaction and is changed into a new compound with different properties.

Plastics are compounds made from long chains of carbon atoms called polymers.

Thermosetting plastics can be melted only once.

Themoplastic materials can be melted again and again like candle wax.

Synthetic fibers are used for clothing because they hold their shape and are dirt and wear resistant.

Pure metals are chemical elements with unique properties.

Metallic ores are refined by heating them to remove oxygen, sulfur, and other impurities.

Alloys are made by melting two or more metals together.

CONCLUSION

Engineers working with the results of basic research are reshaping your world. The materials they have created provide thousands of new products for you to use. Each material changes or improves your life in some way. New uses for concrete and new forms of glass, plastic, and metal are invented every year. These materials can help to make tomorrow's world a better place to live and work.

19. What is the KEY IDEA of this chapter?

CHAPTER

42 Energy and Technology

Power for Today's World

Just think of all the energy it takes to light these Manhattan skyscrapers!

42A INTRODUCTION

People use energy every day to do work. Energy moves your body, runs your family car, and heats your school. Everything you do requires energy. In the last hundred years, people have been using more and more machines to make work easier. Because those machines use energy, people are using more energy today than ever before. As a result, the earth is running short of energy from traditional sources.

Scientists and engineers have been working to develop technology that will help solve the earth's energy shortage. They have developed new equipment and improved old technology. In this chapter, you will study some of the recent developments in energy sources. You will learn how they save energy while providing power for people to use. You will also learn about the need to conserve and use energy wisely.

1. What is energy?
2. Why is the earth running short of energy from traditional sources?
3. How are engineers using technology to solve the earth's energy problems?

This photo shows a solar-powered telephone in the Saudi Arabian desert. The solar cells in the panel at the top of the pole provide all the electricity needed to operate the telephone.

42B SOLAR ENERGY

Engineers are finding ways to use sunlight to provide energy for people. Sunlight is the only earth resource that can never be used up. Because it is available everywhere, solar energy is a cheap and abundant energy source.

Engineers have harnessed sunlight to generate electricity. To provide small amounts of electricity, engineers developed SOLAR CELLS. A solar cell is a round or square plate made of silicon with tiny amounts of other elements. **When sunlight strikes a solar cell, the solar cell changes the light energy into electrical energy.** Solar cells are being used in some areas to power telephones and weather stations and to recharge batteries.

Where larger amounts of electrical power are needed, engineers are testing giant solar power plants. In order for such plants to work, they must be located in places such as deserts, where the weather is mostly sunny. Most solar power plants consist of long rows of curved SOLAR COLLECTORS that rotate to follow the sun. The collectors concentrate the sun's rays on a tube that contains water or some other liquid. The concentrated sunlight heats the liquid and changes it into steam. The steam turns generators that produce electricity.

The solar collectors in this large power plant concentrate the sun's rays to heat water for a laundry.

Solar energy is also being used to heat homes and buildings. PASSIVE SOLAR homes are designed to use the sun's energy without special equipment. Passive solar homes operate on the scientific principle called the GREENHOUSE EFFECT. Light waves pass through the windows of a house without being reflected or absorbed. However, after light waves pass through the windows of a house, they are absorbed by the floor and walls. Then the light energy is changed into heat energy. Unlike light waves, heat waves are reflected back into rooms by windows, trapping the energy in the house.

Passive solar houses are designed to let light in during the winter and keep light out during the summer. During the summer, when the sun is high in the sky, the building's roof and other design features keep the sun out. But during the winter, light enters a passive solar home and is absorbed by brick walls or tanks of water. Then, at night, the stored heat energy is radiated back into the house.

ACTIVE SOLAR systems are also used to heat homes. **Active solar systems use pumps to move a fluid from a storage tank to another type of solar collector.** This kind of solar collector is a box built to absorb energy from the sun and change it into heat energy. Fluid from the storage tank passes through pipes in the rooftop collector where it is heated. The fluid is then returned to the tank. When it is needed, the fluid is used to move the stored heat energy to places in the home that need heat.

Active solar systems can be used in several ways. They may use water, antifreeze, or air to move heat energy from the collectors to a storage area. **Active solar systems can be installed on existing houses. They can also be used to supply part of a home's energy needs by being used to heat water rather than the entire house.**

Active solar systems have advantages, but they also use energy and have moving parts to wear out or break down. Before a builder decides which system to install in a house, many factors must be considered so that the most efficient and economical system may be installed.

4. Explain the Greenhouse Effect. How can it be used to produce heat energy?
5. Describe a passive solar heating system and explain how it works.
6. What is a solar collector?
7. What is the difference between active and passive solar systems?
8. State one disadvantage and one advantage of a passive solar system. An active solar system.

ACTIVITY: Changing Light Energy into Heat Energy

MATERIALS: Light source, meter stick, empty aluminum soft drink cans, cardboard, scissors, white and black paint, thermometers

	Temperature 20 cm	Temperature 40 cm	Temperature 60 cm		
LIGHT SOURCE	°C	°C	°C	Black cans	Before heating
	°C	°C	°C	White cans	
	°C	°C	°C	Black cans	After heating
	°C	°C	°C	White cans	

In this activity, you will learn how light energy is changed into heat energy. Engineers who apply technology to produce products such as solar collectors must understand how the energy in a device will behave. This activity will help you understand some of the problems they face.

a. Cut six pieces of cardboard into circles that fit tightly into the tops of the aluminum soft drink cans.
b. Use your pencil to punch a hole in the center of each cardboard circle and fit the circles onto the tops of the six cans.
c. Check each can to make sure that a thermometer will slide through the hole and down into the can.
d. Paint three of the cans white and three black.
e. Set up your light source on a table.
f. Mark points twenty, forty, and sixty centimeters from the light source.
g. Put a thermometer in each can and place a white and a black can side by side at the three marks.
• h. Construct a table like the one shown to record your data.
i. Record the temperature in each can.
j. Put the light source on for ten minutes.
k. Record the temperature in each can.

9. How did the temperature in the cans vary with their distance from the light source?
10. What difference did the color of the cans make in the temperature at each distance from the light source?
11. What kind of energy change took place between the light source and the cans?
12. Explain how an engineer might use this kind of information in designing a solar collector or choosing the color for a building or automobile.

42C WIND ENERGY

Engineers are constantly searching for new sources of energy. One source of energy they are using is not new. **People have used the wind to move boats, power mills, and pump water for centuries.** In recent years, engineers have worked to harness the wind as a source of electricity.

Modern WIND GENERATORS work almost the same way as ancient windmills. A blade shaped like an airplane propeller is mounted on a large frame above trees or other objects that might block the wind. An electrical generator is connected to the central shaft by a system of gears, and another is used to control the blades of the propeller. When the wind blows, a gearing system or a tail fin points the propeller into the wind. The wind energy is changed into mechanical energy when it turns the propeller. The mechanical energy is then changed into electrical energy inside the generator. **The amount of energy a windmill can generate depends on its size and the speed of the wind.**

Not every part of the United States can be used as a site for a wind generator. **Only places where the wind blows steadily for long periods of time are suitable for wind generators.** Engineers are looking at sites in Oklahoma, Minnesota, Oregon, Ohio, and North Carolina. They are working on very large windmills that will produce large amounts of power.

Small wind-powered generators are being built and used by individual homeowners and farmers to generate electricity. When the wind is blowing, the generators are used to supply power and charge batteries. When the wind dies, homeowners depend on charged batteries or buy electricity from the power company. Small wind-driven power plants are not very dependable, but they help reduce the need for electricity from large power plants.

Wind energy turns the rotor blades on this experimental generator. The windmill is expected to generate enough electricity to power about thirty homes.

13. Explain how wind energy is used to generate electricity.
14. What kind of site is needed for a wind generator?
15. What does the owner of a small wind generator do when the wind dies?

42D ENERGY FROM THE EARTH

The earth provides several unique sources of energy. In areas where magma comes close to the surface, energy can be generated by using magma-heated rocks to make steam. Water seeping down through the rocks comes in contact with the magma and is heated, changing the water into steam. Normally, the steam would return to the surface forming geysers or hot springs, but the steam in such areas can also be used as a source of energy.

To produce GEOTHERMAL energy, engineers drill wells down into the earth. Then they tap the steam being formed as water is heated by the rocks. **The steam is used to turn generators that produce electricity.**

Along many streams in the United States, small dams were used to generate power during the early 1900's. As large power plants were built, the very small generators were abandoned. Today, those small dams are being repaired and the generators are being rebuilt. Each small generator produces only a small amount of electricity, but taken together they are an important source of energy.

Along coastlines around the world, another source of energy is being tapped. **Engineers are working on devices that use energy from the ocean's waves, tides, and currents to generate electricity.** Only a few experimental devices have been constructed. Most of the devices use the motion of the waves to turn levers. The levers move wheels that drive generators.

Other devices use the heat of warm currents of water to drive generators. Each approach presents many problems, but the amount of energy that could be tapped is so large that some kind of generator will most likely be built in the future.

Water changed to steam by hot rocks far below the earth's surface provides the energy for this geothermal power plant.

16. Name three sources of energy from the earth.

17. Describe how geothermal energy is used to make electricity.

18. Why are small dams and generators being rebuilt?

19. Describe one way that waves or tides could be used to generate electricity.

42E ENERGY FROM LIVING MATERIAL

All the living plants and animals of the earth get their energy from the sun. In the last twenty years, engineers have been working to find ways to use that energy as a source of power. The energy trapped by green plants is called BIOMASS. **Today, engineers are using biomass in several ways to generate energy.**

Many large cities are using their garbage as a source of energy. The paper, wood, and plastic in garbage are all made from material that was once living. At specially built plants, the burnable trash is separated from the rest of the trash. When it is burned, the trash produces energy to generate electricity. In addition, the heat is often used a second time to heat nearby buildings and factories.

Other industries are using the same idea. **Furniture plants, lumber mills, and other companies are burning their waste materials.** The resulting energy is used to help power and heat the plant. In large cities, many of these industries also sell their waste heat to nearby apartment and office buildings. The heat they sell makes money for the company and saves energy for the future.

Office waste paper can be converted into storable pellets that can be burned as fuel.

Another way that engineers are using biomass to save energy is by making liquid fuels from plants. One such process uses corn, wood, and other plant materials. The materials are ground up and mixed with bacteria that cause them to ferment. The fermentation produces alcohol. The alcohol is then separated by distillation.

The alcohol produced by such processes is poisonous but contains a great deal of energy. The most common use for such alcohol today is to mix it with gasoline to make GASOHOL. About ten percent of gasohol is alcohol. Therefore, when people use ten gallons of gasohol in their cars, they eliminate the need for one gallon of gasoline.

20. What is biomass?

21. How are cities using trash to save energy?

22. Explain how some industries save energy by using their own waste products.

23. What is gasohol? How is it made?

42F CONSERVATION

CONSERVATION is one of the best ways to save the earth's energy resources. **There are many ways to conserve energy.** You can help preserve energy resources. Your efforts will help make nonrenewable resources last longer.

During the 1970's a great effort was made to stop unnecessary energy use. Unneeded lights were turned off. Smaller, more fuel-efficient cars were built. People were urged to car pool or travel by bus or train. The energy that was saved could be used later and reduced the need for new energy resources. **The need to save energy is greater than ever.**

There are several other ways to conserve energy. Adding insulation to homes cuts down the loss of heat in winter and helps keep heat out in the summer. Insulation around water heaters and furnaces or air-conditioning ducts also helps reduce the amount of energy needed to heat or cool your house. Using less hot water for bathing also saves energy. Hot water heaters can be run by clocks that heat water only when it is needed.

Pulling shades to keep the sun out in summer helps keep your house cooler. During the winter, the same sunlight can be used to help heat your home by closing shades or curtains on the side of the house away from the sun. Such methods are ways to make your home a passive solar system.

Engineers are working to develop new and improved methods of saving energy. Without conservation some of the energy resources you rely on will be used up in less than one hundred years. Long before they run out, the rising cost of energy will change the way you live. **Conservation and the development of new energy sources are the only ways to provide energy for the future.**

24. What is conservation of energy? Why is it important?

25. Describe several ways you can conserve energy.

26. What will happen if people do not conserve energy?

SUMMARY

VOCABULARY

solar cell
solar collector
passive solar
Greenhouse Effect
active solar
wind generator
geothermal
biomass
conservation

KEY FACTS AND CONCEPTS

People use energy every day to do work.

Scientists and engineers have been working to develop technology that will help solve the earth's energy shortage.

When sunlight strikes a solar cell, the solar cell changes the light energy into electrical energy.

Where large amounts of electrical power are needed, engineers are testing giant solar power plants.

Most solar power plants consist of long rows of curved solar collectors that rotate to follow the sun.

The amount of energy a windmill can generate depends on its size and the speed of the wind.

To produce geothermal energy, engineers drill wells down into the earth.

Steam from within the earth is used to turn generators that produce electricity.

Engineers are working on devices that use energy from the ocean's waves, tides, and currents to generate electricity.

The energy trapped by green plants is called biomass.

Engineers are using biomass to save energy by making liquid fuels from plants.

Conservation is one of the best ways to save the earth's energy resources.

Conservation and the development of new energy sources are the only ways to provide energy for the future.

CONCLUSION

Energy is vital to your life. Technology has applied knowledge about energy to make life easier than ever before. But people are also using more energy than ever before. Because there is a limited amount of many energy resources, you must help conserve energy by using it wisely. With the help of new technology and conservation, there will be enough energy for you and future generations.

27. What is the KEY IDEA of this chapter?

CHAPTER

43 Communication and Technology Information for People

43A INTRODUCTION

Communication is the art of exchanging information with other people. You communicate with others every day when you talk, write messages, or telephone your friends. Modern technology makes it possible for you to communicate with people on the other side of the earth in less than a second. **Communications technology has developed as engineers have applied the discoveries made by scientists working with electricity.**

Modern communications devices allow people to see events as they happen in other countries and even on other planets. These devices have changed the world in the last century. Information that once would have taken weeks or months to reach you is now relayed to you in seconds by means of radio and television. New discoveries and inventions are making it easier to communicate every day.

In this chapter, you will study the modern methods people use to communicate. You will learn how the TELEGRAPH, TELEPHONE, RADIO, and TELEVISION were invented and how they work. You will also understand how they help people communicate their ideas to others.

1. What is communication?
2. Describe several types of communication that you use every day.
3. How has modern technology changed communication?

43B SENDING INFORMATION BY WIRE

One of the first discoveries made by scientists studying electricity was that an electric current could flow over long distances in a wire. This discovery was put to work in a device called the telegraph. The telegraph uses electric currents to send messages. In the 1830's, Samuel Morse invented a very simple telegraph that became the prototype for all the telegraphs that were to follow.

Morse's telegraph consisted of a battery, an electromagnetic sounder, and a switch or key. Pressure on the key closed the telegraph circuit, allowing an electric current to flow through the wire to the electromagnet. The current flowing through the electromagnet created a magnetic field that pulled down a strip of metal making an audible click. By pressing and releasing the telegraph key, a series of clicks could be sent to a receiving station.

This drawing shows Alexander Graham Bell and Thomas Watson with the first telephone on the table in the background.

Morse developed a code of long and short sounds, called dots and dashes, that stood for letters and numbers. This became known as Morse code. Thus, the telegraph became the fastest way to communicate at that time. Telegraph lines began going up across the United States. By the time the Civil War began, telegraph lines stretched from the east coast to the west coast. Today, more than ten million kilometers of telegraph lines stretch around the world.

The telephone improved on the telegraph by allowing people to talk over wires. **The first telephone conversation occurred between Alexander Graham Bell and his assistant Thomas Watson on March 10, 1876.** Testing his new invention, Bell called Watson, "Mr. Watson, come here. I want you!" Watson, waiting for the test message, heard the words distinctly over the telephone and ran to congratulate Mr. Bell.

You use the telephone without thinking about its complexity. **The telephone can connect you to people on the other side of the earth.** You could talk to more than forty million people in the United States alone. The modern telephone uses radiowaves, satellites, and cables buried beneath the oceans to transmit conversations from place to place.

When you speak into a telephone, sound waves enter the mouthpiece. **An electric current flowing through the wire carries the sound of your voice to the person on the other end of the line.**

There are two main parts to a telephone: the transmitter and the receiver. The transmitter is located behind the mouthpiece. When you speak, the sound waves strike a thin metal disk in the transmitter called the diaphragm. The diaphragm vibrates at different speeds, depending on the different tones of your voice. The diaphragm presses against carbon grains that conduct electrical current. The pressure on the carbon grains is regulated by the loudness or softness of your voice. As the carbon is pressed, the amount of electrical current being conducted by the carbon changes.

The receiver of the telephone converts electric waves back into recognizable sounds. Two magnets cause the diaphragm in the receiver to vibrate. The vibration is based on the amount of electrical current the magnets receive from the transmitter. The vibrations produce the sound waves that strike the ear of the listener.

The transmitter converts sound into electrical waves that travel over a wire. The receiver converts the electrical waves back into sound.

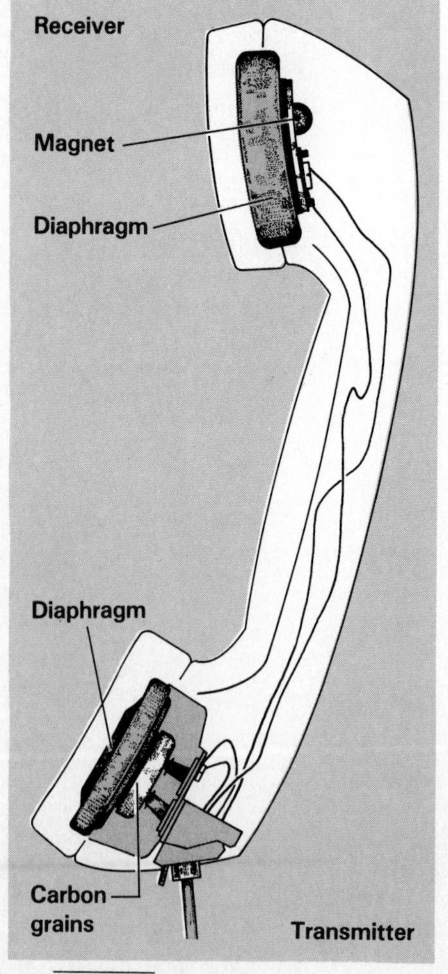

4. What was one of the first discoveries made by scientists who studied electricity?

5. What is a telegraph? Describe how it works.
6. How does the telephone work?

ACTIVITY: Making a Telephone

MATERIALS: Batteries, metal strips, clips, wire, carbon grains, plastic cup, light bulb

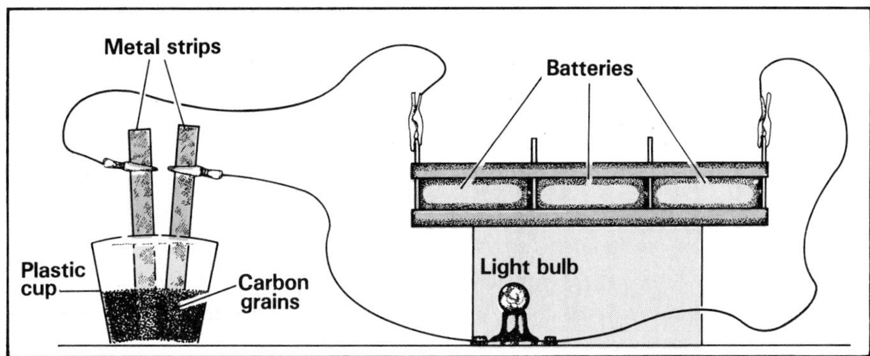

In this activity, you will build a simple device to demonstrate how the carbon grains in your telephone change the flow of electricity.

a. Place two metal strips in either side of a plastic cup.
b. Pour carbon grains into the cup until it is about half full.
c. Connect a wire to one of the strips. Connect the other end to one side of the light bulb.
d. Connect another wire to the other side of the light bulb. Connect the other end to one side of a battery.
e. Connect a third wire to the other strip. Connect the other end to the other side of the battery.
f. Squeeze the two metal strips together.

7. Why does the light bulb light up when you squeeze the two metal strips together?
8. What happens when you stop squeezing the strips?
9. How does pressure on the carbon grains affect the flow of electricity through the wire?
10. What would happen if you could press and release the carbon grains very quickly?

43C Radio

In 1888, a German scientist named Heinrich Hertz discovered that electrical energy could be sent through the air. Six years later, Guglielmo Marconi sent the first radio signal from one place to another. Marconi's device worked by generating an electrical spark, like the spark you see when you touch two wires together. The spark generated electrical energy that traveled in waves to a detector.

The earliest radios sent and received the same Morse code that was used with the telegraph. Marconi's device could send information across the Atlantic Ocean in one eighty-sixth of a second. As a result, people began using radios to send messages, even though the new invention had many problems.

As scientists continued studying the behavior of electrical waves, engineers used the information to develop improved radio systems. They learned how to transmit both speech and music. The first regular radio broadcasts began in the fall of 1920.

Early radio broadcasts often included plays and dramas with many characters. The people in this photo are reading their parts for a 1920's broadcast. The man at the far left is providing the sound effects.

Radio works by changing sounds into radio waves. A radio transmitter then sends these waves through the air at a particular frequency. As you learned in Chapter 27, frequency is the number of vibrations that a sound make each second. The frequency of a particular wave separates it from all the other waves being transmitted. When you tune your radio to a station's frequency, shown by the numbers on the radio dial, the receiver picks out the station's wave from all the others. This is how you tune in to your favorite station.

Before any sounds can be broadcast from a radio station, sound waves must be coded, or modulated, onto the radio wave. Today, a radio program is modulated onto a wave either by AMPLITUDE MODULATION (AM) or FREQUENCY MODULATION (FM). AM and FM signals have different characteristics.

With AM radio, the amplitude, or strength, of the radio wave is changed to match the pattern of the sound wave. With FM radio, the amplitude of the radio wave remains constant but its frequency changes. The frequency of the radio wave changes to match the sound wave patterns sent out by the radio station.

AM radio signals can be transmitted over long distances. Many countries beam AM radio programs around the world. Amateur radio operators also use AM signals to talk to other ham operators thousands of kilometers away. The problem with AM signals is STATIC. **Static is interference from other electrical devices that mix with the AM signal as it travels.** Static sounds like a hissing noise. The farther an AM signal travels and the weaker it gets, the more static you will hear on your radio.

Radios pick up two kinds of signals from transmitters: AM waves and FM waves. In these drawings, notice how the pattern of the FM radio wave differs from the pattern of the AM wave.

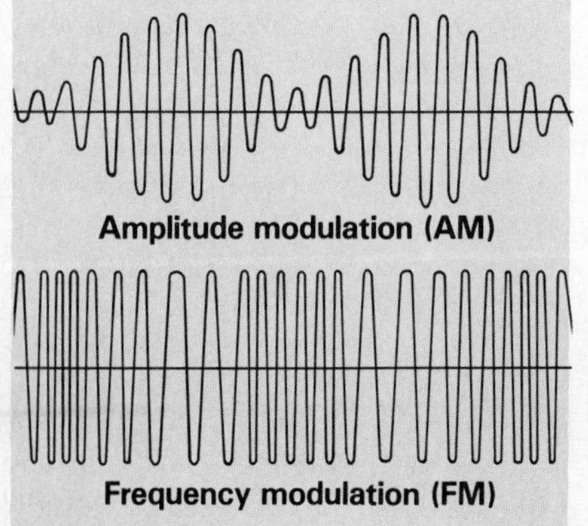

FM radio signals require a great deal more energy to send than AM signals. **FM signals generally travel much shorter distances than AM signals before dying out.** An advantage of FM is that you hear less static on an FM radio station. This is because when the FM signal is strong enough to be received, the signal is also strong enough to eliminate any static. Most modern music systems and television sets use FM radio signals because of the static-free, high-quality sound that is produced.

11. How does radio work?

12. How does a radio station's frequency allow you to pick out that station from all the other stations?

13. Before any sounds can be broadcast from a radio station, what must happen to the sound waves?

14. Explain the difference between an AM signal and an FM signal. Describe the advantages and disadvantages of each.

43D TELEVISION

Television is an electronic system for broadcasting moving pictures and sound. The first practical television system was demonstrated in 1929 by Vladimir Zworykin. By 1939, television was being broadcast on a regular basis from New York and several other large cities. Today, there are hundreds of television stations in this country and thousands around the world.

The picture you see on your television screen begins in a studio many kilometers away. A televison camera is pointed toward a person or scene. Inside the camera, a special camera tube with a light-sensitive plate picks up the image entering through the camera lens. A beam of electrons is scanned back and forth across the plate thirty times every second. The beam divides the picture into 525 lines and breaks each line into hundreds of tiny dots. Each dot is either black, white, or some shade of gray. **A good black and white television picture is made up of 200,000 dots repeated 30 times each second.**

The signal from the television camera and a sound signal is sent by cable to a transmitter. Television transmitters use very high frequencies that travel in straight lines. As a result, television transmission towers are usually more than 300 meters high. Signals from such high towers reach out about 200 kilometers.

When the television signal reaches the antenna at your home, it is very weak. First, the sound and picture signals are separated and amplified. The sound signal is sent to a speaker. Special signals, which were added to the picture at the transmitter, control a scanning beam of electrons in the picture tube. **As the electron beam scans the face of the picture tube, it lights up dots on the screen that match the picture**

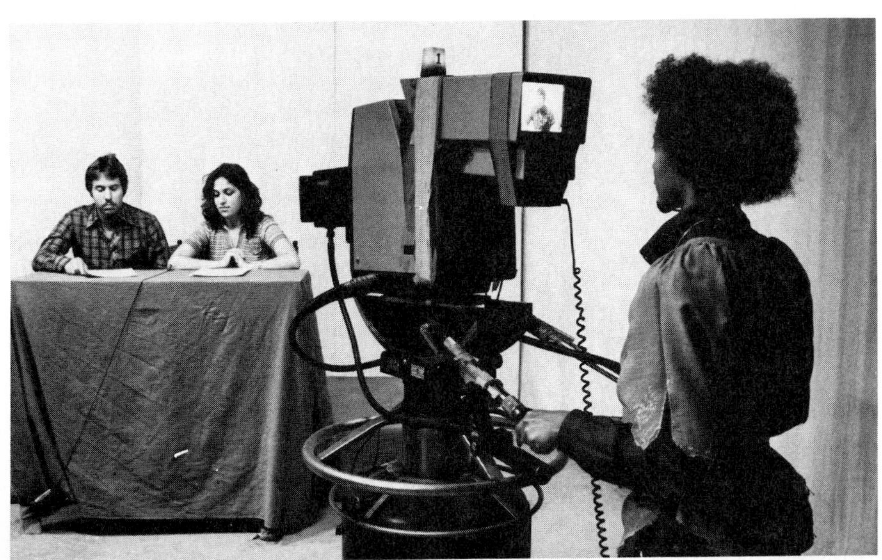

The young cameraperson in this photo is shooting a newsprogram in a college TV workshop.

on the plate in the television camera, recreating the picture entering the camera's lens.

Color television sets work the same way as black and white sets except that each dot on the screen is either red, green, or blue. At the television station, the camera contains three electron beams. Each beam scans one color. The information from all three beams is transmitted to your receiver. Inside the receiver's picture tube, three separate electron beams scan back and forth lighting the red, green, and blue dots. This produces a color picture on your screen.

Device	Inventor	How It Works
Telegraph	Morse	Electrical signals sent through wires
Telephone	Bell	Varying electrical current sent through wires
Radio	Marconi	Code and voice sent through space using electrical energy
Television	Zworykin	Pictures sent through space using electrical energy

15. Explain how a television picture is formed inside a camera.
16. How is a picture recreated inside a television picture tube?
17. How is a black and white television picture different from a color television picture?

43E NEW COMMUNICATION SYSTEMS

During the last five years, engineers have developed new ways for people all over the world to communicate with one another and be informed of world events. **Space satellites are being used to send television signals over great distances.** Television signals are sent to the satellite, which retransmits the signals over a wide area. Small, dish-

Satellites such as *Telstar I,* the first active communications satellite, have made worldwide television broadcasting possible.

shaped antennas are used to pick up the signals. Several hundred television channels can be received from just one satellite. Many homes both in the United States and in other countries now have this type of antenna.

Videotape machines, which store radio and television signals on magnetic tape, allow people to record TV programs and play them back many times. Videodisk machines can store up to two hours of television pictures on a disk that looks like a phonograph record. These disks can be played thousands of times without wearing out. Cable networks carry television and radio signals directly into millions of homes.

New miniature electronic circuits enable you to carry a television set, radio, or telephone in your pocket. All of these devices were developed by engineers using the results of basic scientific research. **Telegraphs, telephones, radios, and televisions keep you in touch with your world.**

18. How have satellites changed television?

19. List six ways in which telegraphs, telephones, radios and televisions keep you informed of local and world events.

SUMMARY

VOCABULARY

telegraph
telephone
radio
television
amplitude modulation (AM)
frequency modulation (FM)
static

KEY FACTS AND CONCEPTS

Communication is the art of exchanging information with other people.

Communications technology has developed as engineers have applied the discoveries made by scientists.

One of the first discoveries made by scientists studying electricity was that an electric current could flow over long distances in a wire.

Samuel Morse's telegraph consisted of a battery, an electromagnetic sounder, and a switch or key.

When you speak into a telephone, an electric current carries the sound of your voice to the person on the other end of the line.

There are two main parts to a telephone: the transmitter and the receiver.

Early radios sent and received the same Morse code that was used with the telegraph.

Radio works by changing sounds into radio waves.

When you tune your radio to a station's frequency, the receiver picks out the station's wave from all the others.

A radio program is modulated onto a wave in one of two ways: amplitude modulation (AM) or frequency modulation (FM).

Radio static is interference from other electrical devices.

Television is an electronic system for broadcasting moving pictures and sound.

A good black and white television picture is made up of 200,000 dots repeated 30 times each second.

Space satellites send television signals over great distances.

Videotape and videodisk machines can store radio and television signals on magnetic tape and disks.

CONCLUSION

Modern electronic devices have changed communication from a process taking weeks or months to one requiring only a matter of seconds. Over the years, the telegraph, telephone, radio, and television have evolved into the systems we use today. Inventors and engineers continue to improve cable and satellite transmissions as well as the quality of videotapes and videodisks.

20. What is the KEY IDEA of this chapter?

CHAPTER

44 Computers and Technology

Handling Information

44A INTRODUCTION

COMPUTERS are electronic machines that process information. Computers take information, process it, and give back new information. The ideas and inventions of many mathematicians and scientists led to the development of the computer.

The first mechanical calculating machines were invented during the 1600's. About two hundred years later, machines were invented that could be programmed. The first programmed machine was a loom that used punched metal cards to control the weaving of cloth. In 1890, Herman Hollerith invented a machine that used holes punched in paper cards to count people for a census. Hollerith's machine counted 63 million cards in a period of three years.

In the 1940's, the first electronic computers were built. One of the early machines, called Eniac, was built in 1946 and contained 18,000 vacuum tubes. Each tube acted like a switch that was either on or off. The computer was capable of performing about 5,000 arithmetic operations a second. Univac, the first commercial computer, was built in 1951. Univac could handle both letters and numbers. Like other early computers, it needed large amounts of electricity, air conditioning, and many people to keep it running.

Today, people have hand-held calculators to help them pay their bills and balance their checkbooks. Small, desk-top computers handle

The automatic loom was invented in 1801 by Joseph Jacquard. The loom was programmed to weave a pattern of cloth. Each part of the pattern was controlled by a punched metal card.

The first electronic computer was called ENIAC, which stands for "Electronic Numerical Integrator and Computer." As you can see in this photo, an entire room was needed to house ENIAC.

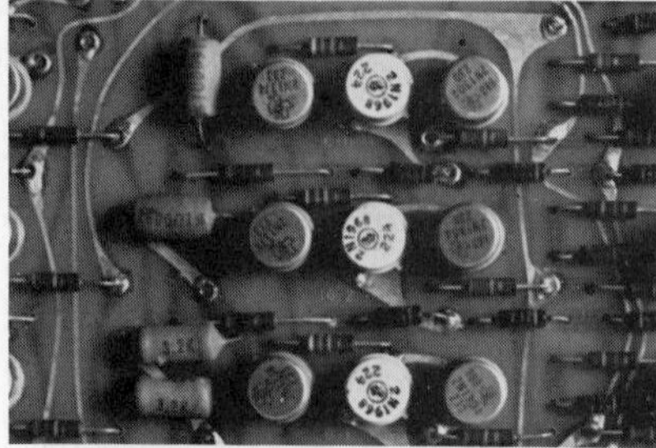

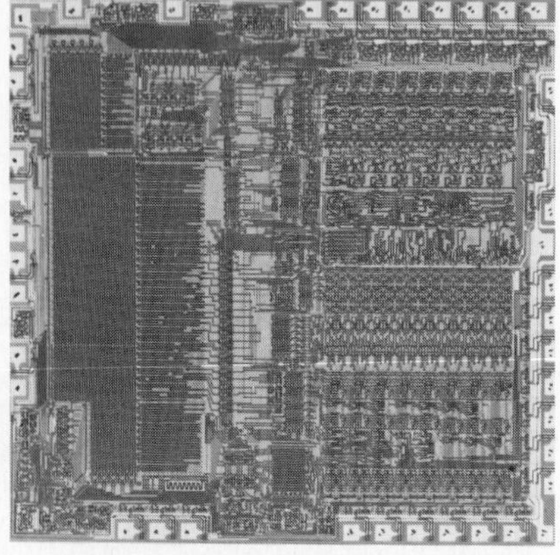

In the first photo, you can see the kind of vacuum tubes that made the first computers possible. In the second photo is a transistor. Transistors resulted in faster, smaller computers. The third photo shows a highly-magnified microprocessor. This microprocessor contains over 7,000 transistors and is as powerful as a small computer.

records and calculations that would have required a very large computer only twenty years ago.

In this chapter, you will learn about computers. You will learn how they handle information and how they are used by people to get jobs done. You will also learn about some ways that computers are changing your life.

1. What is a computer?
2. How have computers changed since the first ones were built?

44B DIFFERENT SIZES OF COMPUTERS

In 1948, scientists at Bell Laboratories developed a device called a TRANSISTOR. **Transistors were solid devices that replaced vacuum tubes.** Because transistors used less electricity and produced little heat, computers containing the transistors were much smaller and easier to use. During the 1970's, engineers made transistors even smaller. Then they learned how to pack thousands of transistors onto a SILICON CHIP about the size of your fingernail. The new chips allowed engineers to build very powerful computers. Today's larger computers can perform millions of mathematical operations a second.

Today's large computers use silicon chips to handle enormous amounts of information. A very large computer, which is called a MAINFRAME, may handle millions of tax records, control stoplights for a large city, or monitor a space shuttle launch. Smaller computers, MINICOMPUTERS, help keep payrolls and perform other business chores. The smallest modern computers, which are called MICROCOMPUTERS, make possible video games, home and hand-held computers, and many modern devices.

3. What is a transistor?
4. What is a silicon chip?
5. What is the difference between a mainframe, minicomputer, and microcomputer?

Computers are grouped into three sizes, shown here. Mainframes are very large computers, minicomputers are medium size, and microcomputers are small units.

44C KINDS OF COMPUTERS

There are three types of computers. ANALOG computers work directly with a quantity, like temperature, rather than with a number, or digit, that represents the quantity. The second type of computer works with digits. Most computers in use today are DIGITAL computers. **The information they use, whether in the form of letters, numbers, or symbols, is represented by digits.** The third type of computer is a HYBRID that changes analog information into digital information.

People have to tell computers exactly what to do. A group of instructions that a computer follows is called a PROGRAM. Every program contains words or symbols that tell the computer to do certain things. Collections of programs are called SOFTWARE. Computers themselves and the machines that surround them are called HARDWARE.

HARDWARE: the physical equipment that makes up a computer

SOFTWARE: the instructions and information used to make a computer carry out a certain function

One way to enter data into a computer is to type it on the keyboard of a terminal. The instructions and information you enter into a computer are called INPUT. There are many other ways to enter data into computers. **Information can be entered on magnetic tape, magnetic disks, or punched cards.**

6. What is an analog computer?
7. How are analog, hybird, and digital computers different?
8. How does a digital computer handle information?
9. What is a program?
10. What is the difference between hardware and software?
11. What is input?

44D INSIDE A DIGITAL COMPUTER

When information is put into a computer it goes to the CENTRAL PROCESSING UNIT (CPU). **The central processing unit is the heart and brain of a computer.** The CPU contains a CONTROL UNIT, an ARITHMETIC LOGIC UNIT, and a MEMORY.

The control unit acts like a traffic cop. It tells each of the other parts of the computer what to do and when to do it. **The arithmetic logic unit adds, subtracts, multiplies, and divides numbers being processed by the computer.** It is capable of doing millions of mathematical operations in a single minute. **The memory holds information until the computer is ready to use it. The memory also stores the new information created as the computer operates.**

The memory within the CPU can function in two ways. A READ ONLY MEMORY (ROM) has information built into it when the computer is built. The ROM usually contains only the information needed to start the computer and load programs of instructions. A second way that memory can function is as RANDOM ACCESS MEMORY (RAM). A computer's RAM is like a scratch pad. RAM holds informa-

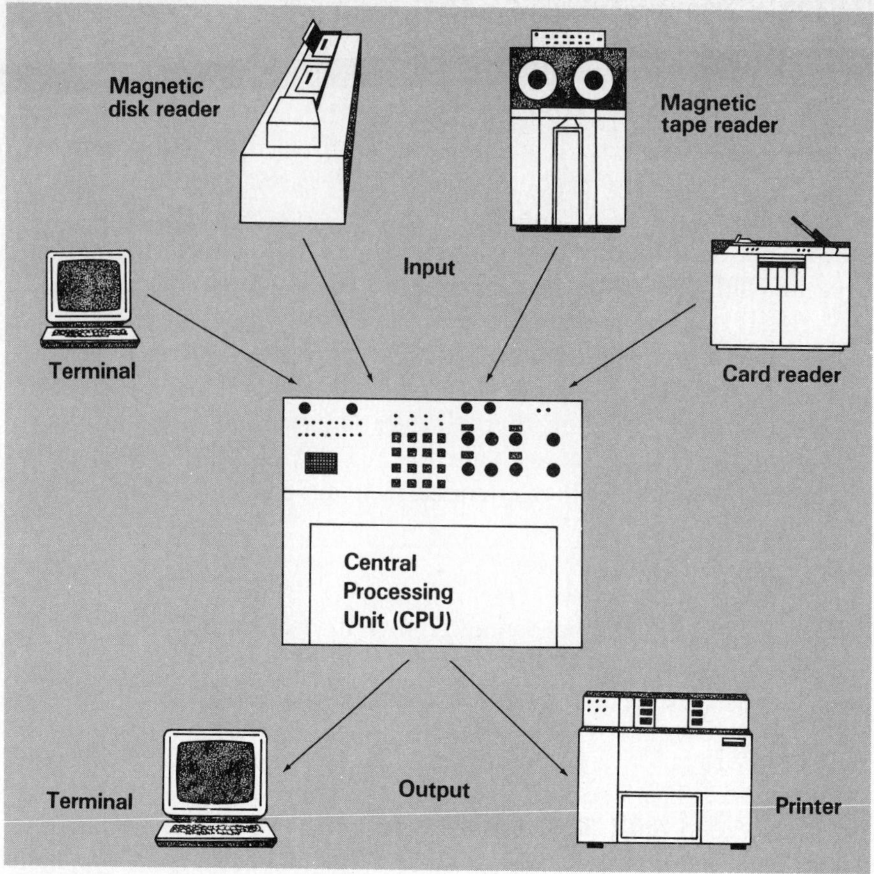

tion while it is being used and may be erased when an operation is completed.

When a computer processes information that needs to be stored for long periods, it uses memory systems located outside the CPU. Information needed or processed by the computer may be read from or written onto MAGNETIC TAPE or a MAGNETIC DISK. Disk or tape memory units will hold very large amounts of information.

When the computer has processed information and stored the product in its memory, the information is available for people to use. Computers communicate their information to people through OUTPUT devices. Most output is printed on paper or displayed on a television-type screen called a terminal. Output may also be recorded on magnetic tape, magnetic disks, or punched cards. Some computers can even generate sounds and "talk" to people.

12. Describe the parts of the central processing unit and explain their functions.
13. How are ROM and RAM different?
14. Explain the uses of magnetic disks and magnetic tape.
15. What is output?

44E HOW DIGITAL COMPUTERS HANDLE DATA

The letters and numbers that computers process are symbols. Each symbol has a meaning like the letter *A* or the number *1*. If you sat down at the keyboard of a small computer and pressed a key, you would be putting a piece of information into the computer. In computers, each

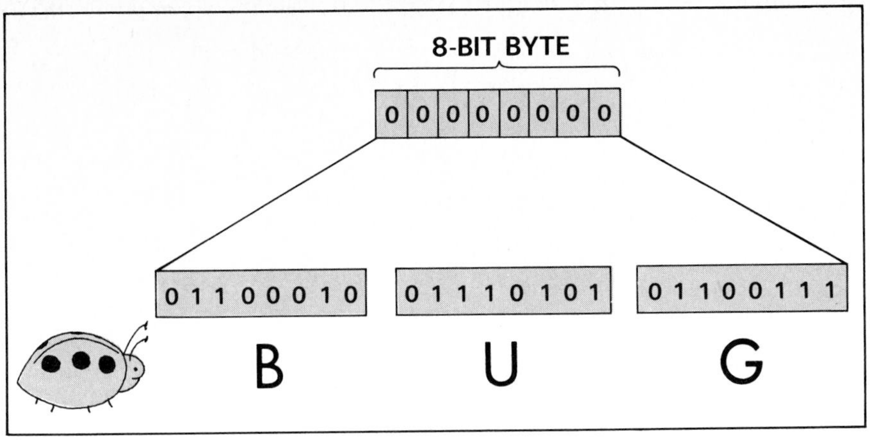

The three bytes shown here represent the word *bug* as it would be recognized by a computer.

symbol is represented by a number. So computers handle data as thousands or millions of numbers.

In order to process numbers, computers must be able to count. Computers count using only 1's and 0's. A single 1 or 0 is called a BIT. Most computers combine bits into groups of eight called BYTES.

Each byte is a pattern of 0's and 1's. Each pattern represents a letter, number, or symbol. For example, when a word like *bug* is entered on the keyboard, the computer receives 01100010 01110101 01100111. Each byte of eight zeros and ones stands for one letter.

Every program that is run in a computer uses thousands of bytes in BINARY CODE, also called machine code, to tell the computer what to do. In order to communicate easily with computers, programmers use special kinds of instructions called LANGUAGES.

Computer languages allow programmers to activate the binary code with familiar symbols like letters or numbers. In each language, certain words or other symbols are interpreted by the computer as an order to do something. Such words are called COMMANDS. A command like *print* might tell the computer to send a certain piece of information to a printer or display it on a screen.

There are many different computer languages. Each language was written to serve a special purpose, and each is known by a special name. FORTRAN is a language designed to handle advanced mathematics. Its name stands for "formula translator." COBOL means "common business-oriented language." COBOL is used to carry out everyday business operations. BASIC stands for "beginners all-purpose symbolic code." BASIC is used by students, hobbyists, and small-business owners who use microcomputers.

COMPUTER LANGUAGES

Name	Use
FORTRAN	scientific mathematics
COBOL	business record keeping
BASIC	general purpose language

All of the major languages follow a standard set of rules that allows each language to be used on many different computers. Therefore, a well-written program can be moved from one computer to another with little difficulty.

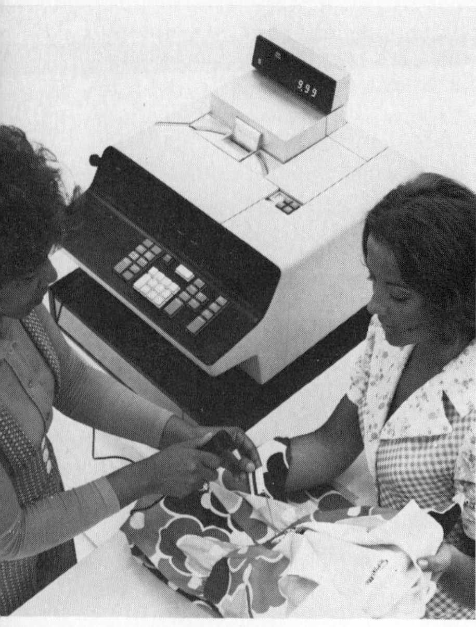

Computers are being used in stores to read product codes and add up customers' bills. Computers also keep store inventories and prepare orders as items go out of stock.

16. What is a bit and a byte? How do computers use them to handle information?

17. What is the difference between binary code and a computer language?

18. Why are there different computer languages?

19. Name three common computer languages and explain their major uses.

44F HOW COMPUTERS ARE USED

Computers began to play an important role in your life the moment you were born. When you were born, your name and the vital information about you were recorded on the hospital's computer. Your school may keep your grades, attendance record, and test scores on a computer. If you have a social security number, your name is part of an enormous information file in Washington, D.C. Every time you work for a company, your salary and work history will be added to your social security file.

A major use of computers is to help stores total your purchases. When you go to the grocery store, the clerk at the checkout counter may check the cost of your items with a computer that reads a printed product code on each item. The computer then checks the code against the price list stored in its memory, determines the price, and adds it to your bill. The computer may even use an artificial voice to read each price aloud. Finally, the computer will help the checkout clerk total your bill and return your change.

Other businesses use computers to keep their inventories, print monthly bills, and credit payments. Even small businesses are using microcomputers to keep their records. In each case, the improved accuracy and speed save the company money.

The student in this photo is learning to be a computer programmer.

Scientists use computers to complete calculations in a few minutes that used to take weeks or months. The National Weather Service prepares weather forecasts with a computer that brings together weather reports from all over North America. The computer prints maps that show conditions in the atmosphere. Then it compares the maps and studies the changes that have occurred over a period of several days. Finally, the computer prints a map that shows how the atmosphere might behave in the coming hours. Meteorologists use the maps to prepare forecasts of tomorrow's weather.

A computer plays some role in your life everyday. In some cars, microcomputers control the engine, helping to control air pollution and improve gas mileage. A computer in a microwave oven can change the temperature, monitor cooking, and tell time. A microcomputer may help you keep household records, control heating and air conditioning systems, and trigger fire and burglar alarms when needed. It may also play games with you in its spare time.

20. Describe two ways in which computers are used by stores.

21. How are computers used to forecast the weather?

22. How are computers being used in people's homes and schools?

SUMMARY

VOCABULARY

computer
transistor
silicon chip
mainframe
minicomputer
microcomputer
analog
digital
hybrid
program
software
hardware
input
central processing unit
control unit
arithmetic logic unit
memory
Read Only Memory
Random Access Memory
magnetic tape
magnetic disk
output
bit
byte
binary code
language
command
FORTRAN
COBOL
BASIC

KEY FACTS AND CONCEPTS

The first mechanical calculating machines were invented during the 1600's.

In the 1940's, the first electronic computers were built.

Transistors were devices that replaced vacuum tubes.

Today's computers use silicon chips to handle enormous amounts of information.

People have to tell computers exactly what to do.

One way to enter information into a computer is to type it on the keyboard of a terminal.

The central processing unit is the heart and brain of a computer.

Memory within the CPU can function in two ways: Read Only Memory (ROM) and Random Access Memory (RAM).

Most output is printed on paper or displayed on a television-type screen called a terminal.

The letters and numbers that computers process are symbols.

In order to process numbers, computers must be able to count.

Computer languages allow programmers to activate the binary code with familiar symbols like letters or numbers.

Each computer language was written to serve a special purpose.

Computers play an important role in your life every day.

CONCLUSION

Computers do only what they are told to do. If a computer makes a mistake, it is because people gave it the wrong instructions. Because computers affect nearly every facet of your life, you need to know how they work and how to use them. If you can make computers work for you, they will help you learn, solve problems, keep records, and make your life simpler in many ways.

23. What is the KEY IDEA of this chapter?

Glossary

This Glossary lists, in alphabetical order, many of the vocabulary words that appear in capital letters in the chapters. A brief definition follows each word. For words that may be difficult to pronounce, a special respelling is given in parentheses.

The following key will help you to pronounce these words correctly. In the respelling, the syllable that is stressed most is printed in capital letters. The syllable or syllables that are not stressed are printed in small letters. This key lists the letters and symbols used for the respelling. It also provides examples of words to show you how this special respelling system works.

Pronunciation Key

SYMBOL	KEY WORD	RESPELLING	SYMBOL	KEY WORD	RESPELLING
a	**act**	(AKT)	uh	**cup**	(KUHP)
ah	**star**	(STAHR)	ə	a as in	
ai	**dare**	(DAIR)		**along**	(ə-LAWNG)
aw	**also**	(AWL-SO)		e as in	
ā	**later**	(LĀT-ər)		**moment**	(MŌ-mənt)
e	**end**	(END)		i as in	
ē	**eat**	(ĒT)		**modify**	(MAHD-ə-fi)
er	**learn**	(LERN)		o as in	
	sir	(SER)		**protect**	(prə-TEKT)
	fur	(FER)		u as in	
i	**hit**	(HIT)		**circus**	(SER-kəs)
ī	**ice**	(ĪS)		**variable**	(VAR-ē-ə-b'l)
ir	**deer**	(DIR)		**open**	(ō-p'n)
	fear	(FIR)	ch	**chill**	(CHIL)
ō	**only**	(ŌN-lē)	g	**go**	(GŌ)
oi	**foil**	(FOIL)	J	**joke**	(JŌK)
	boy	(BOI)		**bridge**	(BRIJ)
or	**horn**	(HORN)	k	**kite**	(KĪT)
ou	**out**	(OUT)		**curtain**	(KER-t'n)
	flower	(FLOU-ər)	ng	**bring**	(BRING)
oo	**hoot**	(HOOT)	s	**sum**	(SUHM)
	rule	(ROOL)		**cent**	(SENT)
yoo	**few**	(FYOO)	sh	**sharp**	(SHAHRP)
	use	(YOOZ)	th	**three**	(THRĒ)
u	**book**	(BUK)	z	**zebra**	(ZE-brə)
	put	(PUT)	zh	**treasure**	(TREZH-er)

abrasion (ə-BRĀ-zhən): the wearing away of rock surfaces by windblown sand

acceleration (ək-sel-ə-RĀ-shən): any increase in speed or change in direction

active solar: systems of pumps, tanks, and collectors used to collect and store solar energy

air mass: a large body of air with nearly uniform characteristics throughout

alkali (AL-kə-lī) **metals:** a group of metals in the periodic table that are very reactive

alloy (AL-oi): a mixture made by melting two or more metals together to produce a substance with a unique set of properties

alpha (AL-fə) **ray:** helium atoms or ions moving at very high speeds

alternate source: using another material to replace a resource that is in short supply

amplitude (AM-plə-tood) the height or depth of a wave from its normal rest position

amplitude modulation (mahd-yoo-LĀ-shən): a method of coding speech or music onto a radio wave by varying its strength

analog (AN-ə-lawg): a computer that works directly with a quantity like temperature rather than with a number

analysis (ə-NAL-ə-sis): the process of breaking a molecule down and identifying its parts

applied science: the application of knowledge gained by basic science to solve practical problems

arithmetic logic unit: the part of a computer's central processing unit that adds, subtracts, multiplies, and divides numbers

asteroids (AS-tə-roids): fragments of rock that orbit the sun in a belt between the inner and outer planets

atmosphere: the layer of air (a mixture of gases, water vapor, dust, and chemicals) that surrounds the earth

atom: the smallest particle of an element

atomic number: the number of protons in the nucleus of an atom

attraction: the force between two different electrical charges that pulls them together

autumnal equinox (aw-TUM-n'l Ē-kwa-nahks): September 22nd, the first day of fall

axes: a horizontal line along the bottom and a vertical line along the side of a graph

axis: an imaginary line that passes through the center of a planet around which the planet rotates

---

balance: an instrument used for weighing objects

bar graph: a graph that uses bars to represent values

BASIC (beginners all-purpose symbolic code): a special computer language used by students and small business owners

basic science: the search for knowledge that results in the laws and theories of science

beta ray: negative particles (electrons) moving at very high speeds

binary (BĪ-nər-ē) **code:** the counting system (base two) used by a computer to represent numbers, letters, and symbols

biochemist (bī-o-KEM-ist): a scientist who studies the chemistry of living things

biomass (BĪ-ō-mas): energy trapped in green plants

bit: a single 0 or 1 in the binary counting system

black hole: a gravity field in space so strong that even light energy cannot escape

block mountains: gigantic masses of uplifted rock

buoyancy (BOI-ən-sē): the force exerted against gravity by an object floating in a more dense liquid or gas

byte (BĪT): a group of eight bits used to represent a letter or number in a computer

---

carburetor (KAHR-bə-rāt-ər): a device used in gasoline engines to mix gasoline with air forming an explosive mixture

cavern (KAV-ərn): a large underground space formed when water dissolves limestone

chain reaction: a nuclear reaction in which atoms are continually splitting and releasing heat

change of state: when matter in one state (solid, liquid, or gas) changes to another state

chemists: scientists who study chemical changes and the properties of matter

chemical bonds: links between atoms that hold molecules together

chemical change: when two substances react to form a new substance with different properties

chemical engineers: people who find uses for chemical reactions discovered by chemists

chemical reaction: the process by which two substances combine to form a new substance

chemical weathering: a group of chemical processes that change minerals into other chemical compounds forming soil

cement: a fine, gray powder that forms a binding paste when combined with water

centi: the metric prefix meaning one hundredth of a unit

central processing unit (cpu): the brain of a computer which includes a control unit, an arithmetic logic unit, and a memory

centripetal (sen-TRIP-ə-t'l) **force:** the force that holds an object in a circular path

COBOL (common business-oriented language): a special computer language used for business record keeping

cold front: a boundary where cooler air moves under warmer air

cinder cone: a steep-sided volcano built from cinder, dust, and ash

column: a vertical arrangement of numbers in a table

comet (KAHM-ət): a ball of frozen gas that orbits the sun far out in space

composite cone: a volcano built of alternating layers of cinders and lava

compound (KAHM-pound): a substance made of more than one element

compression (kəm-PRESH-ən): air compressed or pushed together as in a sound wave

combustion (kahm-BUS-chən): the process of burning a fuel

combustion chamber: the space between the piston and the top of a cylinder in which fuel is burned

computers: electronic machines that process information

concave mirror: a mirror that curves inward

conclusion: part of a scientific paper that states the result of an experiment

concrete: a strong material made by mixing portland cement with sand, gravel, and water

condensation (kahn-dən-SĀ-shən): the change of gas into a liquid

conductor (kən-DUHK-tər): a material that has the ability to conduct heat and electricity

conservation (kahn-sər-VĀ-shən): the practice of preserving and protecting natural resources. Also, the process of saving energy

conservation of energy: the law that states that energy is neither created nor destroyed

constellation (kahn-stə-LĀ-shən): a group of stars forming a recognizable pattern in the sky

constructive forces: forces that build up the land

continents (KAHN-ti-nənts): seven great landmasses that ride on the earth's crustal plates

control: part of an experiment that tests the hypothesis with and without a given factor

control unit: the part of the central processing unit that tells the computer what to do and when to do it

controlled use: planning the use of a resource so that the earth has time to replace the resource before it is used up

convex mirror: a mirror that curves outward

corrosive (kə-RŌS-iv): a material that eats away whatever it comes in contact with

covalent (kō-VĀ-lənt) **bond:** a bond formed when valence electrons are shared between two or more atoms

cirrus (SIR-əs) **clouds:** thin, wispy clouds that form high in the troposphere

cloud: millions of small water droplets floating in the air

climate: long-term trends in the behavior of the atmosphere

clues: guides to the solving of problems

crest: the highest part of a wave

crust: the thin, rigid outer layer of the earth

cumulus (KYOOM-yə-ləs) **clouds:** piled up or "puffy" clouds

cyclonic (sī-CLAHN-ik) **storm:** an area of low pressure with winds blowing counterclockwise about its center

cylinder (SIL-ən-dər): a hollow tube in which a piston is moved back and forth by some force

---

data (DĀT-ə): facts that tell what happened during an experiment. Also, all information used by scientists

data table: a chart that organizes numbers

decade (DEK-ād): a ten-year period of time

deceleration (dē-sel-ə-RĀ-shən): any reduction or slowing in velocity

deci (DES-ə): the metric prefix meaning one tenth of a unit

decibel (DES-ə-b'l): the amount of energy involved in the production of a sound

decompose (dē-kəm-PŌZ): to break a molecule into its parts

deka: the metric prefix meaning ten times the unit

delta: a large, fan-shaped body of mud and sand deposited by a river when it enters a lake or sea

density: the mass per unit volume of a substance

desalinization (dē-sal-ə-nə-ZĀ-shən): the process of removing salt from sea water to produce fresh water

destructive forces: forces that wear down the land

diatomic (dī-ə-TAHM-ik) **molecule:** a molecule made from two atoms of the same element

diesel (DĒ-s'l) **engines:** machines that burn fuel oil under very high pressure to turn a shaft to do work

diffusion (di-FYOO-zhən): the mixing or spreading out of molecules

digital (DIJ-it-'l) **computer:** a computer that works with numbers or letters represented by numbers

displacement: the amount of liquid or gas pushed out of the way by an object

dune (DOON): a hill of sand built by the wind

Earth: the third planet from the sun

earth materials: anything that is taken from the earth and used

earthquake: vibrations moving through the earth caused by motion along a fault

effort: the force applied to a simple machine

effort distance: the distance through which the effort is applied in a simple machine

electron (i-LEK-trahn): a small, negatively-charged particle outside the nucleus of an atom

electron acceptor: an atom that tends to gain valence electrons in chemical reactions

electron donor: an atom that tends to lose valence electrons in chemical reactions

electromagnetic (i-lek-trō-mag-NET-ik) **force:** the force made up of the forces of attraction and repulsion caused by electrical charges and magnetism

electromagnetic spectrum: the full range of electromagnetic waves from long radio waves to short gamma rays

element (EL-ə-ment): a substance that cannot be broken down into simpler substances

elliptical galaxy (i-LIP-ti-k'l GAL-ək-sē): a galaxy with a definite elliptical or oval form

engineers: people who use the discoveries of scientists to design, test, and build the products of technology

equator (i-KWĀT-ər): an imaginary line that cuts the earth in half horizontally

equipment: the part of a scientific paper that tells what supplies and instruments were used in an experiment

erosion (i-RŌ-zhən): processes that move small rocks and soil from one place to another

evaporation (i-vap-ə-RĀ-shən): the change of a liquid into a gas

exosphere (EK-sə-sfir): the uppermost layer of the atmosphere that thins out into the vacuum of space

experiment: an activity designed to test a model or hypothesis

external combustion engine: an engine powered by heat or expanding gases from combustion outside the engine

---

fault: a break in a large mass of rock

flood plains: wide, flat river valleys usually built by slow-moving streams near sea level

focal point: the point at which light rays reflected from a concave mirror come together

folded mountains: mountains formed from bent and folded rocks

force: a push or pull on an object

formula: a group of symbols and numbers which tell what elements are in a molecule and how many atoms of each there are

FORTRAN (formula translator): a special computer language used for scientific mathematics

fossil (FAHS-'l): the preserved remains of plants or animals found in rocks

four-stroke cycle engine: an engine that uses intake, compression, power, and exhaust strokes to make one power cycle

frequency (FRĒ-kwən-sē): a measure of the number of vibrations per second measured in hertz

frequency modulation (mahd-yoo-LĀ-shən): a method of coding speech or music onto a radio wave by varying its frequency

friction: the force between the surfaces of two objects that resist motion

fulcrum (FUL-krəm): the point on a lever at which the lever is supported

full moon: a phase of the moon when it is seen as a completely lighted disk

fundamental tone: the frequency produced when a string vibrates as a whole

fusion (FYOO-zhən): the combining of two hydrogen atoms to form one helium atom with an accompanying release of energy

---

gamma ray: very short, powerful rays that can damage human tissue

gas turbine (TER-bin): an engine in which expanding gas from burning gasoline is used to turn a turbine

gasoline engine: an engine that uses the force of expanding gases formed by burning gasoline to do work

gears: wheels with teeth or cogs that can connect one with another

geothermal (jē-ō-THER-m'l) **energy:** heat energy from the earth's interior that is used to produce electricity

glacier (GLĀ-shər): a very slow-moving sheet of ice

glass: a hard, transparent material made by melting sand, soda, and lime together

gram: the standard unit of mass in the metric system

graph: a method for showing data in picture form

gravity: the force of attraction or pull between all pieces of matter in the universe

Greenhouse Effect: the process of trapping energy by changing light into heat energy inside a glassed enclosure

---

half-life: the time needed for half of a radioactive substance to decay

halogen (HAL-ə-jən): a group of very reactive elements that form salts

harmonics (hahr-MAHN-iks): secondary vibrations also called overtones

hardware: computers and the machines that surround them

heading: the label for a row or column in a table

heat engines: machines that transform energy from fuels, steam, or from air or water under pressure into motion

hecto: the metric prefix meaning 100 times the unit

horizontal: a line drawn from left to right across a page

hour circle: a meridian dividing one time zone from another

hurricane (HER-ə-kān): a very large, violent storm that forms over oceans and has high winds

hybrid (HĪ-brid) **computer:** a computer that changes analog information into digital information

hydration (hī-DRĀ-shən): a process in which hard minerals like mica and feldspar combine with water, changing to clay

hydrometer (hī-DRAHM-ə-tər): a device used to measure the density of a liquid

hypothesis (hī-PAHTH-ə-sis): a scientific or educated guess about why something happens

---

igneous (IG-nē-əs) **rock:** rock formed from cooled magma

inclined plane: a simple machine formed by a sloping surface

inert elements: elements that do not react with any other substances

inertia (in-ER-shə): the tendency of a body to remain at rest or in motion unless acted upon by an outside force

inner planets: the four planets nearest the sun

input: the processes and devices used to put information into a computer

internal combustion engine: an engine in which the fuel that provides power is burned inside the engine

ion (Ī-ahn): an electrically charged atom

ionic bond: a bond formed between oppositely charged atoms through the transfer of electrons

ionizing radiation: alpha, beta, or gamma rays

irregular galaxy: a galaxy with no definite shape

isotope (Ī-sə-tōp): atoms of the same element that have the same atomic number but different atomic mass numbers

---

jet stream: narrow bands of wind in the stratosphere moving at very high speed

joule (JOOL): the amount of work done by a force of one newton acting over a distance of one meter

Jupiter: the nearest of the giant outer planets

---

kilo: the metric prefix meaning 1,000 times the unit

kilogram: 1,000 grams

kinetic (ki-NET-ik) **energy:** energy of motion

---

landform: a constantly changing feature on the earth's surface

language: a special group of words or symbols that tell a computer to carry out certain operations

lava: molten rock that has flowed out onto the earth's surface

law: a condition in nature for which no exceptions have been found

law of constant composition: the law that states that the molecules in a given substance always have the same parts

law of conservation of matter: the law that states that the amount of matter present will always remain the same

lens (LENZ): a transparent substance used to refract light

levels: layers in which electrons travel around the nucleus

lever: a simple machine that consists of a bar supported at one place while a force is applied at another place

life span: the length of time a person lives

lightning: a high-energy electrical discharge that may move from cloud to cloud or cloud to ground

light-year: the distance light can travel in one year

line graph: a graph that uses lines to represent number values

liter (LĒT-ər): the standard metric unit for measuring volume

local time: the time at any particular place in the world

longitude (LAHN-jə-tood): imaginary lines drawn north-south at fifteen-degree intervals around the earth

longitudinal wave: a wave that moves and vibrates in the same direction as the medium

lunar eclipse (LŌŌ-nər ē-KLIPS): a darkening of the moon caused when it passes through the earth's shadow

lunar month: the period of time from one full moon to the next

luster: shininess

---

mainframe: a very large computer

malleable (MAL-ē-ə-b'l): the property that allows a metal to be made into different shapes by pressure or pounding

magma: molten igneous rock beneath the earth's surface

magnetic disk: disk used to store information outside a computer

magnetic tape: a system like a tape recorder used to store information outside of the main computer

mantle: a layer of dense rock on which the earth's crust floats

Mars: the fourth of the inner planets

mass: a measurement of the amount of matter in an object

mass number: the total number of protons and neutrons in the nucleus of an atom

matter: anything that has mass and occupies space

measurement: comparing an unknown amount with a known amount

mechanical advantage: the amount by which any simple machine multiplies force

mechanics: the study of motion and the causes of changes in motion

medium: a substance that will carry sound vibrations

mega: the metric prefix meaning one million times the unit

memory: the part of a computer used to store information

meltdown: a nuclear accident in which the fuel in a nuclear reactor would become hot enough to melt

melting: the change from a solid to a liquid state

melting point: the temperature at which a substance changes from a solid to a liquid

Mercury: the planet nearest the sun

metallic ores: ores mined and refined to produce metals like copper, iron, and zinc

metallurgy (MET-'l-er-jē): the science of purifying metals and preparing them to be used

metamorphic (met-ə-MOR-fik) **rock:** rock formed from other rocks by heat and pressure

metamorphism: the process of changing rock by heat and pressure

meteor (MĒT-ē-ər): the trail or streak of light formed when a meteoroid burns in the atmosphere

meteorite (MĒT-ē-ə-rīt): a meteoroid that passes through the atmosphere and strikes the earth

meteoroid (MĒT-ē-ə-roid): small rocks and dust that float in space

meter: the standard unit of length in the metric system

micro: the metric prefix meaning one millionth of the unit

microcomputer (MĪ-krō-kam-PYOOT-ər): a very small tabletop computer

Milky Way Galaxy: the hazy band of light in the sky formed by the galaxy in which the sun orbits

milli: the metric prefix meaning one thousandth of a unit

minicomputer: small, office-size computer

model: an idea about or design of the way something might work

molecule: the smallest possible piece of a substance

monomer (MAHN-ə-mər): a single link in a long chain of carbon atoms

moons: small bodies in space that orbit the planets

mountains: complicated masses of rock that rise more than 1,000 meters above the surrounding land

music: sound produced by a vibrating body that sends out regular vibrations at regular intervals

---

natural frequency: a special sound produced by any object when it is struck, blown, or plucked

natural resources: something provided by the earth that meets a need

neap (NĒP) **tide:** a smaller than normal tide that occurs when the earth, moon, and sun form a right angle

nebulae (NEB-yə-le): clouds of dust and gas floating in space

negative charge: one type of electrical charge

Neptune: the giant outer planet farthest from the sun

neutral: having no electrical charge

neutron (NOO-trahn): a subatomic particle with no charge found in the nucleus of an atom

new moon: a phase of the moon in which it appears completely dark

newton: the metric unit of force

noble gases: a group of elements that are inert or unreactive

nonmetallic ores: ores mined and refined to produce materials such as glass, cement, and phosphate

nonrenewable resources: resources that cannot be replaced

nova (NŌ-və): a star that increases in brilliance for a short period of time because of an internal explosion

nuclear fission (NOO-klē-ər FISH-ən): the splitting of atoms to release energy usually in the form of heat

nuclear force: the force that holds the nucleus of an atom together

nuclear power plant: a plant that uses nuclear energy to produce electricity

nuclear reactor: a device that controls a nuclear fission chain reaction

nucleus (NOO-klē-əs): the central core of an atom containing protons and neutrons

---

observing: looking carefully for clues as to how the world works

occluded (ə-KLOOD-əd) **front:** front formed when a cool air mass moves underneath an entire warm air mass and lifts it into the atmosphere

orbit: the path followed by a planet as it moves around the sun

ore (OR): metals combined with other elements and concentrated in the earth's crust

organic chemistry: the study of all carbon compounds

organic compounds: chemical compounds containing carbon

outer planets: the five planets farthest from the sun

output: the processes and devices used by computers to communicate information to people

overtones: secondary vibrations produced by a vibrating string

oxidation (ahk-sə-DĀ-shən): a chemical weathering process in which minerals combine with oxygen forming other compounds

---

parallels (PAR-ə-lels): lines drawn east-west around the earth that are used to find location north and south

particle (PAHR-ti-k'l): the smallest piece of matter

particle accelerator (ak-sel-ə-RĀ-tər): a device used to speed up the movement of particles

passive solar: a building designed to use the sun's rays for heating purposes

pendulum (PEN-joo-ləm): a weight hung so that it is free to swing back and forth

periodic table: a table based on the properties of the elements

petroleum: a group name for coal, oil, and natural gas

piston: a short cylinder fitting tightly inside a hollow tube in which it moves back and forth

pitch: the distance between the ridges of a screw. Also, the tone at which a given frequency of sound is heard

phase: the different lighted shapes of the moon as seen from the earth

physical change: a change that does not affect the makeup or properties of a substance

physical weathering: processes that break large rocks into smaller fragments

plains: wide and flat or gently rolling landforms

plane mirror: a mirror with a flat surface

planet: a large, solid body orbiting the sun

plastic: a synthetic material that can be shaped into almost any form

plate tectonics (tek-TAHN-iks): the theory that the earth's crust is broken into plates that are moved by forces within the earth

plateau (pla-TŌ): a wide, flat landform that has been raised by constructive forces

Pluto: the outermost planet

pollution: unnatural chemicals in the environment

polymer (PAHL-i-mər): a molecule made of a long chain of carbon atoms

positive charge: one type of electrical charge

potential energy: stored energy

power: the rate at which work is done

power plant: a plant used to produce electricity

precipitation (pri-sip-ə-TĀ-shən): water, either liquid or frozen into solid droplets, falling from a cloud

prediction (pri-DIK-shən): to guess how something will work without really knowing

prefix (PRĒ-fiks): a syllable put at the beginning of a word to change its meaning

prime meridian (mə-RID-ē-ən): the line of longitude that serves as the starting point for the world's time zones

prism (PRIZ-m): a special type of lens with three sides that refracts white light into colors

procedure: the part of a scientific paper that tells exactly what was done in an experiment

program: instructions that tell a computer what to do

properties: the characteristics used to describe matter

proton (PRŌ-tahn): a subatomic particle with a positive charge found in the nucleus of an atom

prototype (PRŌT-ə-tīp): an original model built to test an idea

pulley: a simple machine made of one grooved wheel and a rope passed over the wheel

pulsar (PUL-sahr): sources of radio energy in deep space that pulse on and off very regularly

purpose: the part of a scientific paper that tells the reader what the paper is all about

quality engineers: people who test a product to insure that it does what it was designed to do

quasars (KWĀ-sahr): faint bluish objects in space that give off a "roar" of radio energy

radio: a method of sending sound through the air in the form of electrical energy

radioactive (rā-dē-ō-AK-tiv) **decay:** the process by which a radioactive atom gives off rays or particles and changes to another element

radioactivity (rā-dē-ō-ak-TIV-ə-tē): powerful rays or particles emitted by certain atoms

random access memory (ram): memory that holds information while it is being used and may be erased when it is no longer needed

rarefaction (rair-ə-FAK-shən): the part of a sound wave in which the molecules of air expand

reactive (rē-AK-tiv) **elements:** elements that react easily with other elements

read only memory (rom): permanent memory that is used to start up the computer and load programs of instructions

real image: an image formed when the image and object are on the same side of the mirror

recycle (rē-SĪ-k'l): the process of conserving a resource by reusing a material

red giant: a very large, old star

refraction (ri-FRAK-shən): the bending of light as it passes from one substance to another

renewable: a resource that can be replaced by natural processes usually within your lifetime

repulsion: the force between two like electrical charges that pushes them apart

resistance: the force of the load being moved by a simple machine

resonance (REZ-ə-nəns): the vibration of an object at its natural frequency caused by the vibration of another object

rock cycle: a group of processes that change rocks from one form to another

rotary (RŌT-ər-ē) **engine:** an engine that has a rotor in place of a piston

row: a horizontal arrangement of numbers in a table

Saturn: a giant outer planet surrounded by rings

scale: a series of standard values used to compare bar or line values on a graph

science: the search for knowledge about how the world works

scientific journals: magazines in which scientific papers are published

scientific report: a written report describing the hypothesis, experiment, data, and the conclusion

scientist: a person whose job is to find out how nature works

screw: an inclined plane that has been wound around a rod in a spiral

season: four periods of differing weather caused by the position of the earth in relation to the sun

sedimentary (sed-ə-MEN-tər-ē) **rock:** rock formed from small pieces or sediments of rock cemented together

shield cone: wide, nearly flat volcanoes built of free-flowing basaltic magma

shoreline: the boundary between land and water

silicon (SIL-i-kən) **chip:** a very small piece of silicon containing thousands of transistors

simple machines: mechanical devices that change the amount of applied force or the direction in which the force acts

smog: chemical pollutants in the air that are dangerous to people's health

software: computer programs

solar cell: a small device made of silicon that converts sunlight into electricity

solar collector: a device for concentrating the sun's rays and changing light energy into heat energy

solar eclipse (ē-KLIPS): a blocking of the sun's light that occurs when the moon passes exactly between the earth and the sun

solar prominence (SO-lər PRAHM-ə-nens): an arching stream of gas that shoots out from the sun's surface

solar system: the earth's family in space

sound waves: waves that carry sound energy through a medium

speed: the rate at which something moves over a distance

spiral galaxy (SPI-rəl GAL-ək-sē): a galaxy with flat arms that spiral about a thick center

spring tide: a higher than normal tide that is caused when the moon and sun are in line with each other

standard: a value that is accepted by a large number of people

star clusters: a loosely organized group of stars

static: electrical interference that sounds like hissing

stationary front: the boundary between two air masses usually where storms form

steam engine: a machine that changes heat energy in the form of steam into mechanical energy to do work

steam turbine (TER-bin): a rotary engine in which steam is directed against blades set in a wheel

storms: violent disturbances in the atmosphere

stratus (STRAT-əs) **clouds:** gray, flat layers of clouds that are usually associated with light rain and drizzle

stratosphere (STRAT-ə-sfir): the second layer of the atmosphere that extends upward from the troposphere

strong nuclear force: the force that holds the nucleus of an atom together

structural formula: a drawing showing the arrangement and number of atoms in a molecule

subatomic (suhb-ə-TAHM-ik) **particles:** particles that make up atoms

sublimation (sub-lə-MĀ-shən): the change of a solid directly into a gas

summer solstice (SAHL-stis): June 21st, the longest day of the year in the northern hemisphere

sunspots: spots on the sun's surface that are cooler than the rest of its surface

supernova: star whose brightness increases hundreds of times when it explodes

symbol: one or two letters used to represent an atom of an element

synthetic (SIN-thə-tik): a manufactured substance

synthetic fibers: plastic fibers such as nylon and rayon

synthetic resins: chemicals made from wood, coal, and oil that are then changed chemically to form plastics

---

technological (tek-nə-LAHJ-i-k'l) **method:** an eight-step method that can be used to develop a product

technology (tek-NAHL-ə-jē): the process of using the knowledge of science to produce useful products

telegraph: a device used to send messages in the form of code over wires

telephone: a device used to send voice messages over wires by varying an electric current

telescope: an instrument used to gather and concentrate the light from distant stars and other bodies in space so they can be seen

television: a method of sending pictures through the air in the form of electrical energy

thermal pollution (THER-m'l pə-LOO-shən): pollution that results when the water temperature of an environment changes and upsets the ecosystem

thermoplastic (ther-mə-PLAS-tik): a kind of plastic that can be formed into different shapes many times by heating

thermosetting (THER-mō-set-ing): a kind of plastic that takes a permanent shape when heated

theory: a hypothesis that has been tested many times and has always produced the same results

threads: the ridges formed on a screw by an inclined plane being wound around a shaft

thrust: the force that pushes a jet or rocket engine forward

thunderstorm: a short, violent storm that may produce lightning and hail

tide: the periodic rise and fall of the oceans caused by the moon's gravity

timbre (TIM-bər): the quality of sound due to the material and shape that makes a musical instrument recognizable

time zone: one of the twenty-four zones of longitude, each of which is fifteen degrees wide

timing system: a system that causes certain things to happen at the right time during an engine power cycle

title: the heading that describes what information is contained in a table

topsoil: the uppermost layer of soil that usually contains decayed plant and animal material

tornado (tor-NĀ-dō): a small, very powerful funnel-shaped cloud accompanied by very high winds

transistor (tran-ZIS-tər): solid-state devices that replaced vacuum tubes in electronic equipment

trend: the general way in which a factor is changing

troposphere (TRAHP-ə-sfir): the layer of the atmosphere nearest the earth where all weather occurs

trough (TRAWF): the lowest part of a wave

two-stroke cycle engine: an engine that uses only an intake-compression stroke and a power-exhaust stroke to make one power cycle

---

units: words used to describe what a number represents

universe: everything in space

ultrasonic (ul-trə-SAHN-ik): sound frequencies too high for the human ear to hear

Uranus (yoo-RĀ-nəs): one of the giant outer planets

---

valence (VĀ-ləns) **electrons:** the electrons in the outermost energy level of an atom

valid hypothesis: a hypothesis proven to be true by experiment

variable stars: stars that flash on and off very precisely

velocity (və-LAHS-ə-tē): the speed at which an object moves in a given direction

Venus: the second planet from the sun, about the same size and mass as the earth

vernal equinox (VER-n'l Ē-kwa-nahks): March 20th, the first day of spring

vertical: a line drawn straight up or down on a page

vibration: the rapid back and forth motion of matter

virtual image: an image that seems to come from inside or behind a mirror

visible spectrum: that part of the electromagnetic spectrum that can be seen by the human eye

viscosity (vis-KAHS-ə-tē): a measure of how fast a liquid will flow

volcanic mountains: mountains made of lava that has erupted from the earth

volume: the amount of space an object occupies

---

warm front: the boundary at which warmer air is pushed up and over cooler air

watt: the metric unit for power measured in joules per second

wavelength: the distance from a point on one wave to the corresponding point on the next wave

weak nuclear force: the force present among particles within the nucleus of an atom

weather: changes in the atmosphere that affect your life

weather forecast: a scientific prediction describing how the atmosphere is expected to behave over a period of time

weathering: the process that causes rock to break into smaller fragments and finally change into soil

wedge: a portable inclined plane

weight: the pull of gravity on matter

wheel and axle: a simple machine in which two wheels of different sizes rotate together

white dwarf (DWORF): a small, very dense white star formed when a red giant collapses

wind belts: belts of moving air formed by the sun's heating of the air and the earth's rotation

wind generator: a device that generates electricity when its propeller is turned by the wind

winter solstice (SAHL-stis): December 21st, the shortest day of the year in the northern hemisphere

work: a force that changes the motion and position of an object

work input: the amount of work put into a simple machine

work output: the amount of work gotten out of a simple machine

Index

E

F

G

H

I

J

K

L

M

N

Photo Credits

Unit 1 Opening Photo **10**: © Richard Wood/Taurus Photos

Chapter 1 **11** (*top*): Wide World Photos, (*bottom*): Dr. Harold E. Edgerton, M.I.T., Cambridge, Massachusetts

Chapter 2 **16**: Runk/Schoenberger from Grant Heilman; **17**: Kitt Peak National Observatory Cerro Tololo Inter-American Observatory

Chapter 3 **22**: The Granger Collection; **23**: 11 Alive WPIX TV

Chapter 4 **25**: © Richard Wood/Taurus Photos; **26**: © Richard Wood/Taurus Photos; **29** (*top*): Adapted from the April 1955 cover of *Scientific American*. © 1955 by Scientific American, Inc. All rights reserved, (*middle*): Bob Fitch/Black Star, (*bottom*): Ken Karp; **30** (*left*): Adapted from the April 1955 cover of *Scientific American*. © 1955 by Scientific American, Inc. All rights reserved, (*right*): Bob Fitch/Black Star

Chapter 5 **32**: The Granger Collection; **33** (*top*): The Bettmann Archive, (*bottom*): Jersey Central Power & Lighting Co.; **35**: © Susan Lapides/Design Conceptions

Chapter 6 **36**: Ken Karp; **37** (*top*): Michigan Department of State Highways, (*bottom*): Runk/Schoenberger from Grant Heilman; **40**: Ken Karp

Chapter 7 **43**: Ken Karp; **44**: Delia Flynn/Stock, Boston

Chapter 9 **57**: Ken Karp

Chapter 10 **63**: Ken Karp; **65**: Cynara; **66** (*top*): Ken Karp, (*bottom*): Ellis Herwig/Stock, Boston

Chapter 11 **68**: Ken Karp; **69** (*bottom*): Owen M.L. from Black Star, (*top left*): Denise A. Heller/DPI, (*top right*): Guy Gillette/Photo Researchers, Inc.; **70** (*left to right*): The Bettmann Archive, Culver Pictures, NASA

Unit 2 Opening Photo **72**: Everett C. Johnson/Leo de Wys, Inc.

Chapter 12 **73**: NASA; **74**: Russ Kinne/Photo Researchers, Inc.; **75**: Ken Karp

Chapter 13 **78** (*left to right*): The Mount Everest Foundation, Australian News and Information Bureau, © Elihu Blotnick/Omni-Photo; **80**: Ken Karp; **81**: Ken Karp

Chapter 14 **83** (*left*): Robert W. Young/DPI, (*right*): Ken Karp, (*bottom*): Ken Karp; **86**: Ken Karp

Chapter 15 **88** (*top*): Ken Karp, (*bottom*): Ken Karp; **89**: Jack Dermid; **91** (*top*): Ken Karp, (*bottom*): Ken Karp

Chapter 16 **93** (*top*): Kitt Peak National Observatory Cerro Tololo Inter-American Observatory, (*bottom*): Ken Karp; **95**: Ken Karp; **96**: Ken Karp

Chapter 17 **98**: Leslie Salt Co.; **100**: Delco Remy Division of General Motors

Chapter 18 **102** (*left to right*): Ken Karp, Myron Wood/Photo Researchers, Inc., © Georg Gersten/Photo Researchers, Inc., © Joel Gordon; **103**: NASA; **105**: Ken Karp

Chapter 19 **107**: The Bettmann Archive; **108**: The Granger Collection; **109**: Ken Karp; **112** (*left to right*): Ken Karp, Ken Karp, USDA Photo

Chapter 20 **117** (*top*): The Bettmann Archive, (*bottom*): Ken Karp; **118**: Ken Karp; **120**: Courtesy of Ward's Natural Science Establishment, Inc.

Chapter 21 **123**: Department of Energy; **124**: The Bettmann Archive; **125**: Brookhaven National Laboratory; **128**: Brookhaven National Laboratory

Chapter 22 **130**: Ira Wyman/Sygman; **131**: © Craig Aurness/Woodfin Camp & Associates; **132**: Runk/Schoenberger from Grant Heilman; **133**: Ken Karp

Unit 3 Opening Photo **136**: Wally McNamee/Woodfin Camp & Associates

Chapter 23 **137** (*top left*): an Exxon photo, (*top right*): © Michal Heron/Woodfin Camp & Associates, (*bottom left*): © 1979 Stern from Black Star, (*bottom right*): Pacific Gas and Electric; **138**: United Press International Photo; **139** (*top*): Ken Karp, (*middle*): The Granger Collection, (*bottom*): The Bettmann Archive; **141** (*top*): Pacific Gas and Electric, (*bottom*): Ken Karp

Chapter 24 **144**: © Gerry Cranham, Rapho/Photo Researchers, Inc.; **146**: Seelinger-Stern from Black Star; **147** (*top*): Henry Monroe/DPI, (*bottom*): NASA; **148**: Ken Karp

Chapter 25 **151**: Ken Karp; **155**: Ken Karp; **156**: © Michal Heron/Monkmeyer; **157**: © Bohdan Hrynewyck/Stock, Boston

Chapter 26 **160** (*left*): Grant Heilman, (*right*): Cunard Line Ltd.; **162**: General Electric Co.; **166**: Mazda; **167**: Lionel Delevingne/Stock, Boston; **168** (*left*): Jeff Albertson/Stock, Boston, (*right*): © Eric Kroll/Taurus Photos

Chapter 27 **171**: Anestis Diakopoulos/Stock, Boston; **172** (*top*): Dentsply International, (*bottom*): NASA; **174**: © Karsh, Ottawa/Woodfin Camp & Associates; **175** (*top*): Ken Karp, (*bottom*): Bill Grimes from Leo de Wys, Inc.; **177**: Stock, Boston; **178**: © Joel Gordon 1981

Chapter 28 **180**: Grumman/DOE; **181**: Ken Karp

Chapter 29 **190**: © Joel Gordon 1982; **191**: Pacific Gas & Electric Co.; **193**: DOE photo from Argonne/West; **197**: Conklin from Monkmeyer; **198**: *The New York Times*

Unit 4 Opening Photo **200**: USGS

Chapter 30 **205**: A. Post/U.S.G.S.; **206**: Courtesy of the American Museum of Natural History; **207** (*top*): Hillers/U.S.G.S., (*bottom*): Oregon State Highway Commission Photo

Chapter 31 **211**: U.S.G.S.; **213** (*top*): U.S. Air Force/U.S.G.S., (*middle*): Rodman/Wanamaker/American Museum of Natural History, (*bottom*): Sergerstrom/U.S.G.S.; **214**: American Museum of Natural History; **215** (*top left*): Bramlette/U.S.G.S., (*top right*): Dale/U.S.G.S., (*middle*): Dwight Bentel/American Museum of Natural History, (*bottom left*): Thane Bierwert/American Museum of Natural History, (*bottom right*): Dwight

Bentel/American Museum of Natural History; **216**: Peter Goldberg/American Museum of Natural History; **217**: American Museum of Natural History

Chapter 32 **219**: American Museum of Natural History; **221** (*top*): American Museum of Natural History, (*bottom*): Elwood Baker from Monkmeyer; **222**: American Museum of Natural History; **223** (*top*): Wahrhaftig/U.S.G.S., (*bottom*): E. D. McKee/U.S.G.S.; **224**: Lanks/Monkmeyer

Chapter 33 **226**: Bureau of Reclamation; **227** (*left*): Field Museum of Natural History, (*right*): I. Howard Spevak/DPI; **228**: © Donato Leo/DPI; **229**: USDA-SCS Photo by Erwin W. Cole; **230**: © Leeanne Schmidt/DPI

Chapter 34 **233**: NASA; **234**: © Jim Anderson 1982/Woodfin Camp & Associates; **237**: Leo de Wys, Inc.; **238**: NOAA, **239** (*top*): John H. Gerard/DPI, (*bottom*): USDA, (*inset*): Walter Dawn

Chapter 35 **241**: NOAA; **245** (*top*): United Press International Photo, (*bottom*): © William Koplitz/DPI; **246**: NOAA

Chapter 36 **249**: NASA; **255**: © Suva/DPI

Chapter 37 **259** (*top*): Mount Wilson and Palomar Observatories, (*bottom*): Royal Greenwich Observatory; **261**: NASA; **263** (*top*): American Museum of Natural History, (*bottom*): American Museum of Natural History/AMNH-Sinclair Aerial Survey; **264**: NASA

Chapter 38 **266**: Lick Observatory; **268**: NASA; **269**: Courtesy of the American Museum of Natural History; **270** (*left*): NASA, (*middle*): Kitt Peak National Observatory Cerro Tololo Inter-American Observatory, (*right*): Lick Observatory Photograph; **271** (*top*): NASA, (*bottom*): Hale Observatories

Unit 5 Opening Photo **274**: Rainbow/Dan McCoy

Chapter 39 **275**: Frederick S. Hagen, Zymos Corporation; **277**: Xerox Corporation; **278** (*top*): Courtesy of Apple Computer, Inc., (*bottom*): © Dick Durrance 1982/Woodfin Camp & Associates; **280**: Roger Ressmeyer

Chapter 40 **281**: Ken Karp, **282**: © Sepp Seitz 1980/Woodfin Camp & Associates; **283** (*top*): © Michal Heron 1981/Woodfin Camp & Associates, (*bottom left*): American Iron and Steel Institute, (*bottom right*): The Chase Manhattan Bank; **284**: Bell Labs; **285**: Ken Karp

Chapter 41 **288** (*left*): Culver Pictures, Inc., (*right*): © Al Stephenson 1981/Woodfin Camp & Associates; **289**: Everett C. Johnson from Leo de Wys, Inc.; **290**: Sigrid Owen/DPI; **291**: Fred Ward/Black Star; **292** (*top*): Bell Labs, (*bottom*): Wide World Photos; **293** (*top*): © Al Stephenson 1980/Woodfin Camp & Associates, (*bottom*): Monkmeyer

Chapter 42 **296** (*top*): Francene Keery from Leo de Wys, Inc., (*bottom*): © Robert Azzi 1982/Woodfin Camp & Associates; **297**: DOE photo by Aratex; **299** (*top*): NASA, (*bottom*): SDG & E; **300**: DOE photo by Jack Schneider; **301**: Ken Karp

Chapter 43 **303**: Sybil Shelton from Monkmeyer; **304**: Culver Pictures, Inc.; **306**: Culver Pictures, Inc.; **307**: Rogers from Monkmeyer; **308**: Bell Labs; **309**: Ken Karp

Chapter 44 **311** (*top*): Culver Pictures, Inc., (*bottom*): United Press International Photo; **312** (*top*): Suva/DPI, (*middle*): Suva/DPI, (*bottom*): Bell Labs, (*bottom left*): Sybil Shackman from Monkmeyer, (*bottom middle*): Hugh Rogers from Monkmeyer, (*bottom right*): Rogers from Monkmeyer; **316** (*top*): United Press International Photo, (*bottom*): © Laimute E. Druskis 1982/Taurus Photos